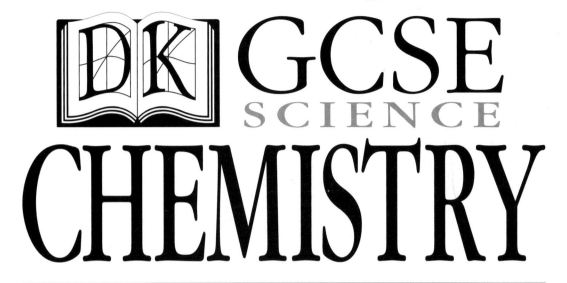

DK GCSE SCIENCE

CHEMISTRY

For Single and Double Awards

LONDON • NEW YORK • SYDNEY • DELHI

www.dk.com

Consultant Tony Cressey

Tony Cressey has had over 35 years experience teaching chemistry and he has been an active examiner for over 30 years

Editor Hannah Wilson
Designer Sue Metcalfe-Megginson
Managing Art Editor Peter Bailey
Production Chris Avgherinos
Jacket Design Andy Smith
DTP Designer Rachel Symons
Proof Reader Slaney Begley

With thanks to Clare Pearson
for editorial help

Illustrators Kessia Beverley-Smith; Moises Chicharro; Matt Clifford; Christina Fairminer; Nathaniel Gale; Genny Haines; Sarah Harvey; Emma Humphries-Davies; Jon-Paul James; Steve Lewin; Jonathan Lord

First published in Great Britain in 1999
by Dorling Kindersley Limited,
9 Henrietta Street, London WC2E 8PS

2 4 6 8 10 9 7 5 3 1

Copyright © 1999 Dorling Kindersley
Limited, London

A CIP catalogue record for this book is available from the British Library.

ISBN: 0-7513-5936-X

Colour reproduction by
First Impressions, UK

Printed and bound in Zrinski, Croatia

Contents

Introduction *4*
Marking system *5*
Revision tips *6*

> ### KEY
> Single and Double Awards
>
> Double Award only

BASIC IDEAS

Safety and laboratory techniques
Introduction and questions 8
Changes of state
Introduction, key facts, and questions 12
Solids, liquids, and gases
Introduction and questions 13
Safety and laboratory techniques
Answers and explanations 15
Changes of state
Answers and explanations 18
Solids, liquids, and gases
Answers and explanations 19

CHEMICAL COMPOUNDS

Physical and chemical changes
Introduction, key facts, and questions 20
Elements, mixtures, and compounds
Introduction, key facts, and questions 21
Physical and chemical changes
Answers and explanations 23
Elements, mixtures, and compounds
Answers and explanations 23

ATOMS AND BONDING

Atomic structure
Introduction, key facts, and questions 26
Chemical bonding
Introduction and questions 27
Molecules and giant structures
Introduction and questions 29
Atomic structure
Answers and explanations 30
Chemical bonding
Answers and explanations 30
Molecules and giant structures
Answers and explanations 33

EXTRACTION AND USES OF MATERIALS

Manufacturing processes
Introduction, key facts, and questions 36
Electrolysis
Introduction and questions 40
Application of materials
Introduction and questions 42
Manufacturing processes
Answers and explanations 44
Electrolysis
Answers and explanations 47
Application of materials
Answers and explanations 49

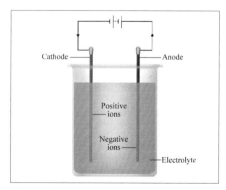

Electrolysis

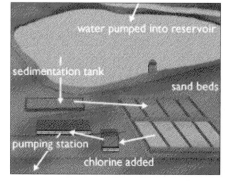

A water treatment works

CHEMICALS FROM OIL

Petrochemicals and organic chemistry
Introduction, key facts, and questions 52
Petrochemicals and organic chemistry
Answers and explanations 56

CHANGING MATERIALS

Chemical changes
Introduction and questions 60
Acids and alkalis – indicators
Introduction and questions 63
Acids and alkalis – salts
Questions 65
Burning and changes to the atmosphere
Introduction and questions 67
Chemical changes
Answers and explanations 68
Acids and alkalis – indicators
Answers and explanations 70
Acids and alkalis – salts
Answers and explanations 71
Burning and changes to the atmosphere
Answers and explanations 72

CHEMICAL FORMULAE

Chemical equations
Introduction, key facts, and questions 74
Chemical equations
Answers and explanations 80

PATTERNS OF BEHAVIOUR

Metals and non-metals
Introduction, key facts, and questions 84
The periodic table
Introduction, key facts, and questions 87
Reactivity series
Introduction and questions 92
Metals and non-metals
Answers and explanations 94
The periodic table
Answers and explanations 96
Reactivity series
Answers and explanations 98

RATES, EQUILIBRIUM, AND ENERGETICS

Reaction rates
Introduction, key facts, and questions 100
Reversible reactions and equilibrium
Introduction, key facts, and questions 103
Exothermic and endothermic reactions
Introduction, key facts, and questions 105
Reaction rates
Answers and explanations 108
Reversible reactions and equilibrium
Answers and explanations 109
Exothermic and endothermic reactions
Answers and explanations 110

THE EARTH

The Earth and its atmosphere
Introduction, key facts, and questions 114
Weathering
Introduction and questions 116
The Earth and its atmosphere
Answers and explanations 117
Weathering
Answers and explanations 118

GEOLOGICAL CHANGES

Formation and deformation of rocks
Introduction, key facts, and questions 120
Structure of the Earth
Introduction and questions 123
Formation and deformation of rocks
Answers and explanations 126
Structure of the Earth
Answers and explanations 128

Glossary *132*

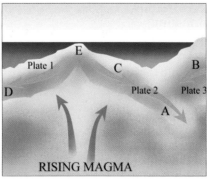

A titration using a burette

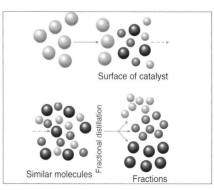

Plate tectonics

Catalytic cracking

Introduction

This book will help you to study and to revise chemistry for GCSE Science. You can use it to test your knowledge and understanding of the subjects covered in your syllabus.

Structure of the book

This book is divided into 11 sections that correspond to the main subject areas in chemistry. These are further divided into chapters. Each section contains key facts, questions, and answers.

• Key facts

The key facts are a brief summary of the important ideas that relate to specific topics within a section. Read them carefully as they provide a basic introduction to subject areas, as well as a quick reminder of important facts.

• Questions

Most of the questions are multiple choice. Use the tick boxes to make your selection (there is only one correct answer for each question). Some questions are easy and others are more difficult. Make sure that you study the questions carefully, because it is often just one word that makes the difference between a right answer and a wrong one.

Don't worry if you have not studied the specific point that is being tested and you cannot pick the correct answer immediately. You may surprise yourself by working out the answer by using your general understanding of chemistry.

• Answers

In many ways, this is the most important part of the book. Check whether your answer is correct or not. If it is – well done! Give yourself a tick in the box next to the appropriate answer. Make sure that you fully understand why the answer you chose was the right one. If your answer is incorrect – do not despair! Make sure that you understand how and why you made a mistake by reading the comprehensive explanation provided with each answer. These explanations will provide you with all the information that you need to answer the question correctly. You will learn a lot by reading over this section carefully, and may like to test yourself on new information learnt by answering the questions again at a later period of revision.

Syllabuses

Check the content of your syllabus carefully because there are several different GCSE Science syllabuses and they vary slightly in their content. They cover a lot of the same material, but you will find that this book includes some areas of chemistry that are not on your syllabus, and that there may be a few topics that you will need to look at separately.

GCSE Science options

There are four options available for the candidate studying chemistry for GCSE Science. They are as follows (attainable grades are in brackets):

Single Science Foundation Level (grades G to C)

Single Science Higher Level (grades D to A*)

Double Science Foundation Level (grades GG to CC)

Double Science Higher Level (grades DD to A*A*)

This books caters for all four options. The contents pages highlights the chapters that relate to both Single and Double Science Awards, and those that relate to Double Awards only. The chapters include questions for both the Foundation and the Higher Level candidate, and may include some that relate to the Higher Level candidate only. You need only study the chapters that relate to you. However, you may find it both interesting and useful to read through some of the other chapters.

GCSE Science coursework

Science coursework makes up 25% of the overall marks of your GCSE Science grade. The coursework is split into four skill areas as follows:

• Planning experimental procedures

• Obtaining evidence

• Analyzing evidence and drawing conclusions

• Evaluating evidence

You will need to check with your school or college that you have provided all the coursework required for each skill area.

Chemical formulae

In chemistry it is important to know the names and formulae of many elements and compounds. Therefore you may need to refer to the sections entitled Chemical Formulae (see page 74) and Patterns of Behaviour (see page 84), which includes a periodic table, when studying other sections.

Marking system

Evaluate your chemistry knowledge and determine which subject areas need the most revision and practice by using this marking system. Add up your correct answers and enter the scores into the relevant boxes below (the totals are cumulative, so higher candidates need only fill in the last column).

Compare results for each section by converting your score into a percentage by using this equation: (100 ÷ [maximum score]) x your score = % score. Eg. (100 ÷ 46) x 30 = 65 %

Use the key at the bottom of the page to assess your results.

SECTIONS		Single and Double Awards	Double Award only	Foundation Level	Foundation and Higher
BASIC IDEAS:		Safety and laboratory techniques		/46 = %	/50 = %
		Changes of state		/20 = %	/20 = %
		Solids, liquids, and gases		/22 = %	/22 = %
CHEMICAL COMPOUNDS:		Physical and chemical changes		/14 = %	/14 = %
		Elements, mixtures, and compounds		/20 = %	/20 = %
ATOMS AND BONDING:		Atomic structure		/7 = %	/7 = %
		Chemical bonding		/21 = %	/34 = %
		Molecules and giant structures		/5 = %	/8 = %
EXTRACTION AND USES OF MATERIALS:		Manufacturing processes		/46 = %	/58 = %
		Electrolysis		/24 = %	/24 = %
		Application of materials		/31 = %	/31 = %
CHEMICALS FROM OIL:		Petrochemicals and organic chemistry		/33 = %	/60 = %
CHANGING MATERIALS:		Chemical changes		/44 = %	/51 = %
		Acids and alkalis – indicators		/29 = %	/29 = %
		Acids and alkalis – salts		/16 = %	/19 = %
		Burning and changes to the atmosphere		/17 = %	/17 = %
CHEMICAL FORMULAE:		Chemical equations		/33 = %	/82 = %
PATTERNS OF BEHAVIOUR:		Metals and non-metals		/35 = %	/40 = %
		The periodic table		/51 = %	/55 = %
		Reactivity series		/18 = %	/18 = %
RATES, EQUILIBRIUM, AND ENERGETICS:		Reaction rates		/34 = %	/34 = %
		Reversible reactions and equilibrium		/0 = %	/12 = %
		Exothermic and endothermic reactions		/14 = %	/35 = %
THE EARTH:		The Earth and its atmosphere		/15 = %	/22 = %
		Weathering		/10 = %	/10 = %
GEOLOGICAL CHANGES:		Formation and deformation of rocks		/40 = %	/41 = %
		Structure of the Earth		/11 = %	/32 = %

				Average Score	
0–25 % Long way to go!	26–50 % Keep going!	51–75 % Nearly there!	76–100 % Excellent!	/656 = %	/845 = %

Revision tips

General tips

Set yourself a reasonable revision timetable and try to stick to it. When you're not revising, relax and do things that you enjoy.

Find a quiet area in which to revise. You will take in much more if you have no distractions, such as the television or music.

Try to revise at a regular time each day. For example, in the holidays you might decide to revise from 10:00 am to 12 noon and from 5:00 pm to 7:00 pm every day.

When you return to your revision after a break, spend a few minutes thinking about the material covered in the last session. This will help you to consolidate what you have already revised.

In an ideal world, you should aim to complete your revision two weeks before the exam. In the final two weeks you should try plenty of past exam questions.

Try to stay fit and healthy – this means you should get plenty of sleep, eat properly, and take regular exercise.

There are lots of people who want you to do well – friends, parents, relatives, and teachers. These people will always be happy to help you.

Your revision sessions

Try to make each revision session about 35 minutes long. A common mistake is to concentrate hard for the first five minutes, daydream for the next 25 minutes, and then to resume a high level of concentration for only the last five minutes. You think that you've done 35 minutes of hard work, but really you have done only ten! The secret of good revision is making the most of these 35 minute sessions. The following tips should help you do this.

• The sessions must be varied. In any one session you should aim to read, answer questions, highlight key words, and possibly produce labelled diagrams. You may find it useful to write your notes onto revision cards to use as a reminder of important facts.

• Before you start, make sure that you have everything that you need.

• The first thing you must do is to make sure that you understand what you are revising. There is no point learning something that you don't understand. Do not be afraid to ask your teachers any questions that you might have – they are there to help you. Make sure you ask at a sensible time, and not at the very last minute.

• Once you understand a topic, make notes on it in your own words. If possible, draw a diagram. It is easier to remember things as pictures rather than as words.

• Test yourself at regular intervals by using the questions in this book. Start by looking at questions that address just one topic, and progress to those that address a wider range of topics.

• As you revise a topic, use a highlighter pen to pick out the key words and points. After going through your notes several times, you will be able to fit enough basic information on to one revision card to remind you of a whole topic. Remember to use these cards often to test yourself on information learnt.

• Keep your notes and cards organized! This is very important but often forgotten – you will lose much of the benefit of your revision if you lose your notes.

• As the exam gets closer, try past questions from your exam board. When you first start answering questions you may have to use your notes to produce a full answer. As your knowledge improves, you will need to refer to your notes less. If you cannot find an answer in a text book or in your notes, ask your teacher. Don't just ignore it – a similar type of question may come up in your exam. Be aware of the time taken to answer a question; your answering speed will increase as your knowledge improves.

The night before the exam

There are several different views as to what to do the night before the exam, ranging from working all night to having the afternoon off school the day before in order to relax. The best solution lies between these two.

We have consulted doctors and examiners to come up with this simple list. It is incredibly easy to follow and will give you the best chance of success in your exam.

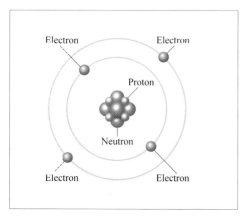

Atomic structure

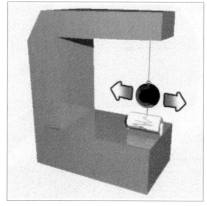

A seismometer

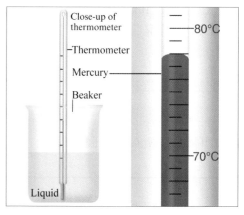

Measuring the boiling point of a liquid

• Have a good meal.

• Go over your revision cards for about an hour early in the evening.

• If you have any questions, ask someone rather than remain silent and worry about it.

• In the hour before your regular bedtime, try to relax. Many people relax by watching television or by listening to music.

• Go to bed at your regular bedtime and try to get a good night's sleep.

The exam

Arrive at least 15 minutes before the exam starts.

Make sure you have everything you need – pens, a pencil, a rubber, a watch, a ruler, coloured pencils, and a calculator.

Read all the instructions for the exam carefully and note the time allocated for the exam. Check whether or not you have to answer all the questions. If you do not, make sure that you understand all the instructions attached to the questions that you do need to answer.

Plan your time carefully. Look at the marks available for the question and determine what proportion they are of the total marks. You should spend a similar proportion of the time available on that question. For example, if a question is allocated 20% of the overall marks, you should spend 20% of the exam period on that question.

The marks available for each question give you a guide as to how much information the examiners are after. For example, a 2-mark question generally requires two separate points or one fully explained point as an answer.

Look out for key words in the question. For example, "calculate" means show your calculations.

Always read the question at least twice.

If your exam contains multiple choice questions, make sure that you answer them all. In multiple choice questions, if you are unsure of an answer, first eliminate the answers that you know are wrong, then make an educated guess between the options that remain. For the extended questions (generally worth 6 marks), the examiner requires several key points. You may wish to briefly plan your answer.

Make sure that all your answers stick to the point. Consider carefully what the question is asking and try not to waffle!

Exam presentation

There is more to doing exam questions than getting the right answer. How you present your answer can gain or lose you valuable points. In GCSE Science there are some rules that will help you pick up as many points as possible.

• If a question requires a calculation, always show your working and use the correct units.

• In a calculation, work with more decimal places than the question requires and then reduce your final answer to the required number of decimal places. This will ensure that your answer is accurate. For example, if the question asks for your answer to 2 decimal places, do the calculation working to at least 3 decimal places. When you have your final answer reduce it to 2 decimal figures.

• If a diagram will aid your answer, use one. Make sure that it is neat, and properly labelled.

• When including graphs, make sure that they have a title and that both axes are labelled. Plot the points on the graph accurately and clearly, and draw the best line of fit with a sharp pencil. If the graph line is straight, use a ruler and position it symmetrically between the points in order to draw the line. If the graph line is not straight, draw a smooth curve that best fits the plotted points.

• If you have any time remaining at the end of the exam, read over all your answers. First check that your answers are correct, and then check your spelling, punctuation, and grammar. (In some exams, 5% of the marks are awarded for correct spelling, punctuation, and grammar.)

And finally...GOOD LUCK!

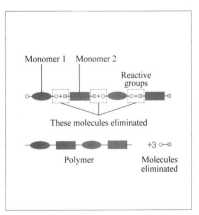

Polymerization

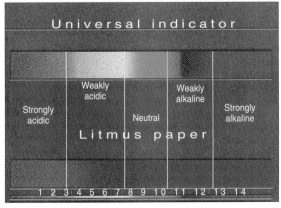

A universal indicator colour chart

A 3-D cross section of the Earth

Basic Ideas

Safety and laboratory techniques *(Single and Double Awards)*

Chemistry is a practical science and so it is important that a range of apparatus can be used safely and accurately. This section will help you to understand the safety measures and the technical skills that are required for laboratory work.

 QUESTIONS

Foundation and Higher Levels

1 Which one of the following sequences describes – in the correct order – the four hazard warning symbols that are illustrated below?

- ☐ (a) Corrosive, flammable, toxic, oxidizing
- ☐ (b) Toxic, harmful, toxic, flammable
- ☐ (c) Flammable, irritant, corrosive, explosive
- ☐ (d) Harmful, oxidizing, toxic, corrosive
- ☐ (e) Oxidizing, corrosive, toxic, flammable

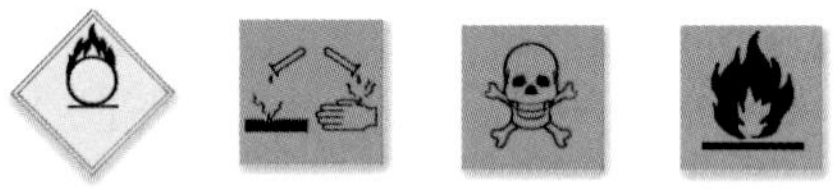

Q1

2 Which one of the following describes the hazard warning symbol that appears on bottles of concentrated sulphuric acid?

- ☐ (a) Flammable
- ☐ (b) Irritant
- ☐ (c) Harmful
- ☐ (d) Corrosive
- ☐ (e) Burns you

3 Give two precautions a student should take when warming a test tube containing dilute sulphuric acid in a laboratory.

....

....

4 Which sequence describes – in the correct order – the four diagrams that follow?

- ☐ (a) Beaker, conical flask, measuring cylinder, test tube
- ☐ (b) Test tube, conical flask, filter funnel, round-bottomed flask
- ☐ (c) Distillation flask, conical flask, measuring cylinder, beaker
- ☐ (d) Conical flask, round-bottomed flask, beaker, measuring cylinder
- ☐ (e) Beaker, measuring cylinder, conical flask, round-bottomed flask

Q4

5 Which apparatus should be used to measure 5 g of sulphuric acid?

- ☐ (a) A burette
- ☐ (b) A measuring cylinder
- ☐ (c) A stopwatch
- ☐ (d) An electronic balance
- ☐ (e) A pipette

6 A piece of magnesium was placed inside a crucible with a lid over the top and its mass recorded. It was then heated until a reaction occurred. Once cooled, the magnesium was weighed again. The diagram below illustrates the masses recorded before and after heating. What was the change in mass?

- ☐ (a) 1.2 g
- ☐ (b) 1.6 g
- ☐ (c) 3.2 g
- ☐ (d) 0.8 g
- ☐ (e) 1.5 g

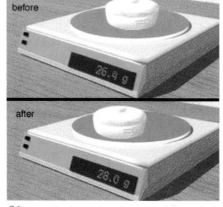

Q6

7 During an experiment to investigate the rate of reaction, a pupil is asked to measure the time taken for a strip of magnesium to dissolve in sulphuric acid. What piece of equipment should the student use to carry out the task?

- ☐ (a) An electronic balance
- ☐ (b) A measuring cylinder
- ☐ (c) A burette
- ☐ (d) A pipette
- ☐ (e) A stopwatch

8 Which one of the following pieces of apparatus should be used to measure 10 cm^3 of a liquid?

- ☐ (a) A stopwatch
- ☐ (b) A measuring cylinder
- ☐ (c) A thermometer
- ☐ (d) An electronic balance
- ☐ (e) A filter funnel

9 What is the reading on the measuring cylinder illustrated in the diagram below?

- ☐ (a) 15.7 cm^3
- ☐ (b) 14.7 cm^3
- ☐ (c) 15.6 cm^3
- ☐ (d) 15.4 cm^3
- ☐ (e) 15.5 cm^3

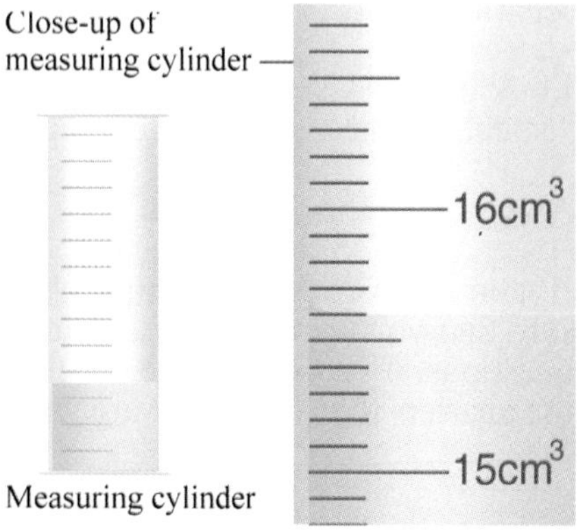

Close-up of measuring cylinder —

—16cm^3

—15cm^3

Measuring cylinder

Q9

10 A stone is placed in a measuring cylinder that contains a recorded volume of water. In the following diagram, the measuring cylinder on the left shows the water level before the stone was added, and the cylinder on the right shows the water level afterwards. What is the volume of the stone?

- ☐ (a) 20.0 cm^3
- ☐ (b) 30.0 cm^3

☐ (c) 25.0 cm³
☐ (d) 22.0 cm³
☐ (e) 30.2 cm³

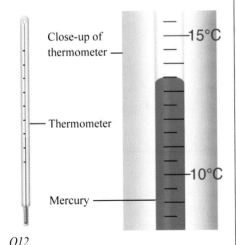

Q10

11 What instrument should be used to measure the temperature rise that occurs during the neutralization of sulphuric acid with sodium hydroxide?

....

12 What is the temperature on the thermometer in the diagram below?

☐ (a) 16.50°C
☐ (b) 13.75°C
☐ (c) 18.00°C
☐ (d) 14.00°C
☐ (e) 13.50°C

Q12

13 A pupil is asked to investigate the rate of reaction between 5 g of zinc and 25 cm³ of hydrochloric acid by measuring the time taken for the zinc to dissolve in the acid. What apparatus should the pupil use?

☐ (a) Measuring cylinder, electronic balance, stopwatch
☐ (b) Stopwatch, burette, pipette
☐ (c) Thermometer, electronic balance, stopwatch
☐ (d) Stopwatch, burette, thermometer
☐ (e) Thermometer, pipette, electronic balance

14 A liquid is heated until it reaches its boiling point, and a thermometer is used to record this temperature. According to the diagram shown below, what is the boiling point of the liquid?

☐ (a) 75°C
☐ (b) 77°C
☐ (c) 80°C
☐ (d) 78°C
☐ (e) 76°C

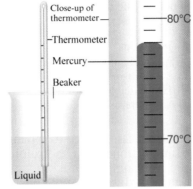

Q14

15 A pupil was asked to determine how long a piece of zinc took to dissolve in a sample of hydrochloric acid. The stopwatch in the diagram below shows the reading at the end of the experiment. What was the time taken, in seconds, for the zinc to dissolve?

☐ (a) 350.00 s
☐ (b) 5.25 s
☐ (c) 162.50 s
☐ (d) 325.00 s
☐ (e) 243.00 s

Q15

16 An electronic balance records the mass of a piece of metal as 234 g. What would the mass be in kg?

....

17 What process is used to obtain salt from a salt solution?

....

18 What is the best method of producing pure water from sea water?

....

....

19 What is the process of filtration?

☐ (a) The separation of two solids
☐ (b) The separation of a liquid and an insoluble solid
☐ (c) The removal of a solid by a magnet
☐ (d) The separation of two liquids
☐ (e) The separation of a liquid and a dissolved solid

20 Why can a mixture of alcohol and water be separated almost completely by fractional distillation?

☐ (a) Because they have different densities
☐ (b) Because alcohol is insoluble in water
☐ (c) Because of the difference in their boiling points
☐ (d) Because alcohol floats on water
☐ (e) Because alcohol is magnetic

21 Why can a solution of salt and water not be separated by filtration?

....

....

22 What would be a suitable method of separating small glass beads from a measure of water?

....

23 What process should a student use to determine how many colours there are in a sample of ink?

....

24 What is chromatography?

☐ (a) A process by which two solids can be separated
☐ (b) A process by which a liquid and an insoluble solid can be separated
☐ (c) A process by which a mixture of dyes can be separated using a solvent
☐ (d) A process by which two liquids can be separated
☐ (e) A process by which a liquid and a dissolved solid can be separated

25 A pupil uses chromatography to investigate the dyes present in two food colourings – X and Y. The results are shown below in a diagram of a chromatogram. Which dye – A, B, C, D, or E – is in both colourings?

....

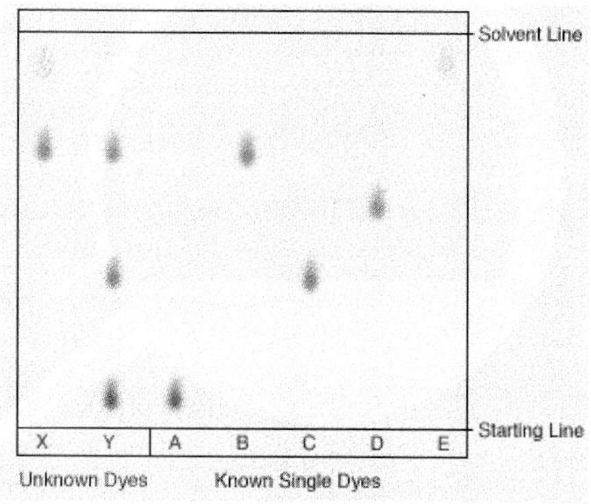

Solvent Line

Starting Line

| X | Y | A | B | C | D | E |

Unknown Dyes   Known Single Dyes

Q25, 26, 27

26 According to the diagram above, which dye is not present in either of the two colourings?

....

27 A chemist uses chromatography to analyse the dyes present in two unknown mixtures – X and Y. The results from the experiment are shown in the diagram above. Which dyes does Y contain?

☐ (a) A only
☐ (b) B and C only
☐ (c) A, B, and C only
☐ (d) A, B, and D only
☐ (e) A, C, and E only

28 Which one of the following processes can be used to separate iron filings from sulphur powder?

☐ (a) Filtration
☐ (b) Chromatography
☐ (c) Magnetic attraction
☐ (d) Fractional distillation
☐ (e) Decanting

29 Which of the following processes can be used to extract copper sulphate crystals from a copper sulphate solution?

☐ (a) Filtration
☐ (b) Chromatography
☐ (c) Magnetic attraction
☐ (d) Separation by use of a funnel
☐ (e) Evaporation

30 A pupil is asked to separate a mixture of sand and common salt in order to produce a sample of each.

What is the correct order of the processes involved?

☐ (a) Dissolution, filtration, evaporation
☐ (b) Dissolution, evaporation filtration
☐ (c) Filtration, dissolution, evaporation
☐ (d) Evaporation, filtration, dissolution
☐ (e) Evaporation, dissolution, filtration

31 Which of the following can be separated by decanting?

☐ (a) Two solids
☐ (b) A liquid and an insoluble solid
☐ (c) A mixture of dyes
☐ (d) Two miscible liquids
☐ (e) A liquid and a dissolved solid

32 A magnet can be used to separate a mixture of iron filings and sulphur powder, but cannot be used to separate a mixture of copper powder and sulphur powder. Why not?

....

....

33 A pupil was asked to measure the temperature rise that occurs during a neutralization reaction. The diagram below shows the temperatures that were recorded before and after the reaction occurred. What was the change in temperature?

☐ (a) 11.5°C
☐ (b) 22.6°C
☐ (c) 13.6°C
☐ (d) 10.5°C
☐ (e) 5.2°C

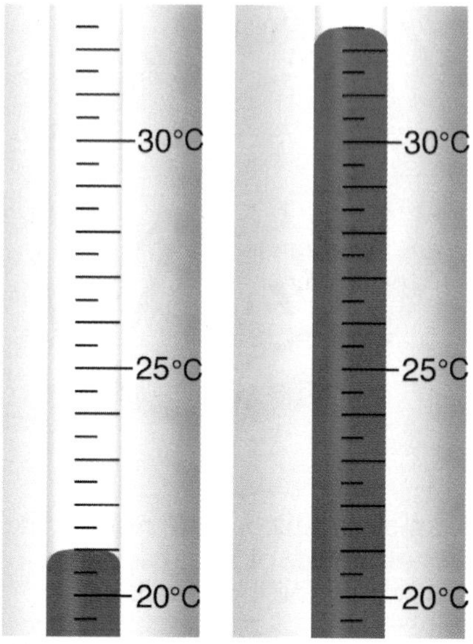

Q33

34 Which one of the following is normally separated by process of fractional distillation?

☐ (a) Two solids
☐ (b) A liquid and an insoluble solid
☐ (c) The pigments present in an ink
☐ (d) A mixture of two liquids
☐ (e) A liquid and a solid dissolved in the liquid

35 By what process can natural colouring materials, such as chlorophyll, be separated into their component parts?

☐ (a) Crystallization
☐ (b) Filtration
☐ (c) Distillation
☐ (d) Chromatography
☐ (e) Evaporation

36 A solid substance was heated until it boiled. As it was being heated its temperature was recorded every 30 seconds and the results plotted on a heating curve, as shown in the diagram below. What is the melting point of the substance?

☐ (a) 87°C
☐ (b) 22°C
☐ (c) 50°C
☐ (d) 0°C
☐ (e) 100°C

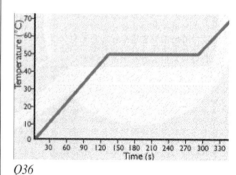

Q36

37 Which one of the following can be achieved by simple distillation?

☐ (a) The separation of two solids
☐ (b) The separation of pigments found in ink
☐ (c) The separation of a solid from a substance by use of a magnet
☐ (d) The separation of a compound into its elements
☐ (e) The separation of a liquid from a solid that is in solution

38 Which of the following can be separated into its component parts by fractional distillation?
i. Crude oil
ii. A mixture of iron and sulphur
iii. The gases in air

☐ (a) i, ii, and iii
☐ (b) ii and iii only
☐ (c) i and iii only
☐ (d) None of them
☐ (e) i and ii only

39 A solid substance was heated until it melted. When it cooled, its temperature was recorded every 30 seconds. These temperatures were plotted on a cooling curve, as shown in the diagram below. What is the melting point of the substance?

☐ (a) 43°C
☐ (b) 46°C
☐ (c) 88°C
☐ (d) 56°C
☐ (e) 89°C

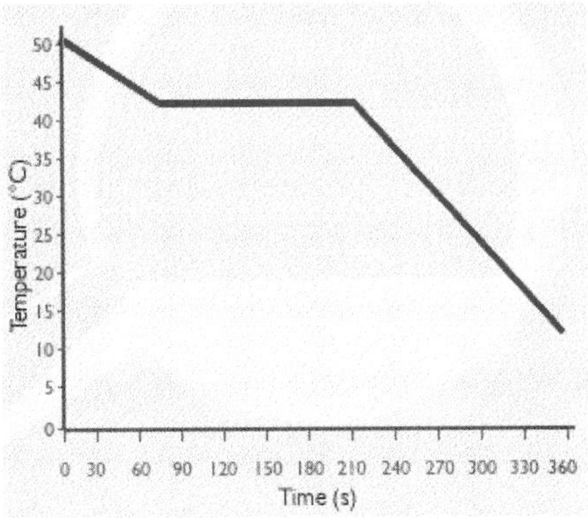

Q39

40 Why is it that filtration can be used to separate sand from water, but not salt from water.

....

....

41 For what reason can crude oil be separated by fractional distillation?

☐ (a) Its compounds have different chemical properties
☐ (b) Its compounds have different boiling points
☐ (c) Its compounds are non-magnetic
☐ (d) Crude oil is insoluble in water
☐ (e) Crude oil is flammable

42 What is the boiling point, in °C, of pure water?

....

43 Why is chlorine added to water?

☐ (a) To extract acids
☐ (b) To add flavour
☐ (c) To filter the water
☐ (d) To extract large solid matter
☐ (e) To kill germs

44 What instrument is used to measure accurately the mass of magnesium oxide that is formed during the oxidation of magnesium?

....

45 Which one of the following is not an accurate description of water?

☐ (a) A solvent
☐ (b) A reactant in the respiration reaction
☐ (c) A source of energy
☐ (d) A coolant in industrial processes
☐ (e) A coolant in mammals

46 Which property differs for sand and salt, and enables them to be separated?

☐ (a) Mass
☐ (b) Solubility in water
☐ (c) Density
☐ (d) Boiling point
☐ (e) None of the above

QUESTIONS

Higher Level only

47 Which of the following should be used during a titration to measure accurately the amount of acid used to neutralize 25 cm^3 of alkali?

☐ (a) A burette
☐ (b) A measuring cylinder
☐ (c) A stopwatch
☐ (d) A pipette
☐ (e) An electronic balance

48 During a titration to determine the concentration of an acid, a pupil is asked to measure 25 cm^3 of sodium hydroxide. Which one of the following pieces of apparatus should the pupil use?

☐ (a) An electronic balance
☐ (b) A 25 cm^3 beaker
☐ (c) A pipette
☐ (d) A thermometer
☐ (e) A measuring cylinder

49 According to the following diagram, what is the volume of the acid that has been released from the burette – assuming that the original reading was 0.0 cm^3?

☐ (a) 24.8 cm^3
☐ (b) 24.6 cm^3
☐ (c) 24.5 cm^3

☐ (d) 25.6 cm^3
☐ (e) 25.4 cm^3

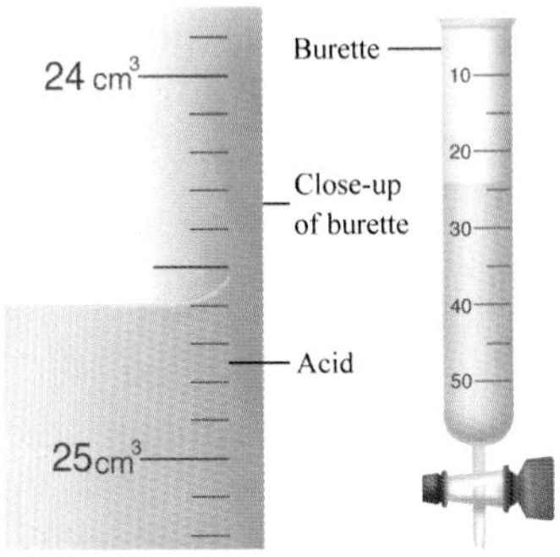

Q49

50 A titration was performed to determine the concentration of an acid. The acid was titrated against a known volume and concentration of sodium hydroxide. Look at the following diagram that illustrates the burette used in the experiment, and determine the volume of acid that was delivered from the titration – assuming that the original reading was 0.0 cm^3?

☐ (a) 13.6 cm^3
☐ (b) 12.6 cm^3
☐ (c) 12.3 cm^3
☐ (d) 12.4 cm^3
☐ (e) 13.7 cm^3

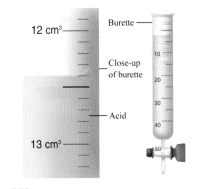

Q50

Changes of state *(Single and Double Awards)*

All substances take the form of one of three states of matter: solid, liquid, or gas. Matter often changes from one state to another when heated or cooled. The following questions examine these basic ideas.

 ## KEY FACTS

• **States of matter:** There are three states of matter: solid, liquid, and gas. All substances can be found in one of these states. Matter is made up of particles, and it is the arrangement of these particles that determines the state of matter. The state of matter can be changed by heating or cooling, and various terms are used to describe these changes. Melting, for example, describes the change from the solid state of matter to the liquid state.

Solid

Liquid

Gas

 ## QUESTIONS

Foundation and Higher Levels

1 What is the process of evaporation?

- ☐ (a) A gas turning into a liquid
- ☐ (b) A liquid, below its boiling point, turning into a gas
- ☐ (c) A solid turning into a liquid
- ☐ (d) A solid turning into a gas
- ☐ (e) A liquid boiling and turning into a gas

2 The following statements are about the properties of liquids at a constant temperature. Which one is false?

- ☐ (a) Liquids have a fixed volume
- ☐ (b) Liquids flow and can be poured
- ☐ (c) Liquids change shape to fit the shape of their container
- ☐ (d) Liquids are denser than gases
- ☐ (e) Liquids can be compressed

3 Why can a large volume of gas be transferred to a small container?

....

....

4 A substance was placed in a boiling tube and heated in a hot water bath, until its temperature was well above its melting point. Then the boiling tube was removed from the hot water and allowed to cool slowly. The temperature was recorded every minute and the results are shown in the chart below. What is the melting point of the substance?

....

5 Oil is used in the hydraulics of a lorry's braking system for a number of reasons. Which one of the following is the main reason?

- ☐ (a) Oil is denser than air
- ☐ (b) Oil does not have a fixed shape
- ☐ (c) Oil cannot be compressed
- ☐ (d) Oil can be changed into a gas
- ☐ (e) Oil takes the shape of its container

6 Which one of the following is not a gas at room temperature?

- ☐ (a) Ammonia
- ☐ (b) Oxygen
- ☐ (c) Carbon dioxide
- ☐ (d) Nitrogen
- ☐ (e) Water

7 Is sodium chloride a liquid at room temperature?

....

8 Which one of the following is a gas at room temperature?

- ☐ (a) Sodium
- ☐ (b) Petrol
- ☐ (c) Neon
- ☐ (d) Mercury
- ☐ (e) Polythene

9 What is meant by the term freezing?

....

....

10 What is formed when water is cooled below 0°C?

....

11 What is meant by the term melting?

....

....

Substance melting point results									
Time (min)	0	1	2	3	4	5	6	7	8	9
Temp (°C)	74	70	64	55	55	55	55	48	40	36

Q4

	Melting point (°C)	Boiling point (°C)
A: iodine	114	183
B: sulphur	119	445
C: mercury	−39	329
D: iron	1540	3000
E: sodium	98	883

Q12

12 Referring to the table above, which one of the following is not a solid at 25°C?

☐ (a) Iodine
☐ (b) Sulphur
☐ (c) Mercury
☐ (d) Iron
☐ (e) Sodium

13 Name the process that occurs when a puddle of water disappears on a sunny day?

....

14 What is meant by condensation?

....

....

15 Bricks are used in the foundations of buildings for a number of reasons. One of the following suggested reasons is false. Which one is it?

☐ (a) Bricks have a definite shape
☐ (b) Bricks cannot be compressed
☐ (c) Bricks have a definite volume
☐ (d) Bricks do not have a definite shape
☐ (e) Bricks are denser than water

16 Which one of the following is a solid at room temperature?

☐ (a) Carbon monoxide
☐ (b) Carbon
☐ (c) Nitrogen
☐ (d) Carbon dioxide
☐ (e) Argon

17 Name the process by which a gas changes into a liquid?

....

18 Which one of the following is not a gas at room temperature?

☐ (a) Hydrogen
☐ (b) Argon
☐ (c) Neon
☐ (d) Chlorine
☐ (e) Sodium

19 Car tyres are filled with air for a number of reasons. One of the following suggested reasons is false. Which one is it?

☐ (a) Air fills the space inside the tyre
☐ (b) Air can be compressed
☐ (c) Air can flow
☐ (d) Air has a fixed volume
☐ (e) Air takes on the shape of the tyre

20 When solid carbon dioxide warms up, it changes into a gas. What name is given to this process?

....

Solids, liquids, and gases *(Single and Double Awards)*

Solids have definite shapes. They contain particles that are very close together, and these particles cannot move out of their positions, but they can vibrate. Liquids have definite sizes, but not definite shapes. Liquids can be poured as the particles can move out of their positions. Gases have neither definite sizes nor shapes. Gases spread out to fill all available space. The particles of a gas are free to move in any direction, and are not in direct contact with each other.

 QUESTIONS

Foundation and Higher Levels

1 Which one of the following statements about the behaviour of particles in a liquid explains why liquids are able to flow?

☐ (a) The particles occupy fixed positions
☐ (b) The particles repel each other
☐ (c) The particles are a long distance from each other
☐ (d) The particles are able to move around
☐ (e) The particles have a constant motion at very high speed

2 What happens to the particles in a liquid when it changes state and forms a solid?

....

3 Which one of the following statements about the particles in a solid is false?

☐ (a) The particles form a regular 3-D arrangement
☐ (b) There are strong attractive forces between the particles
☐ (c) The particles cannot move to new positions
☐ (d) The particles can vibrate
☐ (e) The particles expand when the solid is heated

4 What happens to the salt particles in a crystal when it dissolves in water?

☐ (a) They disappear
☐ (b) They evaporate
☐ (c) They decrease in size
☐ (d) They spread out in the water
☐ (e) They melt

5 Which of the following statements explains why a gas fills the container in which it is kept?
i. The particles in a gas are larger than those in a liquid
ii. The particles in a gas have very small attractive forces between them
iii. The particles in a gas are constantly moving very quickly

☐ (a) i only
☐ (b) ii only
☐ (c) i and ii only
☐ (d) ii and iii only
☐ (e) i and iii only

6 What is the name of the process by which a gas will spread out to occupy all the space available to it?

☐ (a) Sublimation
☐ (b) Brownian movement
☐ (c) Diffusion
☐ (d) Condensation
☐ (e) Dissolution

7 As a liquid boils it will not increase in temperature until it has converted completely into a gas. Which one of the following statements explains why this occurs?

☐ (a) All the energy is used to separate the particles in the liquid
☐ (b) All the energy is used to increase the mass of the particles
☐ (c) All the energy is used to increase the volume of the particles
☐ (d) All the energy is used to increase the attractive forces between the particles
☐ (e) All the energy is used to place the particles in a regular arrangement

8 Why does the pressure of a gas in a sealed container increase when it is heated?

....

....

9 A metal can is filled with air that is 25°C in temperature, and sealed. The can is placed inside a freezer for one hour. What is the effect on the gas in the can?

☐ (a) Its volume increases
☐ (b) Its pressure increases
☐ (c) Its volume decreases
☐ (d) Both its pressure and volume remain constant
☐ (e) Its pressure decreases

10 When a liquid boils, its temperature remains constant even though it is still being heated. Which one of the following statements explains why this occurs?

☐ (a) All the energy that is being supplied is lost to the surroundings
☐ (b) All the energy is used during the separation of the particles
☐ (c) All the energy is absorbed by the particles as potential energy
☐ (d) All the energy is absorbed by the container
☐ (e) None of the above

11 The following diagram shows two jars – A and B – stacked on top of each other and separated by a lid. Jar A contains air and jar B contains chlorine. The lid is removed to form a single container.

What will happen after five minutes?

☐ (a) Both gases remain in place and do not mix
☐ (b) The molecules in air and chlorine mix together and fill both jars
☐ (c) The air molecules dissolve into the chlorine
☐ (d) The molecules in air react with the chlorine to form a new compound which fills both jars
☐ (e) The molecules in air are compressed into a small volume by the chlorine as it spreads into both jars

Q11

12 Why do your hands feel cold when ethanol is spilt on them?

☐ (a) The ethanol molecules are a lower temperature than your skin
☐ (b) The molecules use the heat from your skin to evaporate
☐ (c) The molecules use the heat from your skin to expand
☐ (d) The molecules are a higher temperature than your skin
☐ (e) The molecules freeze on contact with your skin

13 Which one of the following statements explains why a gas feels cool when it is released from a pressurized aerosol container?

☐ (a) The temperature of the gas inside the aerosol is lower than normal room temperature
☐ (b) As the gas is released it uses some of its energy to expand
☐ (c) As the gas is released it uses some of its energy to increase its mass
☐ (d) As the gas is released it uses some of its energy to decrease its volume
☐ (e) The particles of the gas are moving at a high speed

14 Which of the following statements are true?
i. When a solid dissolves the particles disappear
ii. When a solid dissolves the particles are dispersed throughout the liquid
iii. When a solid dissolves the particles melt

☐ (a) i only
☐ (b) ii and iii only
☐ (c) ii only
☐ (d) iii only
☐ (e) i, ii, and iii

15 Which one of the following statements explains why a solid is denser than a liquid?

☐ (a) The particles in a solid have more energy than those in a liquid
☐ (b) The particles in a liquid are lighter than those in a solid
☐ (c) The particles in a solid are closer together than those in a liquid
☐ (d) There are no attractive forces between the particles in a liquid
☐ (e) The particles in a solid are larger than those in a liquid

16 When a gas condenses on a cold surface, the surface increases in temperature. Which one of the following statements explains why this occurs?

☐ (a) The gas removes energy from the surface as it condenses
☐ (b) The gas transfers its energy to the surface as it condenses
☐ (c) The collision of the gas with the surface causes the temperature to increase
☐ (d) The gas is hotter than the surface
☐ (e) The surface removes energy from the gas

17 Which one of the following statements explains why a liquid that has been heated can dissolve a solid more quickly than it can at a lower temperature?

☐ (a) The solid particles are able to melt more quickly
☐ (b) The heat energy provides the particles in the solid with the energy to break free from each other
☐ (c) The heat energy increases the volume of the liquid
☐ (d) The heat energy decreases the volume of the solid particles
☐ (e) The heat energy increases the volume of the solid

18 Which one of the following statements explains what happens to the particles when a liquid changes into a gas?

- ☐ (a) The particles lose energy
- ☐ (b) The particles form a regular arrangement
- ☐ (c) The particles are unaffected
- ☐ (d) The particles move further apart
- ☐ (e) The particles vibrate more slowly

19 Which one of the following statements explains why heat is required to melt a solid?

- ☐ (a) The particles need energy in order to expand
- ☐ (b) The particles need energy to break free from their fixed positions
- ☐ (c) The particles need energy to convert into liquid particles

- ☐ (d) The particles need energy to increase the attractive forces between each other
- ☐ (e) The particles need energy to increase their mass

20 Which one of the following statements explains why solids expand on heating?

- ☐ (a) The particles vibrate more and push each other further apart
- ☐ (b) The particles expand
- ☐ (c) The particles increase in mass
- ☐ (d) The solid particles convert into liquid particles
- ☐ (e) The space between the particles fills with liquid which pushes them apart from each other

21 What is the name of the random and erratic motion of smoke particles which can be observed through a microscope?

- ☐ (a) Kinetic theory
- ☐ (b) Brownian movement
- ☐ (c) Avogadro's motion
- ☐ (d) Diffusion
- ☐ (e) Boyle's motion

22 When smoke is observed under a microscope, its particles follow an erratic path. Which one of the following statements explains the cause of this motion?

- ☐ (a) The smoke particles have an excess of energy
- ☐ (b) The smoke particles are moved about as they collide with the particles of air
- ☐ (c) The smoke particles are affected by the heat from its burning source
- ☐ (d) The smoke particles collide with each other
- ☐ (e) The smoke particles are heated by the light of the microscope

---

● ANSWERS

Safety and laboratory techniques

Foundation and Higher Levels

☐ **1** *(e)*
The four hazard symbols from left to right are as follows: oxidizing, corrosive, toxic, and flammable.

☐ **2** *(d)*
Concentrated sulphuric acid is corrosive.

☐ **3**
A student should take the following precautions during the experiment:
1. Wear eye protection
2. Point test tube away from others
3. Use a test tube holder
4. Perform the experiment standing up
5. Use gentle heat or a low Bunsen flame

☐ **4** *(e)*
The four diagrams – from left to right – represent the following apparatus: beaker, measuring cylinder, conical flask, and round-bottomed flask.

☐ **5** *(d)*
The mass of solids and liquids should be measured by an electronic balance.

☐ **6** *(b)*
The crucible had a mass of 26.4 g before heating and a mass of 28.0 g after heating. Therefore the change in mass is 1.6 g.

☐ **7** *(e)*
A stopwatch should be used to measure the time taken for a strip of magnesium to dissolve in sulphuric acid.

☐ **8** *(b)*
A measuring cylinder should be used to measure accurately 10 cm^3 of liquid.

☐ **9** *(c)*
The volume should be read from the bottom of the meniscus of the liquid in the measuring cylinder.

☐ **10** *(b)*
The volume of the stone is equal to the volume of water that was displaced when the stone was added to the measuring cylinder of water. The displacement can be calculated by subtracting the original volume of water in the measuring cylinder (32 cm^3) from the volume after the stone had been added (62 cm^3). Therefore the answer is 30 cm^3.

☐ **11**
A thermometer should be used to measure the temperature rise that occurs during the neutralization of sulphuric acid with sodium hydroxide.

☐ **12** *(e)*
The temperature should be read from the top of the meniscus of the mercury in the thermometer.

☐ **13** *(a)*
In order to perform this experiment, the pupil will need to measure the mass of the zinc using an electronic balance, and

to measure the correct volume of acid using a measuring cylinder. The time taken for the zinc to dissolve in the acid can be recorded by a stopwatch.

☐ **14** *(d)*
The temperature (in this case 78°C) that is shown on the thermometer is the boiling point of the liquid.

☐ **15** *(d)*
The reading on the stopwatch is given in minutes and seconds. In this instance a time of 5 minutes and 25 seconds has been recorded. As there are 60 seconds in a minute, this gives a total time of 325 seconds.

☐ **16**
1 kilogram (kg) is equal to 1000 grams (g). Therefore 1 g is equal to 0.001 kg. 234 g is equal to 0.234 kg.

☐ **17**
Salt is soluble in water and so it forms a solution when mixed with water. When the solution is heated, the pure water evaporates and leaves behind the salt in crystal form.

☐ **18**
Sea water is a solution of salt and water and it can be purified – and pure water extracted – by distillation. This process involves evaporation and recondensation in order to separate a mixture of liquids. The process requires substances to have different boiling points so that they will evaporate at different times and can be separated from each other. When sea water is

heated, the pure water boils and evaporates leaving salt crystals behind. The water vapour can then be recondensed and pure water is formed. In places with very low rainfall, distillation is used on a very large scale to produce drinking water from the sea.

☐ **19** *(b)*
An insoluble solid will not dissolve in a liquid, and so it will not pass through filter paper as a liquid does. The result of filtration is that the solid will remain in the filter paper after the liquid has passed though, and thus the insoluble solid and liquid are separated. See diagram below.

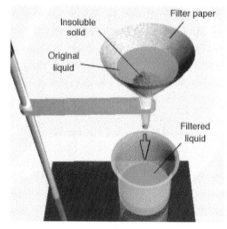

A19

☐ **20** *(c)*
Alcohol and water have very similar densities, and alcohol is soluble in water. Alcohol is non-magnetic. It is the difference in their boiling points that allows them to be separated almost completely by distillation.

☐ **21**
Salt is soluble in water and when it mixes with water a solution is formed. This solution cannot be separated by filtration because the dissolved salt particles are small enough to pass through the filter.

☐ **22**
Glass is insoluble in water, and so the beads can easily be separated from it by the process of filtration or by decanting.

☐ **23**
Chromatography should be used to determine the number of dyes present in an ink. The dyes, according to their different solubilities, will travel at different speeds through the paper and in this way are separated.

☐ **24** *(c)*
Chromatography can be used to

separate the dyes in a mixture. It relies on the varying effects of a solvent on the substances in the mixture. Typical solvents which are used are water and ethanol. The dyes will be absorbed at different speeds by the paper that is dipped into them. The diagram that follows illustrates how the dyes separate and travel to different points on the paper.

A24

☐ **25**
As the food colourings spread up the chromatogram, the dyes contained separate out. As the diagram shows, only the colour spot that indicates dye B corresponds with dye spots in both X and Y. This means that only dye B is present in both of the food colourings, X and Y.

☐ **26**
As the chromatogram shows, the colour spot for the single dye D does not correspond to any of the colour spots representing the dyes present in the colourings X and Y. This means that dye D is not present in either of the two food colourings.

☐ **27** *(c)*
The colouring Y contains three dyes which are represented by the three different colour spots in the Y column of the chromatogram. These spots correspond directly to the colour spots for the single dyes A, B, and C. This means that the colouring Y contains these three dyes.

☐ **28** *(c)*
Iron filings are magnetic whereas sulphur is not. This means that only the iron filings will be physically attracted to a magnet and in this way they can be separated from the sulphur.

☐ **29** *(e)*
Because copper sulphate is water-soluble the process of filtration cannot be used to extract the crystals from the water. In order to separate the copper sulphate

crystals from the water, the process of evaporation can be used. If the solution is left in a warm place or gently heated the water will evaporate – even below the solution's boiling point – leaving the crystals behind.

☐ **30** *(a)*
In order to separate a mixture of sand and salt to provide a sample of each material, water must be added to the mixture. The salt will dissolve in the water but the sand, which is insoluble, will not. This mixture of salt solution and sand can now be filtered to separate the sand. The salt solution is then heated until all the water evaporates, leaving solid salt crystals behind. Hence, the correct order is dissolution, filtration, and evaporation.

☐ **31** *(b)*
If the insoluble solid is denser – and therefore heavier – than the liquid, it will sink to the bottom of the container in which the mixture is placed. The liquid can then be poured out carefully (decanted) leaving the solid at the bottom of the container. This process is illustrated in the diagram below.

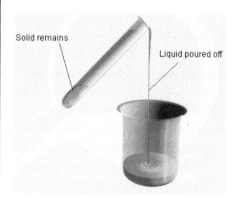

A31

☐ **32**
Copper is a non-magnetic metal and so – like sulphur – it will not be attracted to a magnet. Therefore copper, unlike magnetic iron filings, cannot be separated from sulphur by the use of a magnet.

☐ **33** *(a)*
The change in temperature that occurred during the reaction can be calculated by subtracting the reading on the thermometer at the start of the reaction (21.0°C) from the reading at the end (32.5°C). Therefore, there was a temperature rise of 11.5°C.

☐ **34** *(d)*
It is possible to separate two liquids with similar properties providing that they have different boiling points. The

mixture is heated until the liquid with the lower boiling point begins to boil and evaporate. The vapour is directed down a tube to cool and recondense into its pure liquid form. The other liquid remains at a temperature below its boiling point. This process is known as fractional distillation. It is used on a large scale to separate crude oil into its component parts.

☐ **35** *(d)*
Chromatography can be used to separate out natural colouring materials into their component parts.

☐ **36** *(c)*
As a solid changes into its liquid form – or melts – it uses the energy supplied by the heating process. This energy is absorbed during liquefication as the attractive forces between the fixed particles in the solid are overcome. The energy is no longer converted into heat and so the temperature remains constant when the substance reaches its melting point. The horizontal line on the graph indicates the time during which the temperature is constant – the melting point of 50°C.

☐ **37** *(e)*
Simple distillation can be used to separate a liquid from a solid that is in solution. The liquid evaporates and leaves the solid behind.

☐ **38** *(c)*
Fractional distillation separates liquids according to their different boiling points. Air can only be separated by this process when it is in its liquid form, as its liquid components have different boiling points. Crude oil is a liquid whose component parts have different boiling points and therefore it can be separated by fractional distillation. See diagram below.

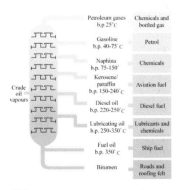

A38

☐ **39** *(a)*
When a substance is heated until it reaches temperatures above its melting point and then left to cool, its temperature will decrease until it reaches the melting point once again. At this point, the temperature remains constant while the particles in the substance arrange themselves into the regular pattern of a solid structure. The horizontal line on the graph indicates the time during which the temperature is constant. In this case this occurs at 43°C, the melting point of this substance.

☐ **40**
Sand is insoluble in water and its particles cannot pass through filter paper. Salt, however, is soluble and dissolves into very small particles that are small enough to pass through filter paper. Thus a solution of salt and water cannot be separated by filtration.

☐ **41** *(b)*
Fractional distillation separates mixtures of liquids into components, or fractions, according to their different boiling points. The fractions with the lowest boiling points boil and evaporate first and are therefore separated from the mixture first. The compounds in crude oil have different boiling points and can therefore be separated by this process.

☐ **42**
Pure water, like all pure substances, has a single precise boiling point. The boiling point of pure water is 100°C.

☐ **43** *(e)*
The diagram below illustrates a water treatment works. First, water is pumped from rivers into a reservoir, which acts as a storage facility. From here the water is channelled into the sedimentation tank where large pieces of solid matter are separated from the water. The water is then filtered through sand beds, which trap the smaller solid particles. Finally, chlorine is added to the water in order to kill the germs. The treated water is then distributed to all users by the pumping station.

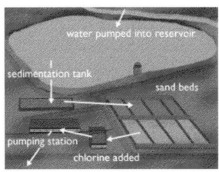

A43

☐ **44**
An electronic balance should be used to measure accurately the mass of magnesium oxide formed during the oxidation of magnesium.

☐ **45** *(b)*
As the equation below shows, water is a product, not a reactant, of the respiration equation. Aerobic respiration requires oxygen, whereas anaerobic respiration does not. Water is an essential compound that acts as a coolant for industrial machinery as well as for mammals in the form of sweat. Water is an important solvent, and it is a source of energy in the form of hydroelectric power.

Aerobic respiration equation

glucose + oxygen → water + CO_2 + energy

A45

☐ **46** *(b)*
Salt is soluble in water whereas sand is not. The two substances can be separated by mixing them with water, causing the salt to dissolve. Filtration extracts the sand, and then the salt solution can be boiled to evaporate the pure water, leaving the salt crystals behind.

Safety and laboratory techniques

Higher Level only

☐ **47** *(a)*
Titration is a process by which the concentration of one of two solutions can be calculated. One solution is added from a graduated vessel – a burette – to another until a chemical reaction occurs. The volumes of both liquids must be known, as well as the concentration of one of them. During a titration it is essential to measure accurately the small quantities of liquids involved. The most suitable apparatus to achieve this is the burette, which usually holds up to 50 cm^3.

☐ **48** *(c)*
A pipette allows the pupil to measure accurately 25 cm^3 of sodium hydroxide. A measuring cylinder should not be used because it is not accurate enough for this type of experiment, which involves very small quantities of liquids.

☐ **49** *(b)*
The volume of liquid released from a

burette can be read from the graduated scale. Remember to take the measurement from the bottom of the meniscus of the liquid inside the burette. See diagram below.

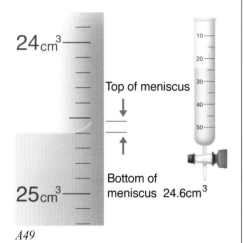

A49

☐ **50** *(d)*
The reading on the burette is 12.4 cm³. This indicates that this volume of acid was released from the burette in order to neutralize the sodium hydroxide during the titration. Once again, remember to take the measurement from the bottom of the meniscus of the liquid inside the burette.

Changes of state

Foundation and Higher Levels

☐ **1** *(b)*
Evaporation is the process by which a liquid that is below its boiling point turns into a gas. When a puddle of water is exposed to the heat of the sun, it will slowly disappear as the water evaporates and forms water vapour. Although boiling also involves a change of state from a liquid to a gas, this is a very rapid process and occurs at a specific boiling temperature.

☐ **2** *(e)*
The following statements are true:
(a) Liquids have a fixed volume
(b) Liquids flow and can be poured
(c) Liquids change their shape to fit the shape of their container
(d) Liquids are denser than gases – gases always float on top of liquids.
However, liquids cannot be compressed. The volume of a liquid only changes with a change in temperature.

☐ **3**
Because the particles in a gas are not in

close contact with each other, they can easily be pushed together.

☐ **4**
As the substance cools, it loses energy and the movement of the particles reduces. The temperature of the substance will decrease until it reaches its melting point. Then the temperature will remain constant as the particles form a regular arrangement. Once this has occurred, the temperature of the solid will decrease again until it matches that of its environment (this may be room temperature). The answer is 55°C.

☐ **5** *(c)*
When the lorry driver applies force to the brake pedal, this force needs to be transferred to the brakes. If a liquid could be compressed, the force would be used up and lost by process of changing the volume of the liquid. However, because the liquid – in this case oil – cannot be compressed, the force can be transferred through it to the brakes.

☐ **6** *(e)*
Water has a freezing point of 0°C and a boiling point of 100°C. It would be a liquid at room temperature (25°C).

☐ **7**
Sodium chloride, or common salt, is a crystalline solid, and not a liquid, at room temperature.

☐ **8** *(c)*
Neon has a boiling point of –246°C and therefore it is a gas at room temperature. When electricity is passed through neon, it glows brightly. For this reason it is often used in lighting systems for advertisements such as those in Times Square, New York.

☐ **9**
Freezing is the conversion of a liquid into its solid form. This starts to happen to each substance at a specific temperature, known as the freezing point. During winter when the temperature drops below 0°C (the freezing point of water) puddles and lakes freeze and become solid ice.

☐ **10**
When a liquid is cooled below its freezing point it will change state and solidify. When water is cooled below its freezing point (0°C) ice forms.

☐ **11**
Melting is the conversion of a solid into its liquid form. This starts to happen to each substance at a specific temperature, known as the melting point. The melting

point for a substance is also its freezing point. It is the temperature at which a substance either begins to liquefy from its solid form, when being heated, or to solidify from its liquid form, when being cooled. For example, water will freeze when cooled below 0°C, and ice will melt when heated above 0°C.

☐ **12** *(c)*
All of the substances apart from mercury convert from a solid to a liquid at temperatures above 25°C. Therefore, only mercury would be a liquid at 25°C.

☐ **13**
The process which occurs is evaporation (the conversion of a liquid into a vapour or gas) at temperatures below its boiling point. The water must change state from a liquid to a gas in order to disappear from the puddle. Evaporation would also occur if the water were to boil. However, the temperature of the water in the puddle will not reach its boiling point even on a very hot day!

☐ **14**
Condensation is the process that occurs when a gas cools and forms a liquid. In the cooling process, the particles of the gas lose their energy, their movement decreases, and the particles condense. When water vapour meets a cold surface, such as a window, it condenses and forms liquid water.

☐ **15** *(d)*
All solids have a definite shape as well as volume. It would be difficult to build with a substance that does not have a fixed shape, such as a liquid!

☐ **16** *(b)*
All forms of carbon, including diamond and graphite, are solid at room temperature (25°C).

☐ **17**
Condensation is the process by which a gas changes into a liquid. Evaporation is the process by which a liquid changes into a gas.

☐ **18** *(e)*
Sodium has a melting point of 115°C and so it is a solid at room temperature.

☐ **19** *(d)*
Air does not have a fixed volume and so it can be compressed. When a car hits a bump in the road the air in the tyre can compress ensuring a smooth ride.

□ 20
Sublimation is the process by which a solid changes directly into a gas, without becoming a liquid. When this occurs, a substance is said to sublime.

Solids, liquids, and gases

Foundation and Higher Levels

□ 1 *(d)*
The particles in a liquid are free to move around. This allows the particles to slide past each other, enabling the liquid to flow and form no fixed shape.

□ 2
As a liquid changes into a solid, the particles lose energy and form a regular fixed arrangement. The particles can still vibrate in their new position. The form of the particles does not change in any way.

□ 3 *(e)*
The particles in a solid form a fixed 3-D arrangement in which they are able to vibrate. When a solid is heated the particles do not expand, but they may move faster and further apart due to an increase in energy from the heat.

□ 4 *(d)*
As the crystal dissolves, the salt particles break off from the bulk of the crystal and spread out in the water. The particles are too small to be seen in the water, and so they seem to disappear.

□ 5 *(d)*
The particles in a gas have very small attractive forces between them, and this allows them to move far apart from each other in all directions. They move very quickly because of the large amount of energy that they possess. This energy enables them to reach the furthest parts of the container.

□ 6 *(c)*
Diffusion is the transportation of matter by the agitation – often caused by heat – of its particles. The tiny particles of a gas are in constant motion which explains how they are able to spread out and occupy all available space.

□ 7 *(a)*
When a liquid changes into a gas, the bonds between the particles are broken. Energy is required for the particles to break free from the liquid. This energy comes in the form of heat and, because this heat is used by the process of evaporation, there is no increase in temperature as the liquid – at its boiling temperature – converts into a gas.

□ 8
As the gas is heated the particles gain more energy and move faster. Unable to move outside the confines of the container, they hit its walls harder and more frequently, causing the pressure of the gas to increase.

□ 9 *(e)*
When the can is placed inside the freezer the gas inside cools and loses energy. This loss of energy causes the particles to slow down and to hit the sides of the container less frequently. This results in a decrease in the pressure of the gas.

□ 10 *(b)*
When a liquid boils, all the supplied energy (heat) is used to disperse the particles and to separate them from the liquid. Because none of the energy is stored, there is no change in temperature.

□ 11 *(b)*
As the lids are removed the molecules of the gases diffuse and spread out, reaching all parts of the jar. They are able to do this because they are small and have lots of energy to move fast.

□ 12 *(b)*
As ethanol evaporates and changes state, it uses energy. This energy – in the form of heat – is taken from your skin, which feels cold as a result.

□ 13 *(b)*
As the gas is released from the aerosol container where it is stored under pressure in a confined space, it expands very quickly. This process requires energy (heat), which it obtains from its own particles, causing the gas to cool.

□ 14 *(c)*
When a solid dissolves the tiny particles break off and disperse throughout the liquid. They become invisible but do not disappear. The form of the particles remains unaltered.

□ 15 *(c)*
The particles in a solid are positioned closely together in a firm 3-D arrangement. When the solid melts its particles break free and the distance between them increases. This means that the volume of the substance will increase but, because the number of particles present remains the same, the density will decrease. The other statements are all false for both solids and liquids.

□ 16 *(b)*
When a gas condenses to form a liquid, bonds are formed between the particles. This is an exothermic process – one that gives out heat. This heat energy warms the surface on which the condensation takes place.

□ 17 *(b)*
In order for a solid to dissolve, the particles need to break free from each other so that they can disperse throughout the liquid. The heat of the liquid provides the particles with the energy to do this, helping them to overcome their attractive forces.

□ 18 *(d)*
As a liquid changes into a gas the particles gain energy and move faster. Eventually, the particles break free from the liquid and move further apart.

□ 19 *(b)*
The solid needs to be heated in order for the particles to gain the energy required to break away from their fixed positions and to move freely. The particles do not change in mass or volume.

□ 20 *(a)*
As the solid is heated the particles gain energy, and vibrate vigorously pushing each other apart.

□ 21 *(b)*
This motion of smoke particles is known as Brownian movement (the botanist Robert Brown first observed it in 1785). Air particles move about in a random manner and collide with the smoke particles and it is these collisions that cause the erratic movement.

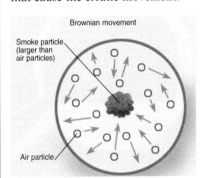

A21

□ 22 *(b)*
The erratic motion is caused by the collision of the smoke particles with the particles of air. The random movement of the smoke particles indicates that the air particles, which are too small to be seen through a microscope, are also moving about in a random manner as they collide with the smoke particles. This random motion is known as Brownian movement.

Chemical Compounds

Physical and chemical changes *(Single and Double Awards)*

The understanding that all matter is composed of many small particles leads to a greater understanding of many different parts of chemistry. The Kinetic Theory explains some of the properties of solids, liquids, and gases in terms of the movement of their particles. Changes in temperature and atmospheric conditions affect particle activity during chemical reactions. The ideas surrounding the behaviour of particles are examined in this section.

 KEY FACTS

• **Physical and chemical changes:**
Physical changes do not produce new substances and the original substances remain. Often a physical change can be reversed. Chemical changes, however, do produce new substances and, in most cases, chemical changes are not easily reversed.

 QUESTIONS

Foundation and Higher Levels

1 What occurs as a result of a chemical reaction?

- ☐ (a) A change in state
- ☐ (b) A new substance
- ☐ (c) A change in mass
- ☐ (d) A change in volume
- ☐ (e) A change in colour

2 A large amount of wood is burnt during a forest fire. What type of reaction occurs when wood is burnt?

- ☐ (a) Substitution
- ☐ (b) Thermonuclear
- ☐ (c) Displacement
- ☐ (d) Chemical
- ☐ (e) Physical

3 For what reason is the process of cooking a cake a chemical reaction?

- ☐ (a) Cooking requires heat
- ☐ (b) Cooking forms new products
- ☐ (c) The products can easily be returned to their raw materials
- ☐ (d) Cooking does not form new products
- ☐ (e) None of the above

4 Which one of the following does not involve a chemical reaction?

- ☐ (a) Making a cake
- ☐ (b) Iron rusting
- ☐ (c) Making a cup of coffee
- ☐ (d) Food rotting
- ☐ (e) Dynamite exploding

5 What type of reaction occurs when coal is burnt?

- ☐ (a) Physical
- ☐ (b) Chemical
- ☐ (c) Nuclear
- ☐ (d) Biological
- ☐ (e) Thermonuclear

6 Iron is produced from iron ore in a blast furnace (see diagram below). What type of reaction is this?

- ☐ (a) Physical
- ☐ (b) Chemical
- ☐ (c) Biological
- ☐ (d) Nuclear
- ☐ (e) Precipitation

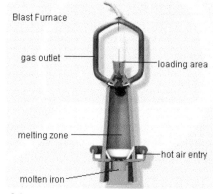
Q6

7 Oxygen condenses at a temperature of –183°C. What type of reaction is this?

- ☐ (a) Physical
- ☐ (b) Chemical
- ☐ (c) Biological
- ☐ (d) Nuclear
- ☐ (e) Chain

8 Water boils at a temperature of 100°C. What type of reaction is this?

- ☐ (a) Nuclear
- ☐ (b) Chemical
- ☐ (c) Biological
- ☐ (d) Physical
- ☐ (e) Chain

9 Which one of the following does not need to be manufactured by a process involving a chemical reaction?

- ☐ (a) Steel
- ☐ (b) Sodium chloride
- ☐ (c) Sodium hydroxide
- ☐ (d) Ammonia gas
- ☐ (e) Sulphuric acid

10 Why is it not possible to reverse the effects of rusting on iron by physical means?

- ☐ (a) Rust is insoluble in water
- ☐ (b) Rust is formed by a chemical reaction
- ☐ (b) Rust is non-reactive
- ☐ (d) Rust cannot be disintegrated
- ☐ (e) Rust is non-magnetic

11 What type of reaction takes place when sodium is heated in air and a white powder is produced?

- ☐ (a) Chemical
- ☐ (b) Physical
- ☐ (c) Biological
- ☐ (d) Neutralization
- ☐ (e) Decomposition

12 Nylon is a synthetic material. Which of the following statements about nylon is true?
i. It is a natural substance
ii. It is formed by a chemical reaction
iii. Two or more substances are required to produce nylon

- ☐ (a) i only
- ☐ (b) i and iii only
- ☐ (c) i and ii only
- ☐ (d) ii and iii only
- ☐ (e) iii only

13 Which one of the following is not a natural substance?

- ☐ (a) Water
- ☐ (b) Salt
- ☐ (c) Gold
- ☐ (d) Glass
- ☐ (e) Sand

CHEMICAL COMPOUNDS: Elements, mixtures, and compounds

14 Some plastics melt when heated. What type of change is this?

- ☐ (a) Chemical
- ☐ (b) Physical
- ☐ (c) Biological
- ☐ (d) Decomposition
- ☐ (e) None of the above

Elements, mixtures, and compounds *(Single and Double Awards)*

This section focuses on the following: elements, which are substances that cannot be decomposed into two or more individual substances; mixtures, which are systems that consist of more than one pure substance; compounds, which are species that are formed by the chemical combination of two or more elements.

KEY FACTS

• **Elements, mixtures, and compounds:**
An element is a substance that contains only one type of atom. It cannot be broken down into a simpler substance. A compound is a substance that contains two or more chemically bonded elements. A mixture contains two or more different substances.

QUESTIONS

Foundation and Higher Levels

1 Which one of the following is an element?

- ☐ (a) Nitrogen
- ☐ (b) Sulphuric acid
- ☐ (c) Chalk
- ☐ (d) Salt
- ☐ (e) Petrol

2 According to the diagram below, which of the clusters of atoms – A, B, C, D, or E – represents a compound?

....

Q2

3 Which one of the following is a compound?

- ☐ (a) Platinum
- ☐ (b) Potassium
- ☐ (c) Phosphorus
- ☐ (d) Polythene
- ☐ (e) Nickel

4 Which one of the following is a compound?

- ☐ (a) Salt
- ☐ (b) Sea water
- ☐ (c) Air
- ☐ (d) Ink
- ☐ (e) Iron

5 Which one of the following is not an element?

- ☐ (a) Oxygen
- ☐ (b) Nitrogen
- ☐ (c) Iron
- ☐ (d) Water
- ☐ (e) Copper

6 Which one of the following properties is different for all the elements which are shown in the periodic table below?

- ☐ (a) Melting point
- ☐ (b) Colour
- ☐ (c) Shape

The periodic table

Group																	0
I	**II**											**III**	**IV**	**V**	**VI**	**VII**	4 He 2
1 H 1																	
7 Li 3	9 Be 4											11 B 5	12 C 6	14 N 7	16 O 8	19 F 9	20 Ne 10
23 Na 11	24 Mg 12											27 Al 13	28 Si 14	30 P 15	32 S 16	35 Cl 17	40 Ar 18
39 K 19	40 Ca 20	45 Sc 21	48 Ti 22	51 V 23	52 Cr 24	55 Mn 25	56 Fe 26	59 Co 27	59 Ni 28	63 Cu 29	64 Zn 30	70 Ga 31	73 Ge 32	75 As 33	79 Se 34	80 Br 35	84 Kr 36
85 Rb 37	88 Sr 38	89 Y 39	91 Zr 40	93 Nb 41	96 Mo 42	Tc 43	101 Ru 44	103 Rh 45	106 Pd 46	108 Ag 47	112 Cd 48	115 In 49	119 Sn 50	122 Sb 51	128 Te 52	127 I 53	131 Xe 54
133 Cs 55	137 Ba 56	139 La 57	178 Hf 72	181 Ta 73	184 W 74	186 Re 75	190 Os 76	192 Ir 77	195 Pt 78	197 Au 79	201 Hg 80	204 Tl 81	207 Pb 82	209 Bi 83	Po 84	At 85	Rn 86
Fr 87	226 Ra 88	277 Ac 89															

Q6

☐ (d) Physical state
☐ (e) Odour

7 According to the diagram below, which of the clusters of atoms – A, B, C, D, or E – represents a molecule?

....

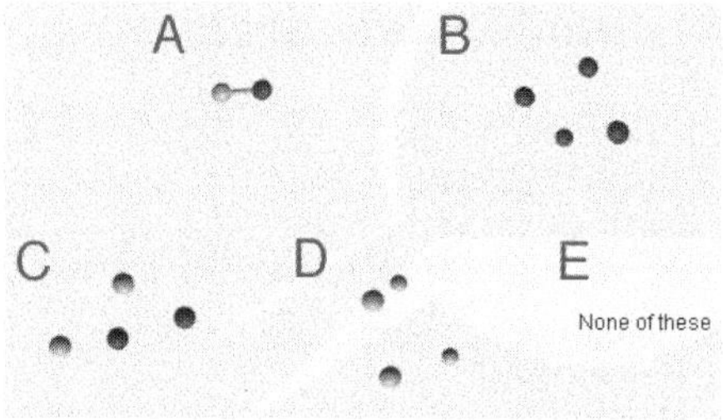

Q7

8 Which one of the following is an element?

☐ (a) Water
☐ (b) Air
☐ (c) Oxygen
☐ (d) Salt
☐ (e) Sand

9 Which one of the following is not a compound?

☐ (a) Ammonia
☐ (b) Polystyrene
☐ (c) Polyvinyl chloride (PVC)
☐ (d) Polythene
☐ (e) Silicon

10 The elements are arranged in the periodic table in groups and periods (see diagram below). How does the electron structure of the elements change as each period is moved across, from left to right?

☐ (a) Each successive element has two less electrons

☐ (b) Each successive element has one more electron
☐ (c) Each successive element has one less electron
☐ (d) Each successive element has two more electrons
☐ (e) There is no pattern

11 What percentage of the air consists of oxygen?

☐ (a) 21%
☐ (b) 78%
☐ (c) 4%
☐ (d) 49%
☐ (e) 90%

12 What term describes the type of mixture that is formed when sugar dissolves in water?

....

13 Which one of the following would enable us to determine that two metal blocks are not the same element?

☐ (a) Shape
☐ (b) Mass
☐ (c) Chemical properties
☐ (d) Volume
☐ (e) Temperature

14 When hydrogen burns in oxygen, water is formed. What happens to the molecules of hydrogen and oxygen during this process?

☐ (a) They form a mixture consisting of one oxygen molecule and two hydrogen molecules
☐ (b) They form a mixture consisting of one oxygen atom and two hydrogen atoms
☐ (c) They form a molecule consisting of one oxygen atom and two hydrogen atoms
☐ (d) They form an atom consisting of hydrogen and oxygen

☐ (e) They form a molecule consisting of any number of hydrogen and oxygen atoms

15 What do compounds consist of?

☐ (a) Identical atoms
☐ (b) Atoms of different elements that have chemically bonded
☐ (c) Molecules of the same atom
☐ (d) A mixture of different atoms
☐ (e) A mixture of different molecules

16 What happens when a compound is formed from two or more elements?

☐ (a) The atoms decrease in size
☐ (b) The atoms bond in a chemical reaction
☐ (c) The density of the atoms changes
☐ (d) The atoms mix together
☐ (e) The atoms change in volume

17 When electrons fill the electron shells surrounding a nucleus, which shells are filled first?

☐ (a) The shells with the lowest energy
☐ (b) The shells with the highest energy
☐ (c) The shells furthest from the nucleus
☐ (d) There is no pattern
☐ (e) The shells that can hold the highest number of electrons

18 Which one of the following statements describes the correct composition of air?

☐ (a) 78% nitrogen, 21% oxygen, noble gases, and variable amounts of carbon dioxide and water vapour
☐ (b) 78% oxygen, 21% nitrogen, noble gases, and variable amounts of carbon dioxide and water vapour
☐ (c) 50% oxygen, 49% nitrogen, carbon dioxide, and water vapour
☐ (d) 78% carbon dioxide, 21% oxygen, noble gases, and variable amounts of nitrogen and water vapour
☐ (e) 50% carbon dioxide, 49% oxygen, noble gases, and variable amounts of nitrogen and water vapour

19 Which substance has all of the following properties?
i. High melting point
ii. Insolubility in water
iii. Electrical non-conductivity (even when the compound is molten or in an aqueous solution)

☐ (a) Sugar
☐ (b) Copper sulphate

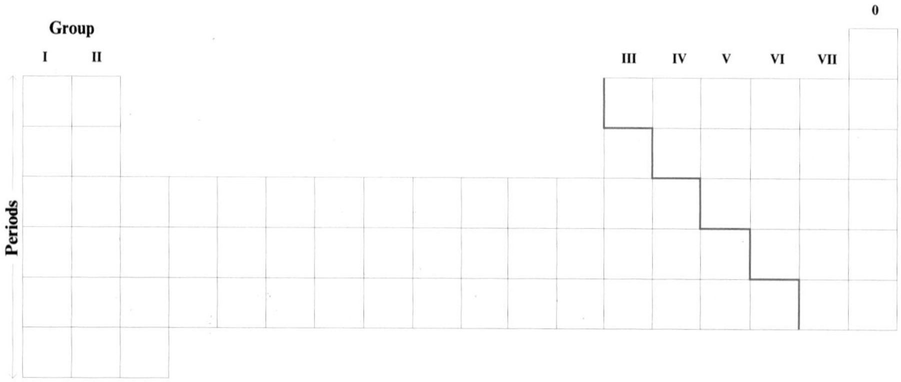

Q10

☐ (c) Diamond
☐ (d) Salt
☐ (e) Iron oxide

20 Sodium and chlorine react to form the compound sodium chloride. What happens to the sodium atoms and the chlorine atoms during this reaction?

☐ (a) Nothing
☐ (b) They form a molecule of sodium chloride
☐ (c) They form sodium ions and chloride ions
☐ (d) They form an atom of sodium chloride
☐ (e) They form a mixture of sodium molecules and chlorine molecules

ANSWERS

Physical and chemical changes

Foundation and Higher Levels

☐ **1** *(b)*
A chemical reaction always involves the formation of a new substance. This distinguishes it from a physical reaction which, like a chemical reaction, may involve changes in state, colour, shape, and volume, but which does not result in a new product.

☐ **2** *(d)*
In this instance, a chemical reaction occurs because new substances are formed. The most significant reaction that occurs when wood burns, is the one between carbon – the main material in wood – and oxygen from the air. This reaction produces a new substance – carbon dioxide.

☐ **3** *(b)*
A chemical reaction occurs when compounds react together to form a new product. The cake ingredients are the compounds (reactants) and the finished cake is the product. Although cooking requires heat, not all chemical reactions do.

☐ **4** *(c)*
A chemical reaction involves the formation of a new product from raw materials. The making of a cup of coffee is a physical reaction because no new product is formed. The coffee dissolves in the water and this new mixture can be separated into its component parts by process of evaporation. The products of a chemical reaction are not returned to their raw materials easily.

☐ **5** *(b)*
A chemical reaction occurs because new substances are formed. When coal – mainly carbon – is burnt, there is a reaction between the carbon and the oxygen, and carbon dioxide is formed.

☐ **6** *(b)*
In the blast furnace iron ore (iron oxide) undergoes a reaction to form iron. Because a new substance has been formed this reaction is a chemical one.

☐ **7** *(a)*
A physical reaction is one by which no new substances are produced. When a substance is heated or cooled to produce a physical reaction there is usually a change in the state of the materials – in this example oxygen changes from a gas into a liquid. In chemical reactions new substances are formed.

☐ **8** *(d)*
The water evaporates and changes state to become a gas, but no new products are formed in the process.

☐ **9** *(b)*
Sodium chloride (common salt) is a substance which occurs naturally and does not need to be manufactured. It is used as a raw material for the production of a number of important chemicals such as sodium hydroxide and chlorine. It is converted into these new substances by process of chemical reaction.

☐ **10** *(b)*
Rust is formed by a chemical reaction between iron and oxygen. The process requires water. Chemical reactions cannot be reversed by physical methods. The products of a chemical reaction can only be returned to the initial materials by another chemical reaction.

☐ **11** *(a)*
A chemical reaction takes place when sodium is heated in air because a new substance, sodium oxide (the white powder), is formed.

Sodium + oxygen → sodium oxide
              (from the air)

☐ **12** *(d)*
Nylon is a synthetic substance and does not occur naturally. It is manufactured from raw materials by a chemical reaction. The diagram following

illustrates the use of two substances to produce a strand of nylon.

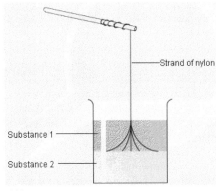

A12

☐ **13** *(d)*
A natural substance is one which occurs in nature of its own accord and which does not have to be manufactured. Glass, which has been used for over 4500 years, is manufactured by use of the reaction that occurs between sand and sodium carbonate. All the other substances listed occur naturally.

☐ **14** *(b)*
A physical change is one by which no new substances are produced. When a substance melts, this is a change of state – a physical change. A chemical change is one by which a chemical reaction takes place and a new substance is produced.

Elements, mixtures, and compounds

Foundation and Higher Levels

☐ **1** *(a)*
An element is a substance that cannot be chemically decomposed into a simpler substance. The periodic table shows all the known elements. A compound is a substance that is composed of two or more chemically bonded elements. Nitrogen is an element, whereas sulphuric acid, chalk, and salt are compounds. Petrol is a mixture of compounds.

☐ **2**
A compound is formed when two or more elements combine in a chemical reaction. E is a compound because two different elements are joined by a chemical bond. A, B, and D are elements because they consist of only one type of atom. C is a mixture because it contains two different elements that have not bonded.

☐ **3** *(d)*
Polythene is a compound consisting of hydrogen and carbon. It is a versatile plastic which can be used as a material for carrier bags. All the other substances are elements.

☐ **4** *(a)*
Salt is a chemical compound of sodium (Na) and chlorine (Cl). Sea water is a mixture of salt and water; air is a mixture of nitrogen, oxygen, and other gases; ink is a mixture of soluble dyes and a solvent; iron is an element. See diagram below.

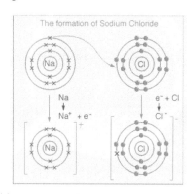

A4

☐ **5** *(d)*
Water is a compound of hydrogen and oxygen. It can be decomposed by the process of electrolysis which relies on ionization which is caused by the flowing of an electric current through the solution. See diagram below.

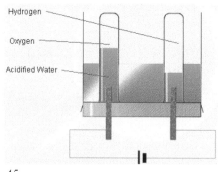

A5

☐ **6** *(a)*
The physical and chemical properties of an element are unique to it. The melting point of an element is a physical property, and therefore it is different for every element. The physical state, including the shape, of an element depends on the temperature. Some elements – many of which are shiny metals – have a distinctive colour, whereas others are colourless.

☐ **7**
Option A represents a molecule because it consists of two or more atoms that are joined by chemical bonds.

☐ **8** *(c)*
An element is a pure substance consisting of one type of atom, and it cannot be decomposed chemically into anything simpler. Oxygen is an element which contains only oxygen. Water is a compound of oxygen and hydrogen; air is a mixture of nitrogen, oxygen, and other gases; salt is a compound of chlorine and sodium; sand consists mainly of silicon dioxide.

☐ **9** *(e)*
A compound is a substance made up of two or more chemically bonded elements, and an element is a substance that cannot be broken down into simpler substances. Silicon is an element, and ammonia, polystyrene, polyvinyl chloride (PVC), and polythene are all compounds.

☐ **10** *(b)*
As the horizontal rows (the periods) are crossed, one electron is added for every element.

☐ **11** *(a)*
Air is 78% nitrogen and 21% oxygen. The remaining 1% is composed of noble gases and variable amounts of carbon dioxide and water vapour.

☐ **12**
It is a solution that is formed when sugar dissolves in water because sugar is soluble in water.

☐ **13** *(c)*
All elements have chemical and physical properties that are unique, and which therefore are distinguishing features. If the chemical properties of the metal blocks are different, the blocks are different elements. Shape, mass, volume, and temperature are properties that constantly vary and do not necessarily indicate a difference in element.

☐ **14** *(c)*
When hydrogen and oxygen react and form water, they form molecules with the constant ratio of two hydrogen atoms to every oxygen atom. The following diagram shows a water molecule.

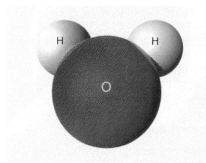

A14

☐ **15** *(b)*
A compound is a single substance that contains two or more different elements that have chemically bonded. An element consists of the same type of atoms. A mixture contains different substances, elements, or compounds.

☐ **16** *(b)*
When a chemical reaction occurs between two or more elements, the atoms form chemical bonds.

☐ **17** *(a)*
The electron shells with the lowest energy levels (those closest to the nucleus) are filled first.

☐ **18** *(a)*
Air is composed of 78% nitrogen and 21% oxygen. The remaining 1% contains noble gases and variable amounts of carbon dioxide and water vapour.

☐ **19** *(c)*
Diamond, which has a giant covalent structure, is the only substance listed that has all of these properties.

☐ **20** *(c)*
When sodium and chlorine react, sodium loses an electron and becomes a positive ion as a result. Chlorine gains an electron and becomes a negative ion. These new ions, which are oppositely charged, are attracted to each other in an ionic bond. The ions form a giant lattice structure and no molecules are formed. See diagram below.

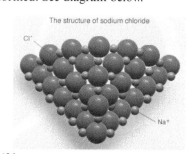

A20

Atoms and Bonding

Atomic structure *(Single and Double Awards)*

For many years it was thought that the smallest particle in matter was an atom. However, in the early part of the twentieth century Ernest Rutherford carried out an experiment that 'split the atom', and the modern atomic theory was born. The idea that atoms contain three fundamental particles – the proton, the neutron, and the electron – has had great success in explaining patterns in the properties of elements. The following questions test knowledge and understanding of simple atomic theory.

 ### KEY FACTS

• **Structure of matter:** The smallest part of an element that can take part in a chemical reaction is an atom. The atom itself is made up of three smaller particles. The protons and neutrons are found in the nucleus of the atom, and the electrons are found around the outside of the atom in electron shells (energy levels).

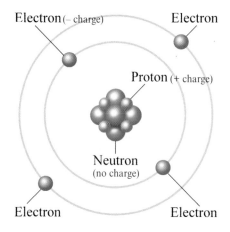

Atomic structure

• **Charge and mass:** The particles of the atom have the following relative charges and mass:

Particle	Charge	Mass
Electron	−1	0 (1/1800)
Proton	+1	1
Neutron	0	1

• **Mass number and atomic number:** An element is given two numbers – a mass number and an atomic number. The mass number is the sum of the number of protons and neutrons in the nucleus of that atom. The atomic number of an atom is the number of protons in the nucleus of an atom. The atomic number is fixed and indicates which element it is. It is also equal to the number of electrons that surround the nucleus. A sample of almost any element will contain some atoms that have a different mass number to the rest. These atoms are known as isotopes. An isotope is an atom of an element that has the same atomic number but a different mass number because it has a different number of neutrons in the nucleus. Examples of two isotopes of carbon are carbon–12 (^{12}C) and carbon–14 (^{14}C). Carbon–12 has six protons and six neutrons in the nucleus of each atom, and carbon–14 has six protons and eight neutrons in the nucleus of each atom.

• **Electron arrangement:** The electrons that surround the atom are arranged into electron shells, which are able to hold a fixed number of electrons. The first shell can hold up to two electrons, the second shell up to eight, and the third shell up to eighteen. Any remaining electrons are placed into the fourth shell. The number of electrons in each energy level (or shell) of an element is known as the electron arrangement (structure) of the element. The shells are filled from the centre outwards and a new shell is only filled when the previous one is full.

 ### QUESTIONS

Foundation and Higher Levels

1 Which of the following does an atom contain?

- ☐ (a) Protons only
- ☐ (b) Protons and neutrons only
- ☐ (c) Protons, neutrons, and electrons
- ☐ (d) Neutrons and electrons only
- ☐ (e) Electrons only

2 What is contained in the nucleus of an atom?

- ☐ (a) Electrons
- ☐ (b) Neutrons only
- ☐ (c) Electrons and protons only
- ☐ (d) Protons and neutrons only
- ☐ (e) Protons, neutrons, and electrons

3 Where are the electrons found in an atom?

- ☐ (a) In the nucleus
- ☐ (b) Orbiting the nucleus
- ☐ (c) On the outer edge of the nucleus
- ☐ (d) Combined with the neutrons
- ☐ (e) Atoms do not contain electrons

4 How many electrons can the second electron shell hold?

- ☐ (a) 8
- ☐ (b) 2
- ☐ (c) 10
- ☐ (d) 18
- ☐ (e) 6

5 What is an ion?

- ☐ (a) An atom, or group of atoms, that is arranged in a special way
- ☐ (b) An atom that shares electrons with another atom
- ☐ (c) An atom, or group of atoms, that has lost or gained electrons
- ☐ (d) An atom, or group of atoms, that has unstable nuclei
- ☐ (e) An atom, or group of atoms, that has different numbers of neutrons

6 A chlorine atom contains 17 protons. What is the electronic structure of chlorine?

- ☐ (a) 2.6.9
- ☐ (b) 10.7
- ☐ (c) 2.8.7
- ☐ (d) 2.8.4
- ☐ (e) 2.3.5.7

7 An element has an atomic number of 15. What will its electronic structure be?

- ☐ (a) 2.7.6
- ☐ (b) 8.7
- ☐ (c) 2.8.7
- ☐ (d) 2.8.5
- ☐ (e) 2.2.6

Chemical bonding *(Double Award only)*

There are over one hundred elements and many millions of compounds. Atoms are able to form bonds with other atoms. There are certain rules relating to the combination of atoms, and this section tests the understanding of these rules.

QUESTIONS

Foundation and Higher Levels

1 How many electrons can the first shell of an atom hold?

- ☐ (a) 36
- ☐ (b) 8
- ☐ (d) 10
- ☐ (d) 18
- ☐ (e) 2

2 An atom contains three protons, four neutrons, and three electrons. What would the atomic number be for this atom?

- ☐ (a) 6
- ☐ (b) 3
- ☐ (c) 7
- ☐ (d) 4
- ☐ (e) 10

3 An atom has an atomic number of 11 and a mass number of 23. How many protons would this atom have in its nucleus?

- ☐ (a) 22
- ☐ (b) 12
- ☐ (c) 11
- ☐ (d) 23
- ☐ (e) 34

4 An atom contains five protons, six neutrons, and five electrons. What would the mass number be for this atom?

- ☐ (a) 11
- ☐ (b) 5
- ☐ (c) 6
- ☐ (d) 10
- ☐ (e) 16

5 A carbon atom has six protons and six neutrons. What is its electronic structure?

- ☐ (a) 2.4
- ☐ (b) 6
- ☐ (c) 8.4
- ☐ (d) 2.8.2
- ☐ (e) 2.2.2

6 An aluminium atom has 13 protons and 14 neutrons.

What is its electronic structure?

- ☐ (a) 8.8.8.3
- ☐ (b) 2.8.4
- ☐ (c) 2.8.8.9
- ☐ (d) 2.8.3
- ☐ (e) 8.5

7 An atom has an atomic number of 14 and a mass number of 29. How many electrons would the atom have in its nucleus?

- ☐ (a) 14
- ☐ (b) 29
- ☐ (c) 15
- ☐ (d) 0
- ☐ (e) 43

8 An atom has an atomic number of 12 and a mass number of 25. How many electrons would the atom have in shells around its nucleus?

- ☐ (a) 0
- ☐ (b) 13
- ☐ (c) 12
- ☐ (d) 25
- ☐ (e) 37

9 An atom has an atomic number of 14 and a mass number of 29. How many electrons would the atom have in shells around its nucleus?

- ☐ (a) 14
- ☐ (b) 15
- ☐ (c) 28
- ☐ (d) 29
- ☐ (e) 43

10 Which of the following explains what happens to a metal atom when it reacts to form an ionic compound?

- ☐ (a) It loses neutrons
- ☐ (b) It gains electrons
- ☐ (c) It shares electrons
- ☐ (d) It becomes negatively charged
- ☐ (e) It loses electrons

11 When an element loses an electron, or electrons, from its outer shell, why does it gain a positive charge?

- ☐ (a) It gains protons at the same time
- ☐ (b) It gains neutrons at the same time
- ☐ (c) It now has more protons than electrons
- ☐ (d) It now has more electrons than protons
- ☐ (e) It now has more neutrons than protons

12 Why do atoms of elements lose or gain electrons in the formation of an ionic bond?

- ☐ (a) So that their outer shell can overlap with other atoms
- ☐ (b) So that they can have a noble gas electronic structure
- ☐ (c) So that they can change into a different element
- ☐ (d) So that they can gain energy
- ☐ (e) So that they can become neutral

13 What happens during the formation of an ionic bond?

- ☐ (a) The atoms share electrons
- ☐ (b) There is a transfer of electrons
- ☐ (c) The atoms join together
- ☐ (d) There is a transfer of protons
- ☐ (e) None of the above

14 Which of the following pairs of elements, when they react to form a compound, form ionic bonds?

- ☐ (a) Oxygen and hydrogen
- ☐ (b) Sodium and chlorine
- ☐ (c) Chlorine and hydrogen
- ☐ (d) Carbon and oxygen
- ☐ (e) Nitrogen and hydrogen

15 Which of the following dot and cross diagrams represents the correct diagram for sodium chloride?

....

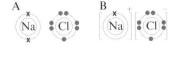

Q15

16 Table salt (sodium chloride) is an ionic compound containing two ions

27

– sodium and chloride. What are the charges on these ions (metal and non-metal respectively)?

☐ (a) +1, –1
☐ (b) +2, –1
☐ (c) +1, –2
☐ (d) +2, –2
☐ (e) –2, +2

17 The solid magnesium fluoride is an ionic compound. What is the charge of the magnesium ion in this compound?

☐ (a) +2
☐ (b) +1
☐ (c) –2
☐ (d) –3
☐ (e) +3

18 What type of compounds do metals form when they react with non-metals?

☐ (a) Simple covalent
☐ (b) Metallic
☐ (c) Ionic
☐ (d) They do not form compounds
☐ (e) Giant covalent

19 Magnesium, a group II metal, reacts with fluorine. Which of the following statements about this reaction are true?
i. The magnesium will form a +2 ion
ii. The electrons from the magnesium will be transferred to one fluorine atom
iii. The compound will be solid

☐ (a) i only
☐ (b) i and ii only
☐ (c) i, ii, and iii
☐ (d) ii only
☐ (e) i and iii only

20 Which of the following dot and cross diagrams represents the correct diagram for magnesium flouride?

....

Q20

21 When magnesium burns in air it forms the compound magnesium oxide. What is the charge on the oxide ion in this compound?

☐ (a) –3
☐ (b) +3
☐ (c) –1
☐ (d) +2
☐ (e) –2

QUESTIONS
Higher Level only

22 When non-metal elements react together they form covalent compounds. The atoms are held together by the sharing of electrons to form covalent bonds. How many electrons are shared in a single covalent bond?

☐ (a) 3
☐ (b) 1
☐ (c) 2
☐ (d) 5
☐ (e) 8

23 What is a covalent bond?

☐ (a) The transfer of electrons between two atoms
☐ (b) The sharing of a pair of electrons between two atoms
☐ (c) The transfer of protons between two atoms
☐ (d) The sharing of a pair of protons between two atoms
☐ (e) The attraction of two oppositely charged particles

24 What happens to the outer-shell electrons when a covalent bond is formed between two atoms?

☐ (a) One atom loses an electron, the other gains one
☐ (b) They both gain electrons
☐ (c) The electrons of both atoms become delocalized
☐ (d) An electron from each atom is shared
☐ (e) A new shell of electrons is added

25 A reaction between which pairs of the following elements would produce covalent bonds?

☐ (a) Sodium and chlorine
☐ (b) Sodium and oxygen
☐ (c) Potassium and chlorine
☐ (d) Hydrogen and chlorine
☐ (e) Magnesium and oxygen

26 Why do ionic compounds have high melting and boiling points?

☐ (a) The bonds between the atoms are very strong
☐ (b) The ions are very big
☐ (c) The bonds between the ions are very strong
☐ (d) Electrons are delocalized and cement the ions together tightly
☐ (e) Protons are free to move and they attract negative ions strongly

27 Oxygen has six electrons in its outer shell, and so needs to gain two electrons to have a full outer shell. Carbon has four electrons in its outer shell, and therefore needs to gain four electrons to have a full outer shell. How many oxygen atoms would have to combine with a carbon atom so that each had a full outer shell of electrons?

☐ (a) 2
☐ (b) 4
☐ (c) 1
☐ (d) 6
☐ (e) 8

28 An oxygen atom reacts with another oxygen atom to form a molecule. How many single covalent bonds does oxygen need to form in order to obtain a full outer shell of electrons?

☐ (a) 4
☐ (b) 2
☐ (c) 1
☐ (d) 3
☐ (e) 6

29 Which of the following dot and cross diagrams represents the correct diagram for water?

....

Q29

30 Which one of the following is not a property of ionic compounds, such as sodium chloride?

- ☐ (a) High melting points
- ☐ (b) Solubility in organic solvents
- ☐ (c) Electrical conductivity when molten
- ☐ (d) Electrical conductivity when in solution
- ☐ (e) Giant crystal lattice structure

31 When a metal and non-metal react together an ionic compound is formed. These compounds are solids and generally have high melting points. How are particles held together in ionic compounds?

- ☐ (a) Ions are formed that join to form one large molecule
- ☐ (b) Oppositely charged ions, which attract each other, are formed
- ☐ (c) Ions are formed, their outer shells overlap, and this holds the compound together
- ☐ (d) Electrons become delocalized and they act as a cement holding the atoms together
- ☐ (e) Electrons from different atoms are shared, and this holds the atoms together

32 Ionic compounds will conduct electricity when molten or in solution, but not when they are solid. Why is this?

- ☐ (a) When molten or in solution, the atoms are free to move
- ☐ (b) The electrons cannot pass through a solid
- ☐ (c) When molten or in solution, the ions are held in position
- ☐ (d) When molten or in solution, the electrons are free to move
- ☐ (e) When molten or in solution, the ions are free to move

33 Sodium chloride will conduct electricity when molten, but not when solid. Why is this?

- ☐ (a) When molten, the ions are free to move
- ☐ (b) When molten, the electrons are free to move
- ☐ (c) When solid, the electrons are free to move
- ☐ (d) When solid, the ions are free to move
- ☐ (e) When solid, the molecules are free to move

34 Sodium and hydrogen both react with chlorine to produce chlorides. What is the difference between the chlorides?

- ☐ (a) Sodium chloride is an ionic compound, hydrogen chloride is a giant covalent compound
- ☐ (b) Sodium chloride is an ionic compound, hydrogen chloride is a simple covalent compound
- ☐ (c) Sodium chloride is a giant covalent compound, hydrogen chloride is a simple covalent compound
- ☐ (d) Sodium chloride is a giant covalent compound, hydrogen chloride is an ionic covalent compound
- ☐ (e) Sodium chloride is a simple covalent compound, hydrogen chloride is an ionic compound

---

Molecules and giant structures *(Double Award only)*

Why are some substances gases and others solids? Ethene is a gas whereas polythene is a solid. Knowledge of the structure of substances helps chemists provide some answers. An understanding of this topic is tested in the following section.

QUESTIONS

Foundation and Higher Levels

1 Both diamond and graphite contain only carbon atoms. Diamond is the hardest known naturally occurring substance, but graphite is a very soft material. Why is there a difference?

- ☐ (a) Carbon atoms in diamond are bonded to five other carbon atoms, making it a stronger structure
- ☐ (b) In graphite, each atom is bonded to three others, forming large layers. There are weak bonds between the layers of atoms
- ☐ (c) All the bonds in diamond are shorter than those in graphite
- ☐ (d) Diamond is an ionic substance and graphite is covalent
- ☐ (e) Carbon atoms in graphite have only two bonds, making it a weaker structure

2 Which of the following is not a natural fibre?

- ☐ (a) Cotton
- ☐ (b) Wool
- ☐ (c) Hemp
- ☐ (d) Silk
- ☐ (e) Polythene

3 Which one of the following statements explains why diamond is the hardest known naturally occurring substance?

- ☐ (a) The bonds between the ions in diamonds are very strong
- ☐ (b) The bonds between the molecules in diamonds are very strong
- ☐ (c) The bonds between the atoms in diamonds are very strong
- ☐ (d) The bonds between the ions in diamonds are very weak
- ☐ (e) There are double bonds between the atoms in diamonds

4 Ceramics have very high melting points. They do not conduct electricity and are very hard. What type of structure is likely to be present in ceramics?

- ☐ (a) Simple ionic
- ☐ (b) Simple covalent
- ☐ (c) Giant covalent
- ☐ (d) Metallic
- ☐ (e) Giant ionic

5 Why is there a difference between the properties of diamond and the properties of graphite?

- ☐ (a) Diamond and graphite contain different atoms
- ☐ (b) Diamond and graphite are different compounds
- ☐ (c) Diamond and graphite contain mixtures of different atoms
- ☐ (d) Diamond and graphite contain the same atoms but have different structures
- ☐ (e) Diamond and graphite are different elements

QUESTIONS

Higher Level only

6 Most simple covalent substances are either gases or volatile liquids, such as bromine. What is the reason for the relatively low melting and boiling points of these simple covalent substances?

- ☐ (a) The bonding between the ions is very strong
- ☐ (b) The bonding between the atoms in the molecules is very strong
- ☐ (c) The bonding between the ions is very weak
- ☐ (d) The bonding between the molecules is weak
- ☐ (e) None of the above

7 Which of the following statements explains why metals are able to conduct electricity?

- ☐ (a) The ions in metals are free to move
- ☐ (b) The electrons that surround the metal ions are free to move
- ☐ (c) The molecules in metals are free to move
- ☐ (d) The bonds between the atoms are weak
- ☐ (e) The bonds between the ions are weak

8 Plastics consist mainly of carbon and hydrogen atoms that are arranged into very long chains known as polymer molecules. Which of the following statements explains why plastics do not conduct electricity?

- ☐ (a) They contain non-metal elements
- ☐ (b) The bonds within the polymer are very strong
- ☐ (c) The polymer molecules are randomly arranged
- ☐ (d) The bonds between the polymer molecules are weak
- ☐ (e) They contain no delocalized electrons

ANSWERS

Atomic structure

Foundation and Higher Levels

☐ 1 (c)
The diagram below represents the atomic structure of an element. The atom of any element contains protons (shown in red) and neutrons (shown in blue), which both form the nucleus, and electrons (shown in green), which orbit the nucleus. The exception is hydrogen, which only contains one proton and one electron.

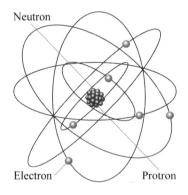

Neutron

Electron   Protron

A1, 2, 3

☐ 2 (d)
The nucleus of an atom contains protons (shown in red in previous diagram) and neutrons (shown in blue). The exception to this is hydrogen, which only has one proton in its nucleus and no neutrons.

☐ 3 (b)
The electrons, which are shown in green in the previous diagram, orbit the nucleus of an atom.

☐ 4 (a)
The electrons in an atom are found in shells around the nucleus. The first shell can hold up to two electrons and the second shell can hold up to eight electrons.

☐ 5 (c)
An ion is formed when an atom, or group of atoms, loses or gains electrons. This results in the ion having either a positive or a negative charge. The only ion to have no electrons at all is the hydrogen ion H^+, which consists of a single proton.

☐ 6 (c)
A chlorine atom contains 17 protons and therefore 17 electrons. The first electron shell can hold up to two electrons and the second up to eight, which means the remaining seven electrons must go into the third shell. The electronic structure of chlorine is therefore 2.8.7.

☐ 7 (d)
The atom of an element that has an atomic number of 15 will also contain 15 electrons. The first two electrons are contained in the first shell and the next eight in the second shell. This means that the five remaining electrons are contained in the third shell. Therefore the electronic structure of this element will be 2.8.5.

Chemical bonding

Foundation and Higher Levels

☐ 1 (e)
The electrons in an atom are found in shells around the nucleus. The first shell can hold up to two electrons, and the second can hold up to eight electrons.

☐ 2 (b)
The atomic number equals the number of protons in the nucleus. Therefore, this atom has an atomic number of three. Its mass number is seven (mass number = the number of protons + the number of neutrons).

☐ 3 (c)
The atomic number equals the number of protons in the nucleus, and so this atom's nucleus will contain 11 protons. It will also have 11 electrons in shells around the nucleus (the number of protons = the number of electrons) and 12 neutrons in the nucleus (the number of neutrons = the mass number minus the atomic number).

☐ 4 (a)
The mass number equals the number of protons plus the number of neutrons in the nucleus. Therefore, this atom has an mass number of 11 (5 + 6). Its atomic number is 5 (atomic number = the number of protons in the nucleus).

☐ 5 (a)
A carbon atom contains six protons and therefore six electrons. The first electron shell can contain up to two electrons and the second up to eight. The

electronic structure of carbon is therefore 2.4.

□ **6** *(d)*
An aluminium atom contains 13 protons and therefore 13 electrons. The first electron shell can contain up to two electrons, the second up to eight electrons, and the third up to eighteen. The electronic structure of aluminium is therefore 2.8.3. See diagram that follows.

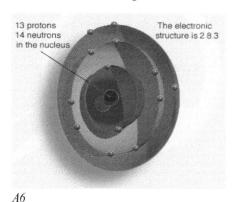

13 protons
14 neutrons
in the nucleus

The electronic
structure is 2.8.3

A6

□ **7** *(d)*
Electrons are never found in the nucleus, they are always in shells around the nucleus. As the atomic number equals the number of protons in the nucleus, this atom's nucleus will contain 14 protons. It also has 14 electrons in shells around the nucleus, as the number of protons equals the number of electrons. There are 15 neutrons in the nucleus (the number of neutrons = the mass number minus the atomic number).

□ **8** *(c)*
The atomic number equals the number of protons in the nucleus, and so this atom's nucleus will contain 12 protons. It therefore has 12 electrons in shells around the nucleus, as the number of protons always equals the number of electrons. It also has 13 neutrons in the nucleus (the number of neutrons = the mass number minus the atomic number).

□ **9** *(a)*
The atomic number equals the number of protons in the nucleus, and so this atom's nucleus will contain 14 protons. It therefore has 14 electrons in shells around the nucleus, as the number of protons always equals the number of electrons. It also has 15 neutrons in the nucleus (the number of neutrons = the mass number minus the atomic number).

□ **10** *(e)*
When a metal atom reacts with a non-metal to form an ionic compound, it loses electrons in order to obtain a more stable electronic structure. Sodium

(atomic number 11) has 11 electrons and an electronic structure 2.8.1. It needs to lose one electron in order to have the stable noble gas structure of 2.8. As it loses the electron, the sodium will now be positively charged as it has more protons than electrons. This charged particle is called an ion.

□ **11** *(c)*
An atom has the same number of protons and electrons. So, if it loses an electron, it will have more protons than electrons and, therefore, it will have a positive charge. For example, a sodium atom has 11 protons and 11 electrons. When a sodium ion is formed it loses an electron, leaving an ion with 11 protons and 10 electrons, giving a resulting charge of +1. See diagram that follows.

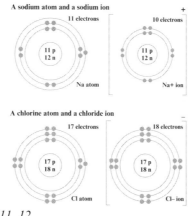

A sodium atom and a sodium ion

11 electrons
11 p
12 n
Na atom

10 electrons +
11 p
12 n
Na+ ion

A chlorine atom and a chloride ion

17 electrons
17 p
18 n
Cl atom

18 electrons −
17 p
18 n
Cl− ion

A11, 12

□ **12** *(b)*
The electronic structure of a noble gas is a stable one and therefore when atoms react they try to obtain this noble gas structure by losing or gaining electrons. When sodium (2.8.1) and chlorine (2.8.7) react there is a transfer of one electron from the sodium atom to the chlorine atom. This results in the formation of two ions, each with an electronic structure of the nearest noble gas (neon 2.8 and argon 2.8.8). See previous diagram.

□ **13** *(b)*
During the formation of an ionic bond there is a transfer of electrons from one atom to another. The metal transfers electrons from its outer shell to the outer shell of the non-metal, and ions are formed that are attracted to each other because of their opposite charges. This attraction is known as an ionic bond. Ionic bonds are formed between metals and non-metals.

□ **14** *(b)*
Only a metal and a non-metal can form an ionic bond. Therefore, from the

suggestions given, only sodium and chlorine would react in this way.

□ **15**
The correct diagram is represented by E. Sodium has an electronic structure of 2.8.1. It loses the one electron in its outer shell to form a positive ion, and so now has the electronic structure 2.8. Chlorine has an electronic structure of 2.8.7, and by gaining the electron from sodium it forms a negative ion 2.8.8. In the diagram below, the electrons of sodium are shown by crosses and those of chlorine by dots.

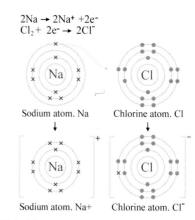

$2Na \rightarrow 2Na^+ + 2e^-$
$Cl_2 + 2e^- \rightarrow 2Cl^-$

Na

Cl

Sodium atom. Na

Chlorine atom. Cl

Na +

Cl −

Sodium atom. Na+

Chlorine atom. Cl−

A15, 16

□ **16** *(a)*
When a compound of sodium chloride is formed, the sodium gives up its one outer-shell electron to the chlorine. The sodium ion now has one more proton than electron, and so has a charge of +1. The chlorine has gained one electron and so has one more electron than proton. It now has a charge of −1. See previous diagram.

□ **17** *(a)*
Magnesium atoms have two electrons in their outer shell, which they lose to obtain a full shell of electrons and so become stable. The resulting ion now has two more protons than electrons, and, therefore, has a charge of +2. These electrons are donated to two fluorine atoms to make two fluoride ions, each with a charge of −1.

□ **18** *(c)*
When a metal and a non-metal react they form an ionic compound that has ionic bonds. An example of this is sodium chloride (common salt). An electron is transferred from sodium to chlorine, producing two oppositely charged ions that are held together by electrostatic forces. This attraction is known as an ionic bond.

☐ **19** *(e)*
When a metal element in group II forms an ionic compound it will need to lose two electrons to gain a noble gas configuration. It will therefore form a +2 ion. As each fluorine atom only needs to gain one electron to reach a noble gas structure, one electron from the magnesium will be transferred to each of two fluorine atoms. The formula of the new compound is MgF_2. All ionic compounds are solids. See diagram below.

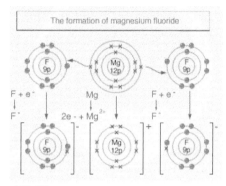

A19, 20

☐ **20**
The correct diagram is D. Magnesium has an electronic structure of 2.8.2. It loses the two electrons in its outer shell to form a positive ion, and so now has the electronic structure 2.8. Fluorine has an electronic structure of 2.7 and, by gaining one of the electrons from magnesium, it forms a negative ion with a structure of 2.8. As magnesium needs to lose two electrons, and a fluorine atom can only accept one, another fluorine atom is needed. The formula of the compound is MgF_2. In the previous diagram, the electrons of magnesium are shown by crosses and those of fluorine, by dots.

☐ **21** *(e)*
When the oxygen atoms in the air react with the magnesium, they form ions by gaining two electrons to obtain a full outer shell of electrons. By gaining two electrons the oxygen ions now have two more electrons than protons, and thus a charge of –2.

Chemical Bonding

Higher Level only

☐ **22** *(c)*
When non-metals react to form compounds they share electrons in order to obtain a full shell of electrons. Each single covalent bond has two electrons that are shared between the

two different atoms. In the diagram that follows, the electrons of hydrogen are represented by crosses, and those of oxygen and nitrogen by dots.

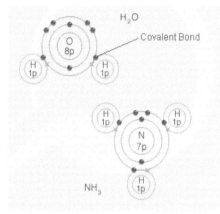

A22, 23

☐ **23** *(b)*
A covalent bond occurs when a pair of electrons is shared between two atoms, so that each atom has a full outer shell of electrons.
See diagram above.

☐ **24** *(d)*
Both the non-metal elements want to get full outer shells of electrons and, in this way, become stable. They do this by sharing electrons when their orbits overlap, as shown in the diagram that follows. An electron from hydrogen is shown by a cross and one from chlorine by a dot. This shared pair of electrons is called a covalent bond.

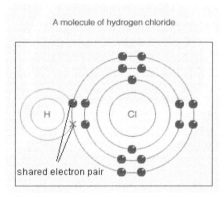

A24, 25

☐ **25** *(d)*
Covalent bonds are formed between atoms of non-metal elements. Therefore, the only pair of elements that would produce a covalent bond are chlorine and hydrogen as they are both non-metals. See previous diagram.

☐ **26** *(c)*
In order for a solid to become a liquid, the bonds between the particles need to break so that the particles are free to

move. If the bonds between the particles are strong it will take more energy to break the bonds, and therefore the melting point will be high. Ionic compounds have strong forces of attraction between the ions and so they have high melting points.

☐ **27** *(a)*
Each of the oxygen atoms share two electrons with the carbon atom, to make two pairs of shared electrons. This results in the two oxygen atoms and the carbon atom having a full outer shell of electrons. The new compound is carbon dioxide, CO_2. See diagram that follows.

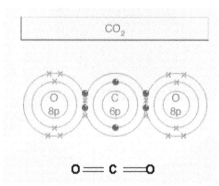

A27

☐ **28** *(b)*
There are six electrons in the outer shell of an oxygen atom and it requires two more to obtain a full outer shell. An oxygen atom will share two of its electrons with another oxygen atom. This means that there are two shared pairs of electrons and each shared pair is known as a covalent bond.

☐ **29**
The correct diagram is A. There are six electrons in the outer shell of an oxygen atom and so it requires two more to obtain a full outer shell. An oxygen atom will share one of its electrons with the electron from a hydrogen atom, forming a covalent bond. This is repeated with another hydrogen atom and so the formula of water is H_2O. See diagram that follows. The electrons of hydrogen are shown by dots and those of oxygen by crosses.

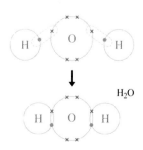

A29

32

□ **30** *(b)*
Organic solvents are non-polar, which means that there are no charges on the molecules. In contrast, ionic solids are made up of positively and negatively charged ions and so they are polar solids. As a general rule, a polar solid will only dissolve in polar solvents, such as water, and non-polar solids will only dissolve in non-polar solvents.

□ **31** *(b)*
Oppositely charged ions are formed and there is a force of attraction between them. This holds them together in a giant three-dimensional structure. The following diagram shows the structure of sodium chloride, which consists of positive sodium ions and negative chloride ions. The structure is a regular one and is known as a lattice.

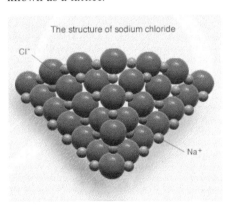

A31

□ **32** *(e)*
In order for an ionic compound to conduct electricity, the ions have to be free to move so that they can act as electricity carriers. When the ionic compound is dissolved in water or melted, the crystal lattice breaks down and the ions become free to move. When the ions are free to move the negative ions are attracted to the positive electrode, where they give up their electrons and become atoms. Positive ions are attracted to the negative electrode, where they gain electrons to become atoms.
See diagram that follows.

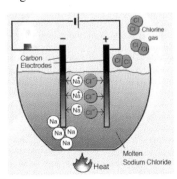

A32, 33

□ **33** *(a)*
Sodium chloride consists of positive sodium ions and negative chloride ions in a three-dimensional crystal lattice. When solid, the ions are fixed in position and are therefore unable to act as a conductors of electricity. When molten, the crystal lattice breaks down so the ions are free to move and can act as electricity carriers. Therefore, molten sodium chloride is a good conductor of electricity.
See previous diagram.

□ **34** *(b)*
The chlorides of metals are usually ionic compounds and the chlorides of non-metals are often simple covalent compounds.

Molecules and giant structures

Foundation and Higher Levels

□ **1** *(b)*
The diagram that follows shows the covalent structures of diamond and graphite. In diamond, each carbon atom is bonded to four others, forming a very strong three-dimensional giant structure. In graphite, each atom is bonded to only three others, forming layers that are weakly held together. These layers can slide over one another easily, making graphite very soft.

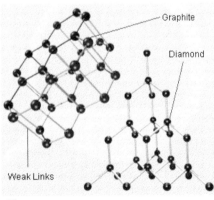

A1

□ **2** *(e)*
Cotton and hemp are natural plant fibres. Silk and wool are natural animal fibres. Polythene is a man-made (synthetic) fibre, produced from a fraction of crude oil.

□ **3** *(c)*
The structure of a diamond consists of a giant three-dimensional covalent molecule that contains no ions. Each atom is strongly bonded by a single

covalent bond to four other atoms. This results in a very strong structure.

□ **4** *(c)*
The properties of ceramics suggest that they are giant covalent structures. See diagram that follows. They consist of a giant covalent arrangement of silicon and oxygen atoms that are bonded together in long chains. These chains are held together by metal ions such as aluminium and so, although the structure is predominately a giant covalent one, it is really a combination of two structures.

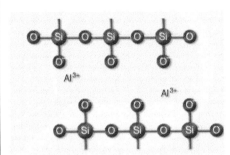

A4

□ **5** *(d)*
Diamond and graphite are both composed of carbon atoms and, therefore, are not different elements. They are not compounds. The difference in properties between the two arises because of the different structural arrangements of the carbon atoms. See diagram that follows.

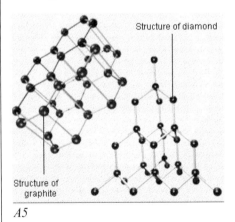

A5

Molecules and giant structures

Higher Level only

□ **6** *(d)*
In order for a substance to change from a liquid to a gas, bonds between the particles have to be broken. If the forces between the particles are weak, the boiling point will be low. For a simple

covalent substance, such as bromine, the bonding between the molecules is weak and so the substance has a low melting and a low boiling point. It is important to remember that the actual covalent bonds are strong and that these are not broken.

□ **7** *(b)*
The following diagram shows the structure of a metal, which consists of positive metal ions embedded in a sea of delocalized electrons. These electrons are free to move, and this allows the conduction of electricity.

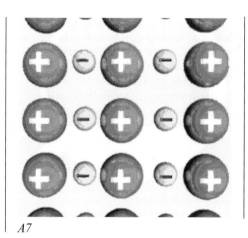

A7

□ **8** *(e)*
The polymer chains in plastics are randomly arranged. All bonding electrons are involved in forming bonds. As a result, there are no delocalized electrons and therefore plastics do not conduct electricity. They are insulators.

Extraction and Uses of Materials

Manufacturing processes *(Double Award only)*

Chemists have found ways to change many natural materials into substances that are more useful to humankind. Some substances, such as steel and ammonia, are manufactured in huge amounts. Knowledge and understanding of some of these important manufacturing processes are tested below.

KEY FACTS

• **Extraction and reactivity:** To obtain pure metals from compounds in the rocks that make up the Earth's crust, an extraction process has to take place. The method of extraction depends upon the type of metal. The more reactive a metal, the harder it is to extract. Very unreactive metals such as gold, silver, and copper can be found as free metal in the Earth's crust. Other metals can be extracted by using reduction with carbon, and by electrolysis.

• **Electrolysis:** Reactive metals such as sodium, potassium, and calcium can only be extracted by the electrolysis of the molten chloride. The chlorides of the elements are heated until they melt and then an electric current is passed through them. The metal collects at the negative electrode, and chlorine is produced at the positive electrode.

• **Reduction with carbon:** Metals that are less reactive than carbon can be extracted using carbon or carbon monoxide as the reducing agent. In the extraction of iron, iron ore (iron oxide), limestone, and coke (carbon) are placed into a blast furnace and hot air is blown in. The coke reacts with the air to produce carbon dioxide, and this carbon dioxide then reacts with more coke to produce carbon monoxide. It is the carbon monoxide that reacts with the iron oxide to produce iron. The limestone in the furnace decomposes to produce calcium oxide, which reacts with the impurities in the ore to produce slag. The molten iron, which is produced, is tapped off from the bottom of the blast furnace.

• **Purification of metals:** The extraction of metals does not always produce pure metals and therefore the metal has to undergo a further process of purification. In the case of copper this is done by electrolysis. The impure copper is made by the anode in an electrolysis cell and a piece of very pure copper is made by the cathode. The electrolyte is copper sulphate solution. When a current of electricity is passed through the cell the copper is transferred from the anode to the cathode and thus the copper is purified. The insoluble impurities, which can include gold and silver, collect at the bottom of the cell.

• **Production of ammonia:** Ammonia is produced in the Haber process by the reaction of nitrogen from the air with hydrogen (obtained from natural gas), as shown by the following equation:
$$N_2 + 3H_2 \rightleftharpoons 2NH_3$$
The reaction is reversible and a 10% yield of ammonia is produced at the conditions chosen. The usual industrial conditions for this reaction are a temperature of 450°C and a pressure of 200 atmospheres, with iron or iron oxide used as a catalyst.

• **Manufacture of fertilizers:** The ammonia produced in the Haber process is used to make fertilizers, which promote the growth of plants and thus increase the yield of plant crops. The fertilizers are produced by first converting the ammonia to nitric acid and reacting this with ammonia to produce ammonium nitrate. Reacting the ammonia with either sulphuric or phosphoric acids can produce other ammonium fertilizers. The excessive use of fertilizers can lead to eutrophication, which results in the death of animal and plant life in rivers and lakes. It has also been suggested that the excess nitrates in the drinking water supply can be a cause of cancer.

QUESTIONS

Foundation and Higher Levels

1 Why is the electrolysis of sodium chloride solution such an important industrial process?

- ☐ (a) It uses unwanted salt deposits
- ☐ (b) It provides the raw materials for a number of other important industrial processes
- ☐ (c) It is a good way of using up excess electricity
- ☐ (d) A plant would provide a vast number of jobs
- ☐ (e) None of the above

2 What are the products formed from the electrolysis of sodium chloride solution?

- ☐ (a) Hydrogen and sodium hydroxide
- ☐ (b) Sodium, hydrogen, and chlorine
- ☐ (c) Chlorine, hydrogen, and sodium hydroxide
- ☐ (d) Sodium hydroxide and hydrochloric acid
- ☐ (e) Chlorine and sodium hydroxide

3 A large sodium chloride electrolysis plant is situated close to a town. What is the main danger associated with this?

- ☐ (a) The salt mined for the plant can cause subsidence
- ☐ (b) Chlorine gas might escape from the plant
- ☐ (c) Sodium hydroxide is a strong base and reacts exothermically with water
- ☐ (d) Chlorine is highly explosive
- ☐ (e) There are no safety problems

4 In the industrial manufacture of ammonia by the Haber process, a catalyst is used. What is the purpose of the catalyst?

- ☐ (a) It increases the yield of ammonia
- ☐ (b) It increases the rate of reaction
- ☐ (c) It reduces the amount of impurities in the ammonia
- ☐ (d) It increases the pressure of the reaction
- ☐ (e) It heats the reaction vessel

5 Calcium carbonate has a number of industrial uses, one of which is the production of quicklime. What is quicklime?

- ☐ (a) Sodium oxide
- ☐ (b) Calcium dioxide
- ☐ (c) Calcium carbonate
- ☐ (d) Calcium oxide
- ☐ (e) Caustic soda

6 When limestone is heated it will undergo thermal decomposition to produce calcium oxide and carbon dioxide. If water is added to the calcium oxide there is an exothermic reaction and a new compound is formed. What is the common name for this compound?

- ☐ (a) Quicklime
- ☐ (b) Slowlime
- ☐ (c) Slagged lime
- ☐ (d) Wet lime
- ☐ (e) Slaked lime

7 What are the solid raw materials that are used for the extraction of iron in a blast furnace

- ☐ (a) Limestone, iron ore, and wood
- ☐ (b) Limestone and iron ore
- ☐ (c) Limestone, coke, and steel
- ☐ (d) Limestone, coke, and iron ore
- ☐ (e) Coke and iron

8 In which of the following processes is limestone used?

- ☐ (a) In the manufacture of sulphuric acid
- ☐ (b) In the manufacture of sodium metal
- ☐ (c) In the manufacture of glass and cement
- ☐ (d) In the manufacture of ammonia
- ☐ (e) In the manufacture of oxygen

9 What substance is formed when calcium oxide (quicklime) is reacted with water?

....

10 What type of reaction does limestone undergo when heated?

- ☐ (a) Electrolysis
- ☐ (b) Thermal decomposition
- ☐ (c) Dissociation
- ☐ (d) Displacement
- ☐ (e) Precipitation

11 Limestone is used in the extraction of iron in the blast furnace to remove the impurities. What is the common name of the compound formed when the impurities are removed?

- ☐ (a) Slag
- ☐ (b) Slog
- ☐ (c) Pig
- ☐ (d) Sled
- ☐ (e) Sludge

12 Limestone will undergo thermal decomposition when heated. What are the products of this reaction?

- ☐ (a) Carbon monoxide and calcium dioxide
- ☐ (b) Carbon calcide and calcium oxide
- ☐ (c) Carbon dioxide and calcium oxide
- ☐ (d) Carbon monoxide and calcium oxide
- ☐ (e) Carbon and calcium

13 Limestone is used in the manufacture of iron in the blast furnace. What is the purpose of adding the limestone?

- ☐ (a) It is a catalyst
- ☐ (b) It removes the impurities
- ☐ (c) It increases the yield
- ☐ (d) It helps to keep the blast furnace hot
- ☐ (e) It contains iron

14 What is the name given to the reaction when a metal is extracted from its metal oxide?

- ☐ (a) Oxidation
- ☐ (b) Displacement
- ☐ (c) Reduction
- ☐ (d) Neutralization
- ☐ (e) Precipitation

15 What are fertilizers used for?

- ☐ (a) To promote plant growth
- ☐ (b) To prevent the growth of weeds
- ☐ (c) To kill pests
- ☐ (d) To reduce the pH of the soil
- ☐ (e) To improve the flavour of crops

16 Which one of the following could be used as a fertilizer?

- ☐ (a) Sodium chloride
- ☐ (b) Ammonium nitrate
- ☐ (c) Potassium chloride
- ☐ (d) Calcium carbonate
- ☐ (e) Copper sulphate

17 Why is it necessary for fertilizers to be water soluble?

- ☐ (a) So that they can be absorbed easily by the plants
- ☐ (b) So that the excess can be washed away by the rain
- ☐ (c) So that they can be stored in solution
- ☐ (d) So that they cannot be eaten by small mammals
- ☐ (e) None of the above

18 Which of the following can be a problem when using many fertilizers?

- ☐ (a) The excess fertilizer can be washed into rivers and streams
- ☐ (b) The fertilizer can be blown away by the wind
- ☐ (c) The fertilizer can be eaten by small animals
- ☐ (d) The fertilizer can damage the crops as it is spread onto the fields
- ☐ (e) None of the above

19 Which one of the following products made from ammonia is not used as a fertilizer?

- ☐ (a) Nitric acid
- ☐ (b) Urea
- ☐ (c) Ammonium nitrate
- ☐ (d) Liquid ammonia
- ☐ (e) Ammonium sulphate

20 Which of the following would be used in the manufacture of nitrogenous fertilizer?

- ☐ (a) Nitric acid and ammonia
- ☐ (b) Sulphuric acid and calcium phosphate
- ☐ (c) Nitric acid and calcium sulphate
- ☐ (d) Hydrochloric acid and magnesium nitrate
- ☐ (e) Sulphuric acid and ammonium nitrate

21 Ammonia is used to produce fertilizers such as ammonium sulphate and ammonium nitrate. What type of reaction is used to make these fertilizers?

- ☐ (a) Oxidation
- ☐ (b) Reduction
- ☐ (c) Displacement
- ☐ (d) Neutralization
- ☐ (e) Polymerization

22 Which one of the following does not have to be manufactured by a chemical reaction?

- ☐ (a) Steel
- ☐ (b) Sodium chloride
- ☐ (c) Sodium hydroxide
- ☐ (d) Ammonia gas
- ☐ (e) Sulphuric acid

23 The Haber process combines nitrogen and hydrogen to form ammonia. A suitable amount of pressure and heat is used, as well as a catalyst, to ensure that the process produces a profitable amount of ammonia. What pressure is usually applied in the Haber process?

☐ (a) 150–350 atmospheres
☐ (b) 0–150 atmospheres
☐ (c) 350–550 atmospheres
☐ (d) 550–750 atmospheres
☐ (e) 750–1000 atmospheres

24 The Haber process combines nitrogen and hydrogen to form ammonia. A suitable amount of pressure and heat is used, as well as a catalyst to ensure the process produces a profitable amount of ammonia. What temperature, in °C, is usually used in the Haber process?

☐ (a) 50–200
☐ (b) 200–350
☐ (c) 350–500
☐ (d) 500–650
☐ (e) 650–800

25 Which raw materials are used to manufacture ammonia?

☐ (a) Nitrogen and hydrogen
☐ (b) Nitrogen and oxygen
☐ (c) Nitric acid and sodium oxide
☐ (d) Lime and water
☐ (e) Sulphuric acid and ammonium nitrate

26 What is the source of the nitrogen that is used in the manufacture of ammonia in the Haber process?

☐ (a) Fertilizers
☐ (b) Natural gas
☐ (c) Air
☐ (d) Green plants
☐ (e) Sunlight

27 What is the source of the hydrogen that is used in the manufacture of ammonia in the Haber process?

☐ (a) Green plants
☐ (b) Air
☐ (c) Sunlight
☐ (d) Methane
☐ (e) Electrolysis of sea water

28 What are the conditions usually required in the Haber process for the manufacture of ammonia?

☐ (a) A pressure of 700 atmospheres and a temperature of 200°C
☐ (b) A pressure of 1000 atmospheres and a temperature of –35°C
☐ (c) A pressure of two atmospheres and a temperature of 245°C
☐ (d) A pressure of 50 atmospheres and a temperature of 45°C
☐ (e) A pressure of 250 atmospheres and a temperature of 450°C

29 Which of the following processes is used to manufacture nitric acid?

☐ (a) The neutralization of sulphuric acid with ammonium hydroxide
☐ (b) The reduction of nitrogen using water
☐ (c) The oxidation of ammonia
☐ (d) The reaction of sodium nitrate and hydrochloric acid
☐ (e) None of the above

30 Nitric acid is produced by the catalytic oxidation of ammonia. What can nitric acid be used for?

☐ (a) The manufacture of fertilizers
☐ (b) The manufacture of plastics
☐ (c) The manufacture of chlorine
☐ (d) The manufacture of steel
☐ (e) The manufacture of aluminium

31 What is the main use of the iron that is produced in a blast furnace?

☐ (a) Conversion to steel
☐ (b) Making cast iron
☐ (c) Making saucepans
☐ (d) Making fireplaces
☐ (e) Making aeroplanes

32 Aluminium is extracted from its ore by electrolysis. What is the name of aluminium ore?

☐ (a) Azurite
☐ (b) Haematite
☐ (c) Magnetite
☐ (d) Malachite
☐ (e) Bauxite

33 Aluminium is extracted from its molten oxide by electrolysis. What is added to the molten oxide to reduce its melting point? See diagram below.

☐ (a) Sulphuric acid
☐ (b) Salt
☐ (c) Cryolite
☐ (d) Oxygen
☐ (e) Carbon

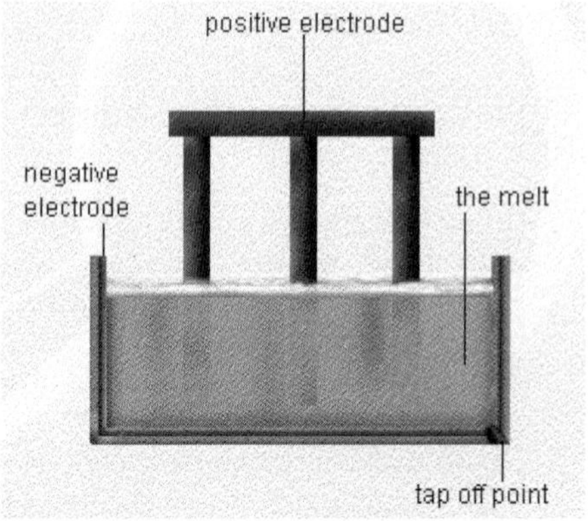

Q33

34 Slag is the mixture formed when the impurities in iron ore react with calcium oxide (formed by the thermal decomposition of calcium carbonate). What is the slag used for once it has been removed from the blast furnace?

☐ (a) It is recycled and the calcium oxide is removed and used again
☐ (b) It is used to make glass
☐ (c) It is used in the foundations of roads
☐ (d) It is dumped in the sea
☐ (e) It is used to produce calcium metal

35 Study the following map and decide which site – A, B, C, D, or E – would be the best location for a new sodium chloride solution electrolysis plant.

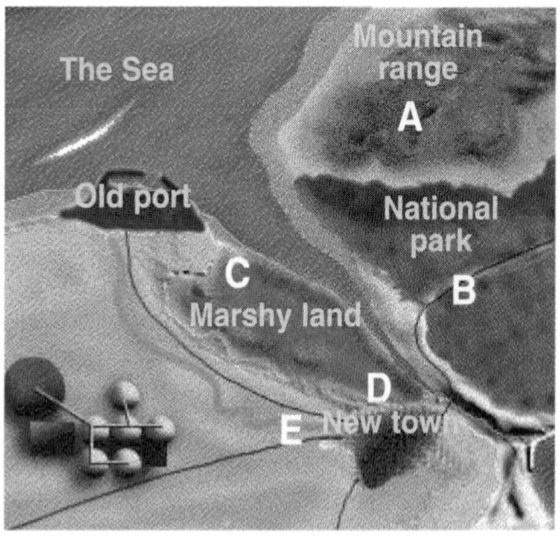

Q35

36 Aluminium is extracted from its molten ore by electrolysis. What material are the anodes made from?

☐ (a) Steel
☐ (b) Copper
☐ (c) Iron
☐ (d) Graphite
☐ (e) Zinc

37 Why would a sodium chloride solution electrolysis plant be situated close to a salt deposit?

☐ (a) The salt is used to make the sodium chloride solution
☐ (b) The salt is used as a fuel
☐ (c) The salt is used to absorb the chlorine produced
☐ (d) The salt is used to remove the impurities from the sodium chloride solution
☐ (e) None of the above

38 Why would a sodium chloride solution electrolysis plant be situated close to a dam?

☐ (a) The plant uses a large amount of water
☐ (b) The dam is a source of hydroelectric power
☐ (c) Water in the dam provides the salt that the plant requires
☐ (d) The river that flows into the dam provides a means of transporting the product and the raw materials to and from the plant
☐ (e) None of the above

39 In the industrial electrolysis of sodium chloride solution, why is sodium not produced at the cathode?

☐ (a) The sodium ions are not free to move
☐ (b) The solution contains no sodium ions
☐ (c) The sodium ions are too reactive to accept electrons when there are other ions in the solution
☐ (d) The sodium ions are only attracted to the anode
☐ (e) The sodium ions are negative

40 What do we call a reaction in which a substance breaks down into other substances when heated?

☐ (a) Thermal decomposition
☐ (b) Dissociation
☐ (c) Displacement
☐ (d) Electrolysis
☐ (e) Precipitation

41 Which one of the following substances will undergo the process of thermal decomposition?

☐ (a) Salt
☐ (b) Calcium carbonate
☐ (c) Gold
☐ (d) Calcium oxide
☐ (e) Carbon

42 When iron is extracted from its ore in the blast furnace, a process called reduction takes place. What does reduction mean here?

☐ (a) The addition of oxygen
☐ (b) Reducing the size of the ore
☐ (c) The removal of oxygen
☐ (d) The removal of impurities
☐ (e) The removal of basic slag

43 Copper is purified by electrolysis, as shown in the diagram that follows. Why is copper, and not hydrogen, discharged at the cathode?

☐ (a) The solution does not contain hydrogen ions
☐ (b) The copper is less reactive than the hydrogen

☐ (c) Hydrogen is discharged at the anode
☐ (d) Hydrogen has a negative charge
☐ (e) None of the above

Q43

44 What is produced at the anode in the purification of copper by process of electrolysis?

☐ (a) Copper metal
☐ (b) Copper (Cu^{2+}) ions
☐ (c) Hydrogen
☐ (d) Oxygen
☐ (e) Chlorine

45 The diagram that follows shows the purification of copper by electrolysis. What is the substance labelled X?

☐ (a) Pure copper
☐ (b) Remains of insoluble copper ore
☐ (c) Impure copper
☐ (d) Copper sulphate
☐ (e) Melted copper ore

Q45

46 What happens at the cathode during the purification of copper by electrolysis?

☐ (a) It gets covered in the impurities
☐ (b) Hydrogen gas is given off
☐ (c) It gets covered in pure copper
☐ (d) It is reduced in size
☐ (e) Metals other than copper are deposited

QUESTIONS

Higher Level only

47 Read the following two statements concerning the industrial electrolysis of sodium chloride solution, and decide if each one is true or false.
i. Sodium is not produced at the cathode
ii. Sodium metal is less reactive than hydrogen gas

	Statement i	Statement ii
☐ (a)	True	True
☐ (b)	False	False
☐ (c)	True	False
☐ (d)	False	True
☐ (e)	Not enough information to answer	

48 Which of the following statements about the electrolysis of sodium chloride solution are true?
i. Chlorine is discharged at the anode
ii. The solution contains two different positive ions
iii. Hydrogen ions are discharged at the cathode

☐ (a) i, ii, and iii
☐ (b) ii and iii only
☐ (c) i only
☐ (d) ii only
☐ (e) iii only

49 Which of the following lists all of the ions that are present in a solution of sodium chloride and water?

☐ (a) Sodium and chloride
☐ (b) Sodium, chloride, and hydrogen
☐ (c) Hydroxide and sodium
☐ (d) Sodium, chloride, hydrogen, and hydroxide
☐ (e) Chloride and hydrogen

50 Which of the following factors will increase the yield of ammonia during the Haber process? (The formation of ammonia is an exothermic process.)
i. An increase in pressure
ii. The addition of a catalyst
iii. An increase in temperature

☐ (a) i only
☐ (b) i and ii only
☐ (c) i, ii, and iii
☐ (d) iii only
☐ (e) ii only

51 Which ions would be left in the solution if the industrial electrolysis of sodium chloride solution was left running for a long time?

☐ (a) Hydrogen and hydroxide
☐ (b) Sodium and chloride
☐ (c) Sodium and hydroxide
☐ (d) Chloride and hydroxide
☐ (e) Sodium only

52 What is the percentage yield of ammonia from the reaction between hydrogen and nitrogen in the Haber process if only 6.4 kg was produced from a total mass of 64 kg of gases?

☐ (a) 100%
☐ (b) 59%
☐ (c) 10%
☐ (d) 25%
☐ (e) 75%

53 In the industrial manufacture of ammonia by the Haber process a temperature of 450°C is used, even though the reaction is exothermic. What is the reason for this high temperature in the process?

☐ (a) It increases the yield of ammonia
☐ (b) It reduces the amount of impurities in the ammonia
☐ (c) It increases the rate of reaction
☐ (d) It decreases the pressure of the reaction
☐ (e) The heat from the reaction reaches this temperature

54 The production of ammonia in the Haber process is an exothermic process. How is the position of equilibrium changed if there is a decrease in the temperature?

☐ (a) The equilibrium moves up
☐ (b) The equilibrium moves to the left
☐ (c) The equilibrium moves to the right
☐ (d) The equilibrium moves down
☐ (e) The equilibrium is not affected by the decrease in temperature

55 If ammonia is removed from the reaction vessel as soon as it is produced, what would happen to the position of equilibrium?

☐ (a) The equilibrium is unaffected
☐ (b) The equilibrium moves to the left
☐ (c) The equilibrium no longer exists
☐ (d) The equilibrium moves to the right
☐ (e) None of the above

56 In the manufacture of sulphuric acid, sulphur dioxide is reacted with oxygen to produce sulphur trioxide, as shown in the following equation:
$$2SO_2(g) + O_2(g) \rightleftharpoons 2SO_3(g)$$
The production of sulphur trioxide is exothermic. How would the position of equilibrium be affected if there is a decrease in temperature?

☐ (a) It moves to the right
☐ (b) It is destroyed
☐ (c) It stays the same

☐ (d) It goes all the way to completion
☐ (e) It moves to the left

57 During the manufacture of sulphuric acid, sulphur dioxide is reacted with oxygen to produce sulphur trioxide, as shown in the following equation:
$$2SO_2(g) + O_2(g) \rightleftharpoons 2SO_3(g)$$
How is the yield of sulphur trioxide affected if a catalyst is used?

☐ (a) The yield is increased
☐ (b) The yield is decreased but it is produced more quickly
☐ (c) The yield and rate remain the same
☐ (d) The yield is increased and it is produced more quickly
☐ (e) The yield is unchanged

58 Which one of the following reactions takes place at the anode during the electrolysis of sodium chloride solution?

☐ (a) Sodium ion + one electron → sodium atom
☐ (b) Sodium atom + one electron → sodium ion
☐ (c) Two chlorine atoms + two electrons → one chlorine molecule
☐ (d) Two hydrogen ions + two electrons → one hydrogen molecule
☐ (e) Two chloride ions → one chlorine molecule + two electrons

Electrolysis (Double Award only)

Electrolysis, which is the conduction of electricity through substances to induce chemical changes, has an important role in modern chemistry. Several substances are manufactured by electrolysis, which is also used in the extraction of metals from their ores. The following questions test knowledge of these processes.

QUESTIONS

Foundation and Higher Levels

1 What is the term for a chemical reaction caused by electricity?

☐ (a) Electrocution
☐ (b) Electrolysis
☐ (c) Electrocation
☐ (d) Displacement
☐ (e) None of the above

2 What is electrolysis?

☐ (a) The passage of electricity through a solid
☐ (b) The transfer of electrons

☐ (c) The transfer of ions
☐ (d) A chemical reaction caused by electricity
☐ (e) A displacement reaction

3 What is the term for liquids that will undergo electrolysis?

☐ (a) Electrodes
☐ (b) Cathodes
☐ (c) Anions
☐ (d) Cations
☐ (e) Electrolytes

4 Which scientist was the founder of electrochemistry?

☐ (a) Faraday
☐ (b) Einstein

☐ (c) John Dalton
☐ (d) Chadwick
☐ (e) Marie Curie

5 Which of the following statements are true?
i. The anode is positive
ii. The cathode is negative
iii. The electrons enter the electrolyte down the anode

☐ (a) i and iii only
☐ (b) i and ii only
☐ (c) ii and iii only
☐ (d) iii only
☐ (e) i only

6 Read the following two statements about the anode electrode and decide if each one is true or false?
i. The anode attracts negative ions
ii. The anode is the negative electrode

	Statement i	Statement ii
☐ (a)	True	True
☐ (b)	False	False

- ☐ (c) True   False
- ☐ (d) False   True
- ☐ (e) Not enough information to answer

7 Read the following two statements about the cathode electrode and decide if each one is true or false?
i. The cathode is the positive electrode
ii. The cathode attracts positive ions

	Statement i	Statement ii
☐ (a)	True	True
☐ (b)	False	False
☐ (c)	True	False
☐ (d)	False	True
☐ (e)	Not enough information to answer	

8 What must all electrolytes contain if they are to conduct electricity?

- ☐ (a) Free electrons
- ☐ (b) Protons
- ☐ (c) Free ions
- ☐ (d) Neutrons
- ☐ (e) Beta particles

9 What is produced at the anode when copper sulphate solution is electrolyzed using copper electrodes?

- ☐ (a) Sulphur
- ☐ (b) Copper metal
- ☐ (c) Oxygen
- ☐ (d) Hydrogen
- ☐ (e) Copper ions

10 What is the process called in which electrolysis is used to put a layer of one metal on the surface of another?

- ☐ (a) Electron-layering
- ☐ (b) Electroplating
- ☐ (c) Spraying
- ☐ (d) Electron-transfer
- ☐ (e) Electrolysis

11 Which one of the following ions would not be attracted to an anode?

- ☐ (a) Chloride
- ☐ (b) Hydroxide
- ☐ (c) Hydrogen
- ☐ (d) Sulphate
- ☐ (e) Nitrate

12 Which of the following is produced at the cathode during the electrolysis of copper sulphate solution using copper electrodes?

- ☐ (a) Sulphur
- ☐ (b) Copper metal
- ☐ (c) Oxygen

- ☐ (d) Hydrogen
- ☐ (e) Copper ions

13 Why is it that ionic solids will not conduct electricity, yet their solutions will undergo electrolysis and conduct electricity?

- ☐ (a) The solids have no ions
- ☐ (b) The ions are not free to move in the solid
- ☐ (c) The solutions contain free electrons
- ☐ (d) The solids contain no free electrons
- ☐ (e) The electrons can only pass through a liquid

14 Why will sodium chloride not conduct electricity but molten (liquid) sodium chloride will?

- ☐ (a) The solid does not contain any electrons
- ☐ (b) The solid does not contain any ions
- ☐ (c) The solid does not contain any free electrons
- ☐ (d) The liquid has ions that are free to move
- ☐ (e) None of the above

15 Which one of the following substances is produced at the anode when molten sodium chloride is electrolyzed?

- ☐ (a) Hydrogen
- ☐ (b) Chlorine
- ☐ (c) Sodium
- ☐ (d) Oxygen
- ☐ (e) Bromine

16 Which one of the following substances is produced at the cathode when molten sodium chloride is electrolyzed?

- ☐ (a) Hydrogen
- ☐ (b) Sodium ions
- ☐ (c) Sodium
- ☐ (d) Oxygen
- ☐ (e) Chlorine

17 Which of the following is produced at the anode if sodium chloride solution is electrolyzed?

- ☐ (a) Hydrogen
- ☐ (b) Chlorine
- ☐ (c) Oxygen
- ☐ (d) Sodium
- ☐ (e) None of the above

18 What is produced at the cathode when a solution of sodium chloride in water is electrolyzed?

- ☐ (a) Hydrogen
- ☐ (b) Chlorine
- ☐ (c) Oxygen
- ☐ (d) Sodium
- ☐ (e) None of the above

19 What is formed at the cathode during the electrolysis of copper chloride solution?

- ☐ (a) Copper
- ☐ (b) Chlorine
- ☐ (c) Oxygen
- ☐ (d) Hydrogen
- ☐ (e) Sodium

20 What is formed at the anode during the electrolysis of dilute sulphuric acid solution, using carbon electrodes?

- ☐ (a) Hydrogen
- ☐ (b) Sulphur
- ☐ (c) Chlorine
- ☐ (d) Oxygen
- ☐ (e) Copper

21 Which of the following is formed at the cathode during the electrolysis of potassium bromide solution, using carbon electrodes?

- ☐ (a) Bromine
- ☐ (b) Potassium
- ☐ (c) Hydrogen
- ☐ (d) Potassium ions
- ☐ (e) Oxygen

22 Which of the following is formed at the anode during the electrolysis of potassium bromide solution using carbon electrodes?

- ☐ (a) Bromine
- ☐ (b) Potassium
- ☐ (c) Hydrogen
- ☐ (d) Potassium ions
- ☐ (e) Oxygen

23 Which of the following statements explains why electrolysis is considered to be a reduction and an oxidation (redox) reaction?

- ☐ (a) Oxygen is released at the cathode
- ☐ (b) There is a loss and gain of electrons
- ☐ (c) Hydrogen is absorbed at the anode
- ☐ (d) Both hydrogen and oxygen can be produced depending on the type of electrolyte
- ☐ (e) None of the above

24 A pupil wanted to plate a ring with nickel. She set up a circuit like the one shown in the following diagram. Which one of the following should be used as the electrolyte?

- ☐ (a) Copper sulphate solution
- ☐ (b) Salt solution
- ☐ (c) Pure water
- ☐ (d) Nickel sulphate solution
- ☐ (e) Hydrochloric acid

Q24

Application of materials *(Double Award only)*

Chemistry is concerned with making substances, and it is important to know what the products of the chemical industry can be used for. The following questions contain many facts and ideas about the various applications of chemical materials.

QUESTIONS

Foundation and Higher Levels

1 Which one of the following is a use for sodium chloride (common salt)?

- ☐ (a) An additive in the food industry
- ☐ (b) Purifying drinking water
- ☐ (c) In the manufacture of steel
- ☐ (d) In the manufacture of aluminium
- ☐ (e) None of the above

2 Which one of the following elements do fuels react with to produce fire?

- ☐ (a) Oxygen
- ☐ (b) Nitrogen
- ☐ (c) Hydrogen
- ☐ (d) Sulphur
- ☐ (e) Carbon

3 Carbon dioxide does not support combustion. Which one of the following properties makes it particularly useful and efficient in putting out fires?

- ☐ (a) It is colourless
- ☐ (b) It is heavier than air
- ☐ (c) It contains oxygen
- ☐ (d) It is acidic
- ☐ (e) It dissolves in water

4 If a chip pan caught fire at home, which of the following should you not use to extinguish the flames?

- ☐ (a) Halon
- ☐ (b) Carbon dioxide
- ☐ (c) Water
- ☐ (d) Dry powder
- ☐ (e) Foam

5 Which one of the following does not need tensile strength?

- ☐ (a) A tent rope
- ☐ (b) A tow bar
- ☐ (c) An anchor chain
- ☐ (d) A house brick
- ☐ (e) A bicycle chain

6 Which of the following is the most important property required for a material that is to be used for the foundations of a large building?

- ☐ (a) Compressive strength
- ☐ (b) Porosity
- ☐ (c) Electrical conductivity
- ☐ (d) Tensile strength
- ☐ (e) Thermal conductivity

7 Which of the following is the most important property required for a material that is to be used for the cables of a suspension bridge?

- ☐ (a) Compressive strength
- ☐ (b) Porosity
- ☐ (c) Electrical conductivity
- ☐ (d) Tensile strength
- ☐ (e) Thermal conductivity

8 Which of the following statements explains why cables made from steel are used to support sections of suspension bridges?

- ☐ (a) Steel has a low tensile strength
- ☐ (b) Steel has a low compressive strength
- ☐ (c) Steel has a high compressive strength
- ☐ (d) Steel has a high tensile strength
- ☐ (e) Steel has a high relative hardness

9 The following table lists data referring to five unknown materials – A, B, C, D, and E. Using the data, select the material that would be the most suitable for the foundations of a large building.

....

	Relative compressive strength
A	0.4
B	3.7
C	1.9
D	4.8
E	1.0

Q9

10 Why are steel cables added to concrete when it is used to manufacture a large span for a suspension bridge?

- ☐ (a) It reduces the cost
- ☐ (b) It increases the compressive strength of the concrete
- ☐ (c) It increases the tensile strength of the concrete
- ☐ (d) It decreases the porosity of the concrete
- ☐ (e) It increases the thermal conductivity of the concrete

11 Why do foods such as margarines contain anti-oxidants?

- ☐ (a) To prevent the foods from becoming saturated fats
- ☐ (b) To make the foods taste better
- ☐ (c) To stop the foods going off
- ☐ (d) To make sure that the foods react with the hydrogen in the air and therefore keep fresh
- ☐ (e) To make sure that the foods keep their colour

12 Overhead cables carry very high voltages of electricity. Which of the following would be the most suitable material for a cover for the cable?

- ☐ (a) Copper
- ☐ (b) Aluminium
- ☐ (c) Rubber
- ☐ (d) Glass
- ☐ (e) Concrete

13 The following table lists data referring to five unknown materials – A, B, C, D, and E. Using the data, which of these materials would be the most suitable for insulating exposed electric wires?

....

	Relative electrical conductivity
A	150.0
B	1.0
C	0.3
D	60.0
E	11200.0

Q13

14 Which one of the following is the best material for the surface of an electric kettle?

- ☐ (a) Perspex
- ☐ (b) Plastic
- ☐ (c) Nylon
- ☐ (d) Polyester
- ☐ (e) Metal

15 Which one of the following is a natural substance?

- ☐ (a) Bronze
- ☐ (b) Brass
- ☐ (c) Gold
- ☐ (d) Steel
- ☐ (e) Pewter

16 Which of the following materials could be used to cut glass, if glass has a relative hardness of 5.5?

Material	Hardness
☐ (a) Steel	7.0
☐ (b) Nickel	5.5
☐ (c) Concrete	5.0
☐ (d) Tin	1.5
☐ (e) Wood	3.0

17 You are developing a new drill for an oil rig. Which of the following materials could be used to drill through bedrock with a relative hardness of 7.5?

Material	Hardness
☐ (a) V	7.0
☐ (b) W	5.5
☐ (c) X	8.0
☐ (d) Y	6.5
☐ (e) Z	3.0

18 What type of shirt would be the most comfortable to wear on a very hot, humid day?

- ☐ (a) Nylon
- ☐ (b) Polyester
- ☐ (c) Wool
- ☐ (d) Polyester and cotton mixture
- ☐ (e) Cotton

19 Which one of the following is a manufactured substance?

- ☐ (a) Wood
- ☐ (b) Coal
- ☐ (c) Steel
- ☐ (d) Gold
- ☐ (e) Wool

20 Which type of rust prevention is most commonly used on dustbins?

- ☐ (a) Chromium plating
- ☐ (b) Painting
- ☐ (c) Oiling and greasing
- ☐ (d) Galvanizing
- ☐ (e) Alloying

21 Which material would be the most suitable for making the cables that support the basket of a hot-air balloon?

Density (Kg/m³)	Strength (Arbitrary units)
☐ (a) 7800	100.0
☐ (b) 11350	1.0
☐ (c) 1850	70.0
☐ (d) 200	2.5
☐ (e) 720	2.0

22 Why is glass fibre used as an insulation material?

- ☐ (a) It has a high conductivity
- ☐ (b) It is porous
- ☐ (c) It has a high tensile strength
- ☐ (d) It has a low thermal conductivity
- ☐ (e) It has a high relative hardness

23 Which one of the following is a valuable natural resource that is used as a source of fuel and chemicals?

- ☐ (a) Soil
- ☐ (b) Water
- ☐ (c) Air
- ☐ (d) Wood
- ☐ (e) Crude oil

24 A saucepan manufacturer is trying to decide what material to use for the saucepan handle. Which one would you suggest?

- ☐ (a) Plastic
- ☐ (b) Glass
- ☐ (c) Wool
- ☐ (d) Metal
- ☐ (e) Metal alloy

25 Referring to the data below, which of the following materials would be the most suitable for a saucepan handle?

Material	Thermal conductivity
☐ (a) V	174.0
☐ (b) W	1.2
☐ (c) X	6.0
☐ (d) Y	1.7
☐ (e) Z	16000.0

26 Which of the following materials would not complete an electrical circuit containing a power source and a light bulb, and therefore would not light the bulb?

- ☐ (a) Gold
- ☐ (b) Copper
- ☐ (c) Sodium
- ☐ (d) Graphite
- ☐ (e) Polythene

27 Which of the following is the most important consideration when choosing a material that is to be used as a radiator?

- ☐ (a) Compressive strength
- ☐ (b) Porosity
- ☐ (c) Tensile strength
- ☐ (d) Cost
- ☐ (e) Thermal conductivity

28 Which one of the following suggestions is a reason why aluminium would be used for the manufacture of window frames instead of iron?

43

☐ (a) Aluminium is cheaper than iron
☐ (b) Aluminium does not corrode as easily as iron
☐ (c) Aluminium has a higher density than iron
☐ (d) Aluminium is a less reactive metal than iron
☐ (e) Aluminium is a poorer conductor of heat than iron

29 Which metal is the most suitable for building aircraft?

....

30 Which one of the following is not a synthetic material?

☐ (a) Nylon
☐ (b) Polythene
☐ (c) Teflon
☐ (d) Cotton
☐ (e) Perspex

31 Why are silver coins, like a 10 p coin, made from an alloy of copper and nickel?

....

⬤ ANSWERS

Manufacturing processes

Foundation and Higher Levels

☐ **1** *(b)*
The electrolysis of sodium chloride solution is an important industrial process because it provides three important raw materials for the rest of the chemical industry. Chlorine is used to produce a wide range of products such as herbicides, pesticides, plastics, and bleach. Hydrogen is used in the production of margarine and ammonia, and is also used as a fuel. Sodium hydroxide is used in the manufacture of paper, soaps, and fibres.

☐ **2** *(c)*
The products of the electrolysis of sodium chloride solution in industry are sodium hydroxide, hydrogen gas, and chlorine gas.

☐ **3** *(b)*
Sodium hydroxide is a very strong base, but the major problem is the highly toxic nature of chlorine gas. If it were to escape from the plant into a populated area it could prove fatal.

☐ **4** *(b)*
The addition of a catalyst in the industrial production of ammonia does not increase the yield of ammonia, but it does increase the rate at which the ammonia is produced.

☐ **5** *(d)*
When calcium carbonate (limestone) is heated, it undergoes thermal decomposition to produce calcium oxide (quicklime) and carbon dioxide, as can be seen from the equation below:

$$CaCO_3 \rightarrow CaO + CO_2$$

☐ **6** *(e)*
The compound that is formed when water is added to calcium oxide is known as slaked lime (calcium hydroxide). A solution of calcium hydroxide is called lime water and this is used in tests for carbon dioxide.

☐ **7** *(d)*
The raw materials used in the extraction of iron in the blast furnace are limestone, coke, and iron ore. The limestone is used to remove the impurities and produce carbon dioxide. Coke is added to act as the reducing agent. It burns to form carbon dioxide, which then reacts with more coke to form carbon monoxide. The carbon monoxide reduces the iron ore to the metal iron.

☐ **8** *(c)*
Limestone is used in the manufacture of both glass and cement.

☐ **9**
When water is added to the quicklime, it reacts to form calcium hydroxide: calcium oxide + water → calcium hydroxide. This is a basic substance that will react with the carbon dioxide in the air to form calcium carbonate: calcium hydroxide + carbon dioxide → calcium carbonate + water

☐ **10** *(b)*
When limestone (calcium carbonate) is heated it decomposes to produce calcium oxide and carbon dioxide. This type of reaction is known as thermal decomposition.

☐ **11** *(a)*
The common name for the compound formed when the impurities are removed is slag (calcium silicate). This is formed by the reaction of calcium oxide with silicon dioxide impurities.

☐ **12** *(c)*
When calcium carbonate (limestone) is

heated, it undergoes thermal decomposition to produce calcium oxide (quicklime) and carbon dioxide:

$$CaCO_3 \rightarrow CaO + CO_2$$

☐ **13** *(b)*
When the limestone is added to the blast furnace it undergoes thermal decomposition to produce calcium oxide and carbon dioxide. The iron ore contains a lot of impurities, mainly silicon dioxide (sand), which is removed by the reaction with the calcium oxide to form calcium silicate (slag). Hence, limestone is used to remove the impurities from the blast furnace.

☐ **14** *(c)*
In chemistry, the word reduction can mean the addition of hydrogen to a substance, as well as the removal of oxygen (or gaining electrons). When a metal oxide is converted to the metal, it loses oxygen and reduction is said to take place.

☐ **15** *(a)*
The purpose of a fertilizer is to promote plant growth. Plants are able to absorb the nitrogen as the ammonium salt in the fertilizers is converted into nitrogen by organisms that live in the soil.

☐ **16** *(b)*
Ammonium nitrate is a popular fertilizer. This is because it is soluble in water and contains a fairly high percentage of nitrogen.

☐ **17** *(a)*
Fertilizers used today are water soluble so that they can be absorbed easily by the plants.

☐ **18** *(a)*
The problem with many fertilizers is that the excess that is placed onto the fields is washed into the rivers and streams. This causes increased algal blooms and plant growth in the rivers and streams.

When the plants die, the bacteria that decompose the plant material use up oxygen. If there is an excess of algae and plants, the bacteria use up so much oxygen that there is not enough left in the water to support fish life. This process is known as eutrophication.

☐ **19** *(a)*
Nitric acid is corrosive and therefore would damage many plants.

☐ **20** *(a)*
Nitrogenous fertilizers can be made by reacting ammonia with an acid such as nitric acid to produce the solid salt, ammonium nitrate. Fertilizers can also be made by the reaction of ammonia with sulphuric acid or phosphoric acid.

☐ **21** *(d)*
Ammonia is a soluble base and therefore will react with acids, such as sulphuric acid and nitric acid, to produce soluble salts. The reaction between an acid and a base, which produces a salt, is a neutralization reaction.

☐ **22** *(b)*
Sodium chloride is a naturally occurring substance and so is not manufactured. It is used as a raw material for the production of a number of important chemicals, such as sodium hydroxide and chlorine. It is converted into these by the use of chemical reaction.

☐ **23** *(a)*
Nitrogen and hydrogen are mixed at a pressure of between 150–350 atmospheres, and at a temperature of between 350–450°C (exact conditions vary from plant to plant). The gases are also passed over an iron catalyst in order to speed up the reaction. At the end of the process enough of the nitrogen has reacted with the hydrogen to ensure that about 10% of the gas that leaves the reaction chamber is ammonia.

☐ **24** *(c)*
Nitrogen and hydrogen are mixed at a temperature of between 350–450°C and a pressure of between 150–350 atmospheres (exact conditions vary from plant to plant).

☐ **25** *(a)*
The raw materials for the manufacture of ammonia are nitrogen and hydrogen. The two gases are reacted together in the Haber process, as shown in the diagram that follows.

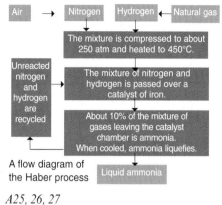

A flow diagram of the Haber process

A25, 26, 27

☐ **26** *(c)*
The nitrogen needed for the manufacture of ammonia in the Haber process is obtained from the air. See previous diagram.

☐ **27** *(d)*
The hydrogen that is used in the manufacture of ammonia in the Haber process is a natural gas. The hydrogen is produced by reacting the methane with steam.

☐ **28** *(e)*
The conditions that are required for the Haber process for the manufacture of ammonia are approximately 250 atmospheres and 450°C. The reaction would favour a low temperature and a very high pressure, but a low temperature produces a very slow rate of reaction. Therefore, a higher temperature and a catalyst are used to speed up the rate of reaction. These conditions result in a 10% yield of ammonia. The following equation shows the reaction that takes place in the Haber process.

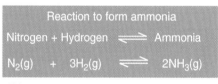

Reaction to form ammonia

Nitrogen + Hydrogen ⇌ Ammonia

$$N_2(g) + 3H_2(g) \rightleftharpoons 2NH_3(g)$$

A28

☐ **29** *(c)*
The diagram that follows shows how nitric acid is manufactured by the oxidation of ammonia using a platinum catalyst. Nitric acid is used in the manufacture of nitrogenous fertilizers.

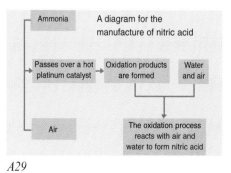

A29

☐ **30** *(a)*
Nitric acid can react with alkalis to produce nitrate salts. These are used as fertilizers because they contain nitrates, which are essential for plant growth. An example is ammonium nitrate, formed when nitric acid reacts with ammonia.

☐ **31** *(a)*
The iron that comes out of the blast furnace contains about 3–4% carbon, which makes it very brittle. The carbon content is reduced to make the metal more useful by converting the iron into steel, which has a carbon content of less than 1%. This is the main use of the iron that is extracted from a blast furnace. The iron is converted into steel by blowing oxygen into the molten iron to burn off the carbon. This is done by an oxygen furnace, as can be seen from the following diagram.

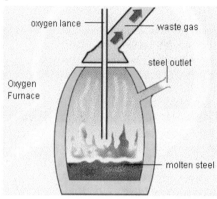

A31

☐ **32** *(e)*
The name of the ore from which aluminium is extracted is bauxite. Bauxite contains approximately 45% aluminium oxide.

☐ **33** *(c)*
The melting point of aluminium oxide is very high (2050°C). To reduce the melting point, cryolite is added to the molten oxide. This brings the melting point down to about 1000°C.

☐ **34** *(c)*
The slag produced does not have many useful properties and so it is used in the foundations of roads and buildings.

☐ **35**
The site of a new sodium chloride solution electrolysis plant needs a number of things including cheap land, a work force, a large supply of salt nearby, a large supply of cheap electricity, and good road and rail links to transport the raw materials and products. Site E is therefore in the best position to satisfy these requirements.

☐ **36** *(d)*
The anodes used in the extraction of aluminium are made from graphite, an allotrope of carbon. Oxygen gas is released at the anode and it reacts with the carbon in the anode to form carbon dioxide. As a result, the anodes need to be replaced regularly. See diagram below.

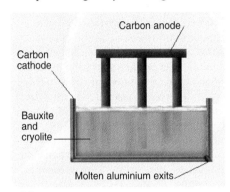

A36

☐ **37** *(a)*
A sodium chloride solution electrolysis plant would be sited close to a large deposit of salt because the process requires a large amount of salt.

☐ **38** *(b)*
A sodium chloride solution electrolysis plant needs a large amount of electricity to power the electrolysis cells. The dam could therefore provide a source of cheaper electricity in the form of hydroelectric power.

☐ **39** *(c)*
When a solution of sodium chloride in water is electrolyzed, the positive ions in solution are attracted to the cathode. If there are more than two types of ion in solution, then the least reactive one will gain electrons and become atoms before the other. In the case of sodium chloride, the solution contains positive hydrogen ions. The sodium ions are more reactive than the hydrogen ions, and therefore the hydrogen ions are discharged first.

☐ **40** *(a)*
A reaction in which a substance breaks down into other compounds is called a decomposition. When heat is required to bring this about, it is known as a thermal decomposition.

☐ **41** *(b)*
Only a compound can undergo thermal decomposition. The only compound of the suggestions given that will undergo thermal decomposition is calcium carbonate. Calcium carbonate breaks down to give calcium oxide and carbon dioxide, as the following equation shows:
$$CaCO_3 \rightarrow CaO + CO_2$$

☐ **42** *(c)*
The iron ore used in the blast furnace is iron oxide, so here the meaning of the word reduction is the removal of oxygen (or gain of electrons). During the reduction process, the oxygen is removed from the iron oxide, leaving the metal.

☐ **43** *(b)*
The solution contains both copper Cu^{2+} ions and hydrogen H^+ ions, but because the copper ions accept electrons more easily than the hydrogen ions, they are discharged first.

☐ **44** *(b)*
Copper ions are produced at the anode during the purification of copper using electrolysis, which is shown by the equation below:

$$Cu(s) \rightarrow Cu^{2+}(aq) + 2e^-$$

☐ **45** *(b)*
The substance labelled X is sludge of insoluble copper ore.

☐ **46** *(c)*
The negative cathode will attract the positively charged ions in the solution. Only the least reactive ions in solution will be discharged and, as copper is less reactive than hydrogen, the cathode will become covered in a layer of pure copper. Any metals less reactive than copper do not dissolve and so remain in the sludge.

Manufacturing processes

Higher Level only

☐ **47** *(c)*
Although the solution contains both sodium ions and hydrogen ions, sodium is not produced at the cathode because the hydrogen ions are discharged first. This is because hydrogen is less reactive than sodium. Hence the first statement is true and the second is false.

☐ **48** *(a)*
Sodium chloride solution does contain two positive ions, sodium (Na^+) and hydrogen (H^+). Chlorine is discharged at the anode, and hydrogen is discharged at the cathode. Hence all the statements are true.

☐ **49** *(d)*
The ions contained in a solution of sodium chloride and water are sodium and chloride ions from the sodium chloride, and hydrogen and hydroxide ions from the water.

☐ **50** *(a)*
Le Chatelier's principle states that 'when conditions are changed, a system in equilibrium will adjust itself in such a way as to minimize the effect of the change'. Applied to this system, an increase in pressure will tip the equilibrium towards the right-hand side (decrease in the number of molecules of gas) whereas an increase in temperature will favour the left-hand side, as the reaction will proceed in the endothermic direction. A catalyst will not alter the yield, just the rate of reaction. See equation that follows.

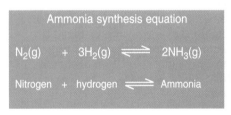

A50

☐ **51** *(c)*
The ions left in the solution after the industrial electrolysis of sodium chloride solution are sodium and hydroxide. Hence the by-product of the process is sodium hydroxide solution. The solution will also contain a few hydrogen and chloride ions, as the cell is never left long enough for all of them to be removed. See diagram following.

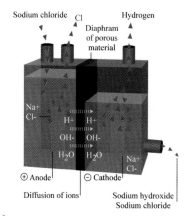

A51

□ 52 *(c)*
To calculate the percentage yield use the following equation:

Percentage yield = (actual yield ÷ maximum possible yield) x 100
The maximum possible yield is the mass that could be produced if all the reactants are converted into products. The actual yield is the mass produced by the reaction. So, using the equation above, the percentage yield for the above reaction can be calculated as follows:
(6.4 ÷ 64) x 100 = 10

□ 53 *(c)*
Even though the production of ammonia is exothermic, and therefore an increase in temperature will reduce the yield of ammonia, a high temperature of 450°C is used to increase the rate at which this yield of ammonia is produced. The use of this temperature produces a yield of about 10%, and the gases that are unreacted are recycled.

□ 54 *(c)*
Le Chatelier's principle states that "when conditions are changed, a system in equilibrium will adjust itself in such a way as to minimize the effect of the change". A decrease in temperature will make the reaction proceed in the exothermic direction. As the production of ammonia is an exothermic process, the position of equilibrium will move to the right.

□ 55 *(d)*
If the ammonia is removed as it is produced, the equilibrium is disturbed and the reaction will try to re-establish the equilibrium by producing more ammonia. Therefore, the position of the equilibrium moves to the right.

□ 56 *(a)*
Le Chatelier's principle states that "when conditions are changed, a system in equilibrium will adjust itself in such a way as to minimize the effect of the change". Therefore, a decrease in

temperature will force the system to produce more heat and so the reaction will proceed in the exothermic direction. The production of sulphur trioxide is exothermic, so the forward reaction will be favoured and the position of equilibrium will move to the right. See equation that follows.

Sulphur trioxide equation
Sulphur dioxide + Oxygen $\rightleftharpoons$ Sulphur trioxide
$2SO_2(g)$ + $O_2(g)$ $\rightleftharpoons$ $2SO_3(g)$

A56

□ 57 *(e)*
A catalyst only increases the rate of a reaction, it will not affect the yield. In a reversible reaction the rate of the forward and reverse reaction are both increased and therefore the yield of the product remains the same.

□ 58 *(e)*
The negative ions in solution will be attracted to the the anode, where they will lose electrons to become atoms. In the case of sodium chloride solution, the negative ions are chloride ions. These will be attracted to the anode, where they will lose their electrons to form atoms. In this example, two ions will form one molecule of chlorine and two electrons.
$2Cl^-(aq) \rightarrow Cl_2(g) + 2e^-$

Electrolysis

Foundation and Higher Levels

□ 1 *(b)*
The term for a chemical reaction caused by electricity is electrolysis. See diagram that follows.

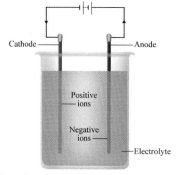

A1, 2, 3

□ 2 *(d)*
Electrolysis is a chemical reaction that occurs when a compound is decomposed by electricity. See previous diagram.

□ 3 *(e)*
Liquids that will undergo electrolysis are known as electrolytes. An electrolyte must contain ions that are free to move. See previous diagram.

□ 4 *(a)*
Faraday's work on electrolysis in the 19th century laid the foundation stone for this branch of chemistry.

□ 5 *(b)*
The anode is positive and the cathode is negative, hence the first two statements are true. However, the electrons come down the cathode (see diagram that follows) and therefore the third statement is false.

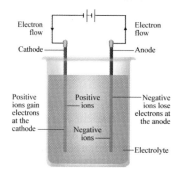

A5, 6, 7, 8

□ 6 *(c)*
The anode is positively charged and will therefore attract the negatively charged ions. Hence, the first statement is true and the second one is false. See previous diagram.

□ 7 *(d)*
The cathode is the negatively charged electrode, so statement i is false. As it is the negative electrode, it attracts positive ions, so statement ii is true. See previous diagram.

□ 8 *(c)*
All electrolytes must contain ions that are free to move if they are to conduct electricity. The ions in the solution or the liquid act as electron carriers. See previous diagram.

□ 9 *(e)*
During the electrolysis of copper sulphate solution, copper ions are produced at the copper anode.
$Cu(s) \rightarrow Cu^{2+}(aq) + 2e^-$

□ 10 *(b)*
Electroplating is used on jewellery and cutlery. A cheap metal (like steel), which is plated in silver, is far less expensive than a solid silver item. Silver-plated items are often marked with EPNS (electroplated nickel silver).

☐ **11** *(c)*
As the anode is positive, it will only attract negatively charged ions or produce positively charged metal ions. When the negative ions reach the anode they lose their electrons and become atoms. Hydrogen has positively charged ions and would therefore not be attracted to the anode.

☐ **12** *(b)*
As the cathode is negative it attracts the positive ions in the solution, i.e. the copper ions. When the copper ions reach the cathode, they gain electrons and become copper atoms. Although there are hydrogen ions present from the water they do not react because the copper is discharged more easily.

$$Cu^{2+}(aq) + 2e^- \rightarrow Cu(s)$$

☐ **13** *(b)*
In order for an electrolyte to conduct electricity it must contain free ions to act as electricity carriers. Ionic solids do contain the ions, but the ions are fixed in a crystal lattice and cannot act as electricity carriers. When the solid dissolves the crystal lattice breaks down, and the ions are free to move.

☐ **14** *(d)*
For salt to conduct electricity, its ions must be free to move. The solid sodium chloride does contain ions, but they are fixed in a crystal lattice and are therefore unable to move. When it is molten, the lattice breaks down and the ions become free to move. Hence the molten sodium chloride is able to conduct electricity, as can be seen from the diagram below.

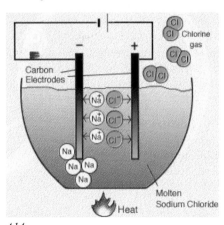

A14

☐ **15** *(b)*
Sodium chloride will only undergo electrolysis when its ions are free to move. When it is solid the ions are held in the crystal lattice and therefore are not free to move, but when it is molten the lattice breaks down and the ions are free to move. The negative ions will move towards the anode, where they will lose electrons and become atoms. In the case of sodium chloride, the negative ions are chloride ions and therefore chlorine gas is given off at the anode.

☐ **16** *(c)*
When sodium chloride is solid it will not conduct electricity, but when it is molten it will because the ions are free to move. The positive sodium ions will be attracted to the negatively charged cathode where they lose electrons to form sodium metal.

$$Na^+ + e^- \rightarrow Na$$

☐ **17** *(b)*
When a solution of sodium chloride is electrolyzed the negative chloride ions in solution will move towards the anode, where they will lose electrons and become atoms. Two atoms will bond together to form a chlorine molecule. There will also be hydroxide ions in the solution from the water, but the chloride ions are discharged more easily.

☐ **18** *(a)*
When a solution of sodium chloride in water is electrolyzed, the positive ions in the solution will be attracted to the cathode. If there are more than two ions in the solution, the least reactive one will gain electrons and become atoms before the others. In the case of sodium chloride, the solution will contain positive hydrogen ions and sodium ions. The sodium ions are more reactive than the hydrogen ions and therefore the hydrogen ions are discharged first, and so hydrogen is produced.

☐ **19** *(a)*
The cathode is negatively charged and so will attract the positively charged ions in the solution. The solution contains two positive ions, hydrogen and copper. As the copper ions are lower in the activity series they are more likely to accept electrons and form atoms. Hence copper is formed at the cathode.

☐ **20** *(d)*
The positive anode attracts the negatively charged hydroxide and sulphate ions. The sulphate ions are complex and difficult to discharge. Therefore, it is the hydroxide ions that give up an electron to the anode. This results in the formation of oxygen and water.

☐ **21** *(c)*
Hydrogen is produced at the cathode when potassium bromide solution is electrolyzed using carbon electrodes. Potassium is not deposited, even though its ions are positive, because it is too high in the reactivity series. The only other positive ions available are hydrogen ions from the water. These are attracted to the cathode instead, and gain an electron to form hydrogen gas.

☐ **22** *(a)*
The following diagram shows the electrolysis of potassium bromide solution. The positive anode attracts the negative bromide ions. At the electrode, the bromide ions lose electrons to become bromine atoms. These atoms join together to form bromine molecules. Negative hydroxide ions from the water are also present, but the bromide ions are discharged first.

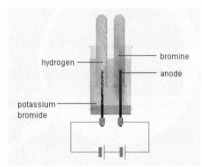

A22

☐ **23** (b)
Any electrolysis reaction involves the loss and gain of electrons. The anode is positive and will attract the negative ions. When the negative ions reach the anode they lose their extra electrons and are oxidized (oxidation is the loss of electrons). The cathode has a negative charge and will attract the positive ions. When the positive ions reach the cathode they gain electrons and are reduced (reduction is the gain of electrons). Hence, both oxidation and reduction take place during electrolysis.

☐ **24** *(d)*
When a current of electricity is passed through the electrolyte, the positive ions in the electrolyte will be attracted to the cathode. In order for the object to be coated with a layer of nickel, the ions in the solution must be nickel ions.

Application of materials

Foundation and Higher Levels

☐ **1** *(a)*
Sodium chloride is often used in the food industry as a preservative or as a flavour enhancer. Sodium chloride is also used in the manufacture of chlorine. The chlorine can then be used in the manufacture of plastics and antiseptics.

☐ **2** *(a)*
A fuel is a substance that produces heat when burnt in oxygen.

☐ **3** *(b)*
Because it is heavier than air, carbon dioxide is able to extinguish the fire by preventing oxygen from reaching it.

☐ **4** *(c)*
The burning fat will float on the water, and some of it will sizzle and spit into the air, possibly starting a new fire.

☐ **5** *(d)*
If a material has tensile strength it will not break when it is pulled or stretched. Only the house brick does not need to have this property because, when used for building purposes, the forces acting upon it are compressive.

☐ **6** *(a)*
The foundations of a large building need to be able to support the weight of the building without being crushed. The building needs to have foundations with a high compressive strength.

☐ **7** *(d)*
The cables of a suspension bridge need to be able to support the weight of the bridge without breaking. Therefore they must have a high tensile strength.

☐ **8** *(d)*
Suggestions *(a)* and *(b)* are false. Suggestions *(c)* and *(e)* are true but do not effect the use of the cable in this case. Steel does have a high tensile strength, and can therefore support the weight of the bridge.

☐ **9**
To support the weight of a large building the material has to have a high compressive strength. Therefore material D, with the highest compressive strength, would be the best material to use in this case.

☐ **10** *(c)*
Concrete has a high compressive strength, but a very low tensile strength. The addition of steel cables increases the tensile strength, allowing it to be used to span large areas.

☐ **11** *(c)*
Foods that have unsaturated fats in them contain two carbon atoms with double bonds between them. These double bonds are quite reactive, and as a result they will react readily with the oxygen in the air. This results in the formation of acids and so the food goes off. The addition of anti-oxidants to the food will prevent this from happening.

☐ **12** *(c)*
The cover of an electrical cable has to be a non-conductor of electricity. Copper and aluminium are both metals and therefore good conductors of electricity. Glass and concrete are both non-conductors of electricity, but are not flexible and will not be able to withstand any movement of the cable. The most suitable material is rubber, as it is a non-conductor and highly flexible.

☐ **13**
Material C has the lowest relative electrical conductivity and therefore does not allow electricity to flow through it. Insulation material needs to have a low relative electrical conductivity to prevent electric shock. Hence, C is the most suitable.

☐ **14** *(b)*
Plastic is a good insulator and therefore will prevent heat from escaping. Metals and perspex conduct heat well so the surface of the kettle would get too hot. Polyester and nylon are synthetic materials used in the clothing industry.

☐ **15** *(c)*
Gold is the only one that is a natural substance and can be found in its pure form in nature. Gold is an element, whereas the other suggestions given are all alloys. An alloy is a man-made mixture of different metals (or non-metals). Steel is an alloy of the metal iron and the non-metal carbon.

☐ **16** *(a)*
For a material to cut another it has to have a higher relative hardness. Only steel would be able to cut the glass.

☐ **17** *(c)*
In order for the drill to cut through the bedrock it needs to be made of a material with a relative hardness higher than that of the bedrock. The only material with a relative hardness of more than 7.5 is material X.

☐ **18** *(e)*
Cotton absorbs moisture and is comfortable on hot days. Polyester and nylon are more hard wearing but do not absorb moisture, and wool is the ideal material for keeping you warm.

☐ **19** *(c)*
Steel is an alloy of iron that contains less than 1% carbon. It is produced by blowing hot oxygen through the impure molten iron that comes out of the blast furnace (see diagram that follows). The other substances are all found in nature and do not have to undergo any manufacturing process.

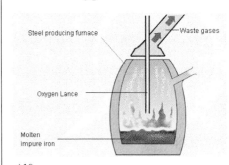

A19

☐ **20** *(d)*
Rust is formed when oxygen reacts with iron to form iron oxide. Therefore it is possible to prevent rusting by stopping the oxygen getting to the iron by coating the iron with another substance. Galvanizing is the process by which iron is coated with a layer of zinc, which stops oxygen reaching the iron. Even if the zinc layer is scratched and the iron beneath is revealed, the iron does not rust because zinc is above iron in the reactivity series so it will react with the oxygen first.

☐ **21** *(c)*
The cables of a hot-air balloon have to be light-weight but very strong. Although materials *(d)* and *(e)* both have low density and therefore would be light, they have very little strength. Material *(b)* is unsuitable as it has both a very high density and low strength. Materials *(a)* and *(c)* are both strong but the lower density of *(c)* makes this the most suitable material.

☐ **22** *(d)*
To be a good insulation material glass fibre needs to prevent heat from passing through it. This property is known as low thermal conductivity.

☐ **23** *(e)*
Crude oil is a valuable resource for fuel and chemicals. It consists of many different chemical compounds. Some are fuels (eg. petrol), while others are used for

the manufacture of numerous chemicals and materials. See diagram that follows.

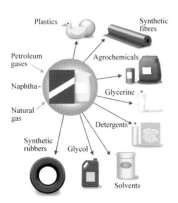

A23

☐ **24** *(a)*
Plastics act as heat insulators and therefore do not transfer the heat of a pan to its handle. All the other options conduct heat.

☐ **25** *(b)*
The handle of a saucepan needs to stay cool when it is in use. Therefore, the material must have a low thermal conductivity and so the best option is material W.

☐ **26** *(e)*
To make the bulb light, the material must be an electrical conductor. The only one that is not an electrical conductor is polythene.

☐ **27** *(e)*
The function of a radiator is to heat the room where it is situated and so it has to be a good conductor of heat.

☐ **28** *(b)*
Although aluminium is positioned above iron in the table of reactivity, it is very resistant to corrosion because it is coated with a protective layer of aluminium oxide. In contrast, it is very difficult to stop iron corroding. Hence aluminium is the preferable material.

☐ **29**
Aluminium has a very low density for a metal and therefore is very light. It is also very strong (in alloys) and resistant to corrosion, making it ideal for use in the building of aircraft.

☐ **30** *(d)*
Cotton grows naturally whereas the others are all man-made polymers.

☐ **31**
The copper and nickel alloy is ideal for use in coins as it is very hard and resistant to frequent handling.

Chemicals from Oil

Petrochemicals and organic chemistry *(Single and Double Awards)*

Crude oil is an extremely important raw material. It is used as a source of fuels and is the starting material for a vast array of everyday products, ranging from plastics and paints to dyes and drugs. Organic chemistry is a study of the reactions of the compounds of the element carbon. Many millions of carbon compounds are known and chemists have developed a good understanding of their properties and reactions. The following questions will help test your knowledge and understanding of this important branch of chemistry.

 KEY FACTS

• **Crude oil:** Crude oil is a mixture of hydrocarbons (compounds that contain hydrogen and carbon atoms only). The number of carbon atoms in each compound affects certain properties of the hydrocarbon. For example, as the number of carbon atoms in the compound increases, so the viscosity increases, the flammability decreases, and the colour gets darker. Each hydrocarbon also has a different boiling point – the higher the number of carbon atoms in the compound, the higher the boiling point. Crude oil can be separated into components or fractions by fractional distillation, a process which relies on all the fractions having different boiling points.

• **Combustion:** The fractions of crude oil have many different uses, one of the most important of which is as fuels such as natural gas, petrol, and paraffin. The energy contained in these fractions is released by combustion. If the air supply is plentiful, the combustion of hydrocarbons produces carbon dioxide and water in addition to energy. In a more limited supply of air, carbon monoxide and water are produced. The combustion of hydrocarbons also produces pollutants such as sulphur dioxide, as the fuels contain sulphur-based impurities.

• **Hydrocarbons:** Hydrocarbons can be divided into groups that contain molecules with the same general formula. Alkanes, with a general formula C_nH_{2n+2}, are saturated hydrocarbons, which means that they contain only single covalent bonds between the carbon atoms. Their main use is as fuels such as methane (CH_4), ethane (C_2H_6), and petrol (C_8H_{18}). The group known as the alkenes has the general formula C_nH_{2n}. Examples include ethene (C_2H_4), and propene (C_3H_6). Alkenes are unsaturated hydrocarbons, which means that they contain one double covalent bond between carbon atoms. The main use of alkenes is their conversion into polymers.

• **Polymers:** Some of the larger molecules obtained by the fractional distillation of crude oil have very little use. These larger molecules are cracked into smaller molecules, which include alkenes, by passing them over a hot catalyst. These alkenes are converted into more useful addition polymers by passing them over a catalyst or reacting them under high pressure. A polymer is a very long chain molecule (often over 20000 carbon atoms) that contains a repeating monomer unit. For example, the repeating unit in polythene is CH_2–CH_2. Addition polymers have a large number of uses including plastic bags (polythene), non-stick coatings (Teflon), polystyrene foam, and PVC.

 QUESTIONS

Foundation and Higher Levels

1 What is the main purpose of the extraction of crude oil and its refinement into different fractions?

- ☐ (a) It makes lots of money for the oil companies
- ☐ (b) It produces a large amount of pollution
- ☐ (c) It produces a vast range of useful products that improve the quality of life for millions of people
- ☐ (d) The work provides employment for thousands of workers
- ☐ (e) None of the above

2 If a sample of crude oil was separated by the process of fractional distillation, which of the following fractions would come off at the top of the column?

- ☐ (a) Petroleum gases (boiling point of 25°C)
- ☐ (b) Diesel oil (boiling point of 220–250°C)
- ☐ (c) Fuel oil (boiling point of 350°C)
- ☐ (d) Lubricating oil (boiling point of 250°C)
- ☐ (e) Naphtha (boiling point of 75–150°C)

3 Which one of the following statements explains why crude oil can be separated into different fractions by fractional distillation?

- ☐ (a) Crude oil is a mixture of liquids with different boiling points
- ☐ (b) Crude oil is a mixture of liquids with the same boiling points
- ☐ (c) Crude oil is a mixture of substances with different densities
- ☐ (d) Crude oil is one large molecule that breaks down when it is heated
- ☐ (e) Crude oil is insoluble in water

4 Which one of the following statements explains why crude oil is such a valuable natural resource?

- ☐ (a) It contains enormous amounts of alcohol
- ☐ (b) It is easy to obtain
- ☐ (c) It contains a vast supply of raw materials that are used in the chemical industry
- ☐ (d) It is expensive
- ☐ (e) It contains metal minerals

5 Which one of the following is not found in crude oil?

- ☐ (a) Petrol
- ☐ (b) Diesel
- ☐ (c) Oxygen
- ☐ (d) Kerosene
- ☐ (e) Bitumen

6 Which of the following fractions of crude oil is the most viscous?

- ☐ (a) Naphtha
- ☐ (b) Petroleum gases
- ☐ (c) Diesel oil
- ☐ (d) Kerosene
- ☐ (e) Fuel oil

7 Which of the following fractions of crude oil is used to power large ships and industrial machines?

☐ (a) Naphtha
☐ (b) Petroleum gases
☐ (c) Diesel oil
☐ (d) Bitumen
☐ (e) Fuel oil

8 Crude oil is a valuable natural resource for many substances. Which of the following can be obtained from crude oil?
i. Petrol
ii. Diesel oil
iii. Nitrogen
iv. Chemicals

☐ (a) All of them
☐ (b) i and ii only
☐ (c) i and iv only
☐ (d) i, iii, and iv
☐ (e) i, ii, and iv

9 Which of the following can be obtained directly from the fractional distillation of crude oil?

☐ (a) Bitumen
☐ (b) Ethanol
☐ (c) Plastics
☐ (d) Fibres
☐ (e) CFCs

10 Which one of the following fractions of crude oil is used to manufacture chemicals such as paints, plastics, and detergents?

☐ (a) Naphtha
☐ (b) Kerosene
☐ (c) Diesel oil
☐ (d) Bitumen
☐ (e) Fuel oil

11 Which one of the following fractions of crude oil contains the highest number of carbon atoms in its molecules?

☐ (a) Naphtha
☐ (b) Petroleum gases
☐ (c) Diesel oil
☐ (d) Bitumen
☐ (e) Fuel oil

12 What is the process by which large hydrocarbon molecules, such as fuel oil, are converted into smaller molecules, such as gasoline (petrol)?

☐ (a) Distillation
☐ (b) Fractional distillation
☐ (c) Cracking
☐ (d) Polymerization
☐ (e) Reforming

13 After the fractional distillation of crude oil some of the fractions undergo cracking. What does the process of cracking involve?

☐ (a) The breaking of large molecules into smaller, more useful ones
☐ (b) Reacting small molecules together to produce larger molecules
☐ (c) The breaking of the fraction into carbon and hydrogen
☐ (d) Reacting the compounds with minerals to produce solid fuels
☐ (e) The rearrangement of the atoms in the molecules

14 Which one of the following is a natural material?

☐ (a) Nylon
☐ (b) Polythene
☐ (c) Polystyrene
☐ (d) Cotton
☐ (e) Teflon

15 Which statement is not true?

☐ (a) Plastics burn easily and give off poisonous fumes
☐ (b) Polystyrene foam is a hard plastic
☐ (c) Polythene is very flexible
☐ (d) A plastic shopping bag is less dense than water
☐ (e) Plastics are good insulators

16 Which of the following is the main use of polymers?

☐ (a) Catalysts
☐ (b) Plastics
☐ (c) Electrical conductors
☐ (d) Electronic data storage
☐ (e) Thermal conductors

17 In the process of cracking, large hydrocarbon molecules are broken down to form smaller molecules. What is the purpose of cracking large molecules into smaller ones?

☐ (a) To produce a compound that is more stable
☐ (b) To produce a compound that is less volatile
☐ (c) To produce a compound that is more viscous
☐ (d) To produce a compound that is more useful
☐ (e) To produce a compound that is less flammable

18 The apparatus shown in the following diagram was set up to investigate the products formed during the burning of a candle. The air and combustion products

were drawn through lime water and a liquid was collected in the U-tube, which was tested using white (anhydrous) copper sulphate. What happens to the lime water and the copper sulphate?

☐ (a) The lime water goes milky and the copper sulphate turns blue
☐ (b) The lime water is unchanged and the copper sulphate turns blue
☐ (c) The lime water goes milky and the copper sulphate remains white
☐ (d) The lime water is unchanged and the copper sulphate remains white
☐ (e) The lime water goes milky and the copper sulphate turns pink

Q18, 19

19 When the experiment shown in the previous diagram was carried out, it was found that the lime water turned milky. What does this tell you about the products of the combustion of the candle?

☐ (a) One of them is chlorine
☐ (b) One of them is carbon monoxide
☐ (c) One of them is nitrogen
☐ (d) One of them is water
☐ (e) One of them is carbon dioxide

20 Which one of the following is not a fossil fuel?

☐ (a) Peat
☐ (b) Oil
☐ (c) Coal
☐ (d) Lignite
☐ (e) Wood

21 Which one of the following raw materials are plastics made from?

☐ (a) PVC
☐ (b) Ceramics
☐ (c) Textiles
☐ (d) Nylon
☐ (e) Crude oil

22 When a hydrocarbon burns, which products are formed?

☐ (a) Carbon dioxide only
☐ (b) Hydrogen and carbon dioxide
☐ (c) Water and hydrogen
☐ (d) Carbon dioxide and water
☐ (e) Hydrogen only

23 Why does the burning of fuels such as coal cause acid rain?

☐ (a) Coal contains hydrogen chloride gas
☐ (b) Coal contains small amounts of sulphur
☐ (c) Coal contains small amounts of chlorides
☐ (d) Coal contains small amounts of metals
☐ (e) Coal contains small amounts of nitrogen

24 Which one of the following is made from chemicals obtained from crude oil?

☐ (a) Sodium chloride
☐ (b) Stainless steel
☐ (c) Plastics
☐ (d) Calcium oxide
☐ (e) Washing soda

25 The process of condensation polymerization usually produces thermosetting plastics. What is a thermosetting plastic?

☐ (a) A plastic that sets hard only when it has been heated to very high temperatures
☐ (b) A plastic that can be melted and set solid many times
☐ (c) A plastic that can only be melted and set solid once
☐ (d) A plastic with a low melting point
☐ (e) None of the above

26 What is the definition of a thermosoftening plastic?

☐ (a) A plastic that sets hard only when it has been heated to very high temperatures
☐ (b) A plastic that can be melted and set solid many times
☐ (c) A plastic that can be melted and set only once
☐ (d) A plastic that has a very high melting point
☐ (e) None of the above

27 Yeast converts glucose (a sugar) into carbon dioxide and ethanol. What is the name of this process?

☐ (a) Electrolysis

☐ (b) Displacement
☐ (c) Fermentation
☐ (d) Combustion
☐ (e) Neutralization

28 What is the missing product from the following equation?
Sugar + yeast → ? + carbon dioxide

☐ (a) Methanol
☐ (b) Ethane
☐ (c) Ethanol
☐ (d) Butanol
☐ (e) Methane

29 Which of the following equations represents fermentation?

☐ (a) Sugar + carbon dioxide → ethanol
☐ (b) Carbon dioxide + ethanol → sugar
☐ (c) Sugar + ethanol → carbon dioxide
☐ (d) Sugar → carbon dioxide + ethanol
☐ (e) Ethanol + carbon dioxide → sugar and water

30 Which of the following statements about fermentation are true?
i. It is an exothermic reaction
ii. Carbon dioxide is needed for the reaction to proceed
iii. Ethanol is produced during the reaction

☐ (a) i and ii only
☐ (b) ii and iii only
☐ (c) i only
☐ (d) iii only
☐ (e) i and iii only

31 What happens during the process of fermentation?

☐ (a) An acid is neutralized
☐ (b) A displacement takes place
☐ (c) A chemical reaction produces electricity
☐ (d) Yeast converts sugars to ethanol and carbon dioxide
☐ (e) A combustion reaction occurs

32 The diagram that follows shows an experiment taking place, in which the lime water turns milky. What causes this?

☐ (a) The carbon dioxide that is produced in the reaction
☐ (b) The water that is produced in the reaction
☐ (c) The presence of yeast
☐ (d) The energy produced
☐ (e) The ethanol that is produced in the reaction

Q32

33 Fermentation is the release of energy from sugars by yeast in anaerobic conditions. What are the other products of the process?

☐ (a) Water only
☐ (b) Water and carbon dioxide only
☐ (c) Carbon dioxide only
☐ (d) Ethanol and carbon dioxide only
☐ (e) Water, carbon, and ethanol

⬤ QUESTIONS

Higher Level only

34 What is the name of the molecule shown in the diagram below?

☐ (a) Methane
☐ (b) Ethane
☐ (c) Propane
☐ (d) Butane
☐ (e) Pentane

Q34

35 Which one of the following represents the structural formula of a molecule of ethane?

☐ (a) C_2H_8
☐ (b) CH_4
☐ (c) C_2H_4
☐ (d) C_2H_6
☐ (e) CH_3

36 What is the name of the molecule shown in the diagram that follows?

- ☐ (a) Methene
- ☐ (b) Methane
- ☐ (c) Ethane
- ☐ (d) Ethene
- ☐ (e) Propene

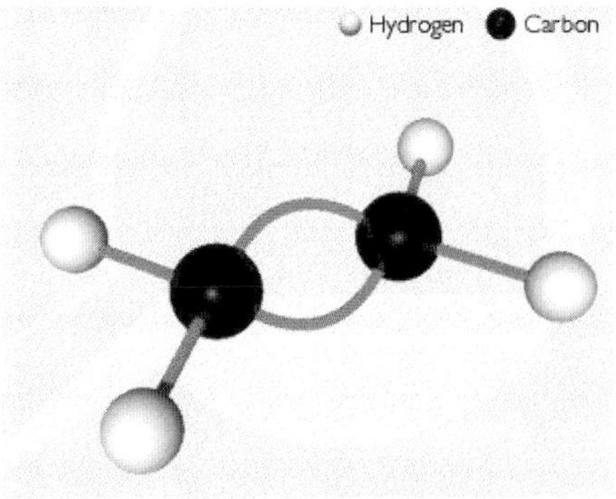

Q36

37 What is the name of the hydrocarbon represented by the structure in the following diagram?

- ☐ (a) Butene
- ☐ (b) Butane
- ☐ (c) Propane
- ☐ (d) Propene
- ☐ (e) Pentene

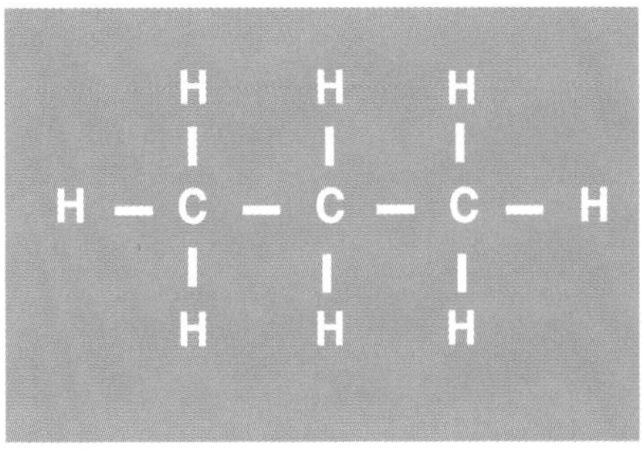

Q37

38 Why are alkanes so unreactive?

- ☐ (a) They are all gases
- ☐ (b) They have a full outer shell of electrons
- ☐ (c) They are saturated hydrocarbons
- ☐ (d) They are non-polar molecules
- ☐ (e) They are polymers

39 What is the formula for ethene?

- ☐ (a) CH_2
- ☐ (b) C_2H_2
- ☐ (c) C_2H_6
- ☐ (d) C_2H_5OH
- ☐ (e) C_2H_4

40 What is the name of the hydrocarbon with the structural formula C_2H_6?

- ☐ (a) Methane
- ☐ (b) Propane
- ☐ (c) Propene
- ☐ (d) Ethene
- ☐ (e) Ethane

41 What is the name of the molecule shown in the diagram that follows?

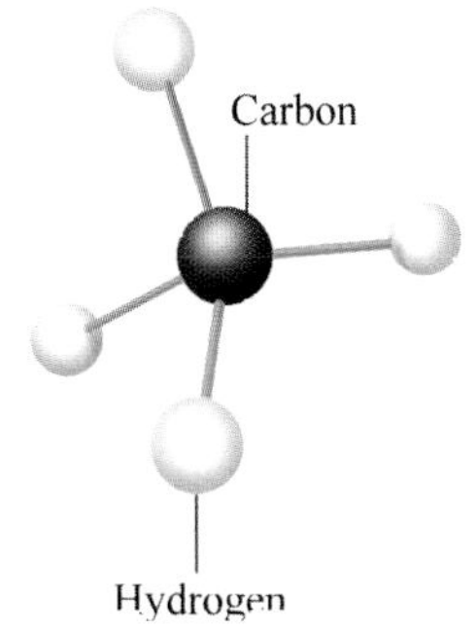

Q41

42 What is the name of the hydrocarbon with the structural formula C_3H_8?

- ☐ (a) Ethene
- ☐ (b) Propene
- ☐ (c) Ethane
- ☐ (d) Propane
- ☐ (e) Butene

43 What is addition polymerization?

- ☐ (a) A process by which large molecules are broken down to form smaller ones
- ☐ (b) A process by which small molecules are joined together to form large long chain molecules and no other product
- ☐ (c) A process by which nitrogen and hydrogen are joined together to form ammonia
- ☐ (d) A process by which copies of molecules are manufactured
- ☐ (e) A process by which small molecules are joined together to form large long chain molecules, with the elimination of a molecule of water or hydrogen chloride

44 Polythene is made by the polymerization of a smaller hydrocarbon monomer.
What is the name of this monomer?

- ☐ (a) Methane
- ☐ (b) Propane
- ☐ (c) Ethane
- ☐ (d) Butane
- ☐ (e) Ethene

45 Methane and propane are very good fuels, and they are relatively unreactive. What makes them unreactive?

- ☐ (a) They have weak bonds between the molecules.
- ☐ (b) They are saturated compounds
- ☐ (c) They are both solids
- ☐ (d) They are both gases
- ☐ (e) They have strong bonds between the molecules

46 Which of the following is produced during the reaction between an alkene and hydrogen?

- ☐ (a) An alkane
- ☐ (b) An alcohol
- ☐ (c) An acid
- ☐ (d) An ester
- ☐ (e) A polyamide

47 What is the name of the molecule shown in the diagram that follows?

- ☐ (a) Propane
- ☐ (b) Propene
- ☐ (c) Butane
- ☐ (d) Butene
- ☐ (e) Ethane

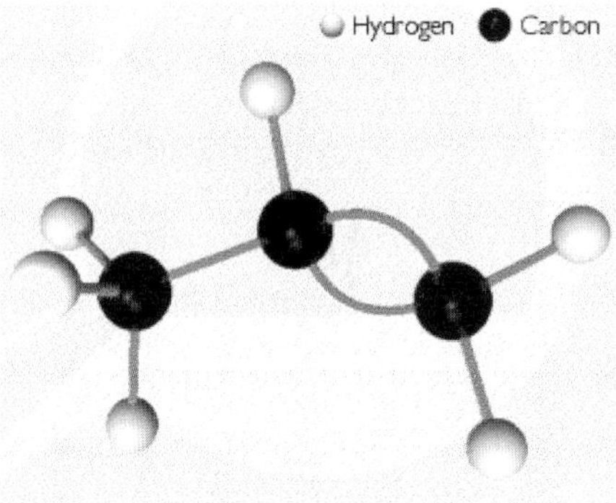

Q47

48 Which of the following can be used to distinguish between saturated hydrocarbons and unsaturated hydrocarbons?

- ☐ (a) The number of carbon atoms
- ☐ (b) Reaction with helium
- ☐ (c) Combustion products
- ☐ (d) Melting point
- ☐ (e) Reaction with bromine water

49 Alkenes can be identified by their reaction with bromine water. What happens when an alkene reacts with bromine water?

- ☐ (a) The bromine water is decolourized
- ☐ (b) A brown gas is produced
- ☐ (c) The bromine water turns green

□ (d) A displacement reaction takes place
□ (e) There is no reaction with alkenes

50 Which of the following conditions are needed for the polymerization of ethene to form polythene?

□ (a) Both high pressure and a heated catalyst
□ (b) Low pressure and water
□ (c) A heated catalyst only
□ (d) Low pressure and a catalyst
□ (e) A heated catalyst and hydrogen

51 Methane and oxygen will only react when a small amount of energy is added at the start of the reaction. What is the name given to this energy?

....

52 Which of the following can be used to distinguish between saturated hydrocarbons and unsaturated hydrocarbons?

□ (a) The structure of the molecule
□ (b) The combustion products
□ (c) The number of carbon atoms in the molecules
□ (d) The melting point
□ (e) The rate at which the hydrocarbon reacts with helium

53 How are alkenes manufactured?

□ (a) By cracking
□ (b) By polymerization
□ (c) By fractional distillation
□ (d) By extraction from their ore
□ (e) In the blast furnace

54 What is the name given to the type of polymerization undergone by ethene to form polythene?

□ (a) Condensation polymerization
□ (b) Addition polymerization
□ (c) Elimination polymerization
□ (d) Substitution polymerization
□ (e) Multiple polymerization

55 What is the name of the hydrocarbon with the structural formula C_3H_6?

□ (a) Propene
□ (b) Propane
□ (c) Ethene
□ (d) Ethane
□ (e) Butane

56 Although methane and oxygen react vigorously together in a bunsen burner flame, why can they be mixed together at room temperature without any reaction taking place?

□ (a) Bonds need to be made before they can be broken
□ (b) They only react when there is a bright light
□ (c) The reaction needs an input of energy before it will start
□ (d) The reaction that occurs is not very exothermic
□ (e) The reaction that occurs is slightly endothermic

57 Which of the following is a property of the alkanes?

□ (a) They react with hydrogen to produce alkenes
□ (b) They burn in air to produce carbon dioxide and water
□ (c) They undergo polymerization
□ (d) They react with bromine
□ (e) They react with elements from group VIII

58 According to the diagram that follows, which one of the polymers would be produced from the monomer propene?

....

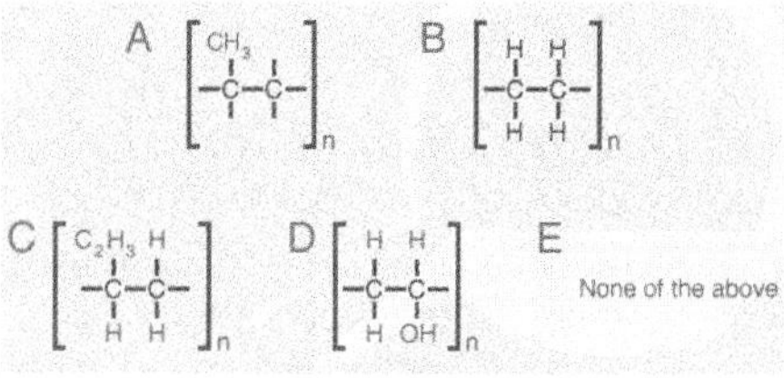

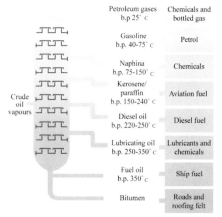

Q58

59 Plastics are made from units called monomers. What is formed when many monomers join together?

....

60 What type of reaction is shown in the diagram that follows?

□ (a) Addition polymerization
□ (b) Cracking
□ (c) Distillation
□ (d) Condensation polymerization
□ (e) Reforming

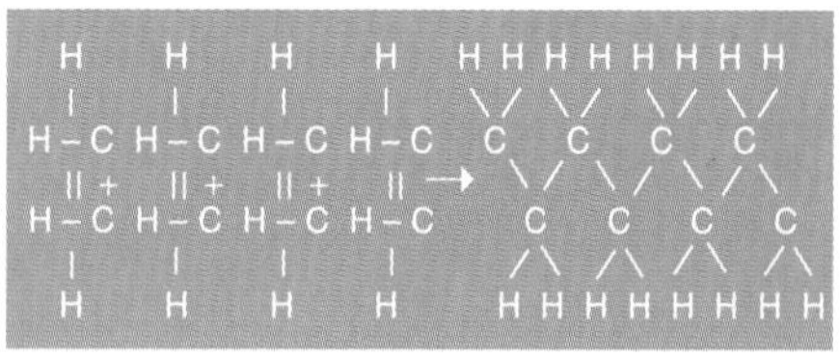

Q60

ANSWERS

Petrochemicals and organic chemistry

Foundation and Higher Levels

□ **1** *(c)*
The extraction of crude oil and its subsequent refinement into the different fractions produces a vast range of products that have improved the quality of life of many millions of people around the world.

□ **2** *(a)*
In the process of fractional distillation the fractions are separated because of their different boiling points. The fraction with the lowest boiling point will be collected at the top of the column where it is coolest, as shown in the diagram on the right.

□ **3** *(a)*
Fractional distillation relies on the components of the mixture being separated having different boiling points. The liquid with the lowest boiling point will come off at the top of the column. See diagram that follows.

A2, 3

☐ **4** *(c)*
Crude oil is a valuable natural resource because it contains vast amounts of different compounds that can be made into many different materials.

☐ **5** *(c)*
Crude oil is formed by the decay of organic material under high pressure with little oxygen present. As a result, all the other substances are found in crude oil except oxygen.

☐ **6** *(e)*
A viscous liquid is one that does not pour very easily as it is thick and gluey. Fractions with a greater number of carbon atoms in the molecules have higher boiling points and are more viscous. Fuel oil has the highest boiling point of the fractions mentioned and so it will be the most viscous.

☐ **7** *(e)*
Fuel oil is used to power large ships and industrial machines. Fuel oil has a high ignition temperature so it is sprayed into the combustion chamber as a fine mist, and this helps it to ignite.

☐ **8** *(e)*
Crude oil is a valuable natural resource as it contains vast amounts of different chemical compounds. These include fuels, such as petrol and diesel, and also petroleum gases. Crude oil also contains many other chemicals that can be used to manufacture plastics, drugs, etc. Nitrogen is not present in crude oil.

☐ **9** *(a)*
Crude oil is a valuable source of chemicals and fuels. One of the compounds that can be obtained from the fractional distillation of crude oil is bitumen. All the other suggestions can be produced from crude oil, but they are not actually present.

☐ **10** *(a)*
The naphtha fraction has a boiling point between 75–150°C. The compounds in this fraction have a vast number of uses, which include the manufacture of paints, plastics, and detergents.

☐ **11** *(d)*
The greater the number of carbon atoms in the molecules, the higher the boiling point will be. Bitumen has the highest boiling point of all the fractions and therefore contains the molecules with the most carbon atoms (i.e. the longest carbon chains).

☐ **12** *(c)*
The name for the process in which large hydrocarbon molecules are converted into smaller hydrocarbon molecules is known as cracking. In the cracking process, the vapour of the large molecules is passed over a hot catalyst and the molecules break to form smaller ones. See diagram that follows.

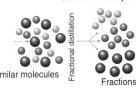

CRACKING

Surface of catalyst

Similar molecules

Fractional distillation

Fractions

A12, 13

☐ **13** *(a)*
The crude oil fractions such as petrol and naphtha are more useful than the large molecules in the fuel oil and bitumen fractions. These large molecules can be broken into smaller, more useful ones, such as petrol, by the process of cracking. This is done by passing the large molecules over a heated catalyst (aluminium oxide or silicon (IV) oxide). See previous diagram.

☐ **14** *(d)*
Polythene, polystyrene, nylon, and teflon are all manufactured materials, while cotton is a natural plant product.

☐ **15** *(b)*
Polystyrene foam is a soft plastic used to make items like disposable insulators.

☐ **16** *(b)*
The main use of polymers is as plastics, such as polythene and nylon.

☐ **17** *(d)*
The purpose of cracking large molecules into smaller ones is to produce a more useful compound. Not enough petrol is obtained from crude oil by fractional distillation. Therefore, the large molecules such as fuel oils and bitumen are cracked into smaller molecules such as petrol.

☐ **18** *(a)*
The candle contains both carbon and hydrogen and as they burn in the air carbon dioxide and water are formed. The water condenses in the U-tube and this is shown by the white copper sulphate turning blue (a positive test). As the carbon dioxide gas is drawn through the lime water it turns milky. This is a positive test for carbon dioxide.

The lime water goes milky because the carbon dioxide reacts with it to form a white solid (calcium carbonate).

☐ **19** *(e)*
The fact that the lime water turns milky indicates that one of the combustion products is carbon dioxide. This is a positive test as the carbon dioxide reacts with the lime water to form calcium carbonate. This is insoluble and so it forms a cloudy precipitate.

☐ **20** *(e)*
Fossil fuels are formed by the anaerobic (without oxygen) decay of organic matter. The answers except for wood are all examples of fossil fuels – the difference between them is the length of time the matter has been decaying, and the pressure that the material has been placed under. Peat and lignite (sometimes referred to as brown coal) have not been decaying for as long as coal and oil. Also, coal and oil have been formed under very high pressures.

☐ **21** *(e)*
Crude oil is refined to separate its products and 4% of the oil is used to manufacture plastics.

☐ **22** *(d)*
All hydrocarbons burn to produce carbon dioxide and water. Many fuels are hydrocarbons.

☐ **23** *(b)*
Fossil fuels, such as coal, contain small amounts of sulphur. When combustion takes place, the sulphur reacts with oxygen in the air to form sulphur dioxide. This is an acidic gas that dissolves in the water, is held in clouds, and then produces acid rain.

☐ **24** *(c)*
Crude oil contains a vast number of useful compounds that can be used to manufacture a large number of other chemicals. These include plastics, fibres, agrochemicals, medicines, and fuels.

☐ **25** *(c)*
A thermosetting plastic is one that can only be melted and set solid once. When the plastic is first melted, the long chains become crosslinked and a huge 3D structure is built up. If it is melted again, the plastic breaks down.

☐ **26** *(b)*
Thermosoftening plastics are materials that can be melted and then cooled to a solid many times, without the plastic breaking down. An example of a thermosoftening plastic is polythene.

☐ **27** *(c)*
The name of the process in which yeast converts glucose to carbon dioxide and ethanol is fermentation.

☐ **28** *(c)*
The equation represents the fermentation of sugar to produce carbon dioxide and ethanol. Therefore, the missing product is ethanol.

☐ **29** *(d)*
During the process of fermentation the sugar is broken down to produce ethanol and carbon dioxide.

☐ **30** *(e)*
Fermentation is the process whereby yeast releases the energy in sugars in anaerobic conditions. It is an exothermic process, and the products of the reaction are ethanol and carbon dioxide. As carbon dioxide is a product of the reaction, it is not needed for the reaction to proceed. Fermentation is used in the brewing industry and baking.

☐ **31** *(d)*
Fermentation is the process by which yeast converts sugars into ethanol and carbon dioxide.

☐ **32** *(a)*
A fermentation reaction will take place between the glucose and yeast, and this produces carbon dioxide and ethanol. The carbon dioxide gas will bubble through the lime water and this will make the lime water go milky. The lime water test is used to detect the presence of carbon dioxide.

☐ **33** *(d)*
During fermentation the yeast breaks down the sugars into carbon dioxide and ethanol, and energy is also released.

Petrochemicals and organic chemistry

Higher Level only

☐ **34** *(b)*
The structure is that of an alkane molecule containing two carbon atoms. It represents a molecule of ethane.

☐ **35** *(d)*
Ethane is a member of a family of hydrocarbons with the general formula C_nH_{2n+2}. Ethane has two carbon atoms and therefore must contain six hydrogen atoms.

☐ **36** *(d)*
The molecule has two carbon atoms so will begin with eth-. The structure contains a carbon-carbon double bond and so is an alkene. Hence, the structure represents a molecule of ethene.

☐ **37** *(c)*
The molecule has three carbon atoms so will begin with prop-. It complies with the general formula C_nH_{2n+2}, with n equalling three so it is an alkane. Hence the name is propane.

☐ **38** *(c)*
The alkanes are so unreactive because they are saturated hydrocarbons. This means that the molecules only contain single bonds, resulting in a very stable molecule and hence making the alkanes unreactive. They do, however, undergo combustion and are therefore used as fuels. For example, methane is used as fuel for domestic cookers.

☐ **39** *(e)*
The name of the molecule begins with eth- so it will therefore have two carbon atoms. It is also an alkene, due to the fact that the name ends with -ene, so it must fit into the general formula C_nH_{2n}. As there are two carbons in the molecule, with n equalling two, the formula must be C_2H_4.

☐ **40** *(e)*
All hydrocarbons with the general formula C_nH_{2n+2} belong to the alkane family and therefore have the suffix -ane. Hydrocarbons with two carbon atoms have the prefix eth-. Therefore, the name of the hydrocarbon with the formula C_2H_6 is ethane.

☐ **41**
This represents the simplest hydrocarbon, methane.

☐ **42** *(d)*
Hydrocarbons with the general formula C_nH_{2n+2} are members of the family of hydrocarbons known as the alkanes. Hydrocarbons with three carbon atoms are given the prefix prop-. The name of this hydrocarbon is therefore propane.

☐ **43** *(b)*
Addition polymerization is the process whereby small molecules with double bonds are joined together to form large long chain molecules. There are no other products formed during the reaction.

☐ **44** *(e)*
Polythene is made by the polymerization of the monomer ethene, by passing the ethene over a heated catalyst at high pressure. This is an example of addition polymerization. Polythene is used to make plastic bags, kitchenware etc.

☐ **45** *(b)*
Methane and propane are alkanes. Alkanes are known as saturated hydrocarbons, which means that there are no double bonds between the carbon atoms. This makes the alkanes relatively stable and unreactive. The alkanes do, however, undergo combustion to form carbon dioxide and water, hence their use as fuels.

☐ **46** *(a)*
The reaction of hydrogen and an alkene results in the formation of an alkane. The alkene contains a double bond and the hydrogen is added into the molecule across this double bond to form the alkane. For example, ethene will react with hydrogen to produce ethane, as can be seen from the diagram that follows.

$$H_2C=CH_2 + H_2 \rightarrow H_3C-CH_3$$

Ethene   Ethane

A46

☐ **47** *(b)*
The molecule has only three carbons so its name will begin with prop-. It also falls into the general formula C_nH_{2n}, with n equalling three, so the formula is C_3H_6. Therefore, it is an alkene and the name will end with -ene. The fact that it has a double bond reinforces the idea that this must be an alkene. The name for this molecule is propene.

☐ **48** *(e)*
The saturated hydrocarbons contain only single bonds, which makes them unreactive and so they do not react with bromine water. Unsaturated hydrocarbons, on the other hand, contain multiple bonds, which are more reactive. Unsaturated hydrocarbons, such as ethene, will react with bromine water turning it from orange to colourless. The orange colour is removed as the bromine reacts with the ethene to produce dibromoethane. See equation that follows.

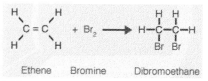

Ethene   Bromine   Dibromoethane

A48

☐ 49 *(a)*
Bromine water will react with ethene to form 1,2-dibromoethane and hence remove the colour of the bromine water. See equation that follows. This is used as a test for alkenes.

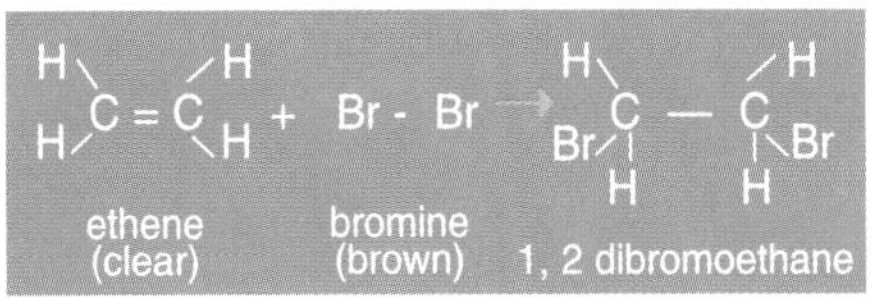

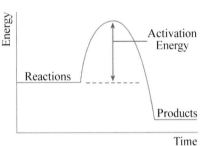

A49

☐ 50 *(a)*
Ethene will undergo polymerization to form polythene under high pressure and in the presence of a heated catalyst.

☐ 51
The energy input required before a reaction will start is known as the activation energy. This is used to overcome the energy barrier at the start of the reaction, and when this has been overcome the reaction can proceed. The activation energy needed to start a reaction between methane and oxygen can be put in using a lighted match.

☐ 52 *(a)*
The structure of a hydrocarbon can be used to distinguish between a saturated and unsaturated hydrocarbon. Saturated hydrocarbons, such as ethane, contain only single bonds between the atoms, whereas unsaturated hydrocarbons, such as ethene, contain multiple bonds.

☐ 53 *(a)*
Alkenes are manufactured by the process of cracking. Cracking is a process whereby large saturated hydrocarbon molecules are broken up into smaller unsaturated hydrocarbon molecules such as alkenes. Hydrogen is also produced in this process as the unsaturated molecules contain less hydrogen than the saturated molecules.

☐ 54 *(b)*
The name given to the polymerization undergone by ethene to form polythene is addition polymerization.

☐ 55 *(a)*
The molecule has three carbons, so it will begin with prop-. It also falls into the general formula C_nH_{2n}, with n equalling three, so the formula is C_3H_6. The substance is an alkene, and its name, therefore, is propene.

☐ 56 *(c)*
Methane will react with oxygen to produce carbon dioxide and water, but an input of energy is needed to get the reaction started, as can be seen from the diagram that follows. This energy is used to overcome the energy hurdle at the start of the reaction and is known as the activation energy. Once the reaction has started it is exothermic and some of the energy released is used to keep the reaction going.

Reaction activation energy

A diagram with Energy on the vertical axis and Time on the horizontal axis, showing a curve rising from "Reactions" level over a hump labelled "Activation Energy" and falling to a lower "Products" level.

A56

☐ 57 *(b)*
The alkanes are saturated hydrocarbons. The molecules only contain single bonds, which makes the alkanes relatively unreactive. They do, however, undergo combustion to produce carbon dioxide and water and hence are used as fuels. For example, methane is used as a fuel in domestic central heating.

☐ 58
Diagram A depicts polypropene, which is the polymer of the monomer propene. The diagram that follows shows a propene molecule to the left of the arrow. The fact that it is in brackets with an 'n' outside the bracket means that many propene molecules join together to form polypropene. A section of the polypropene molecule is shown in the brackets to the right of the arrow.

A58

☐ 59
Many single molecules or monomers may be joined together to form a polymer. The polymer is usually given the name of the monomer with the prefix of poly-. For instance, many ethene molecules joined (or bonded) together form poly(ethene), which is often known as polythene.

☐ 60 *(a)*
The reaction shown in the equation is an addition polymerization reaction. Thousands of monomer molecules (in this example the monomer is ethene) are joined together to form a long chain molecule of polythene. This is an addition polymerization process because the double bonds open up and there are no other products formed.

Changing Materials

Chemical changes *(Single and Double Awards)*

Chemistry is about changing substances to other substances. There are many types of chemical change and it is important to know the main types of change and to be able to classify a particular change into one of these types. The following questions relate to chemical changes.

QUESTIONS

Foundation and Higher Levels

1 Which of the chemical symbols shown in the diagram below represents a mixture?

....

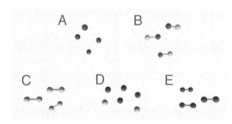

Q1

2 Rusting is a corrosion reaction of which metal?

- ☐ (a) Sodium
- ☐ (b) Iron
- ☐ (c) Gold
- ☐ (d) Silver
- ☐ (e) Magnesium

3 Which element in the atmosphere does iron react with to form rust?

- ☐ (a) Carbon
- ☐ (b) Hydrogen
- ☐ (c) Nitrogen
- ☐ (d) Oxygen
- ☐ (e) Sulphur

4 Which of the following must be present for rusting to take place?

- ☐ (a) Oxygen and iron
- ☐ (b) Oxygen, iron, and water
- ☐ (c) Iron and water
- ☐ (d) Iron, water, and salt
- ☐ (e) Oxygen, aluminium, and water

5 When iron is exposed to the atmosphere, a red-brown solid appears slowly on the surface. What is the name of this reaction?

- ☐ (a) Rusting
- ☐ (b) Neutralization

- ☐ (c) Tarnishing
- ☐ (d) Electrolysis
- ☐ (e) Displacement

6 What is a corrosion reaction?

- ☐ (a) The transformation of a gas into a solid
- ☐ (b) A reaction between oxygen and a metal
- ☐ (c) A reaction between a metal and hydrogen
- ☐ (d) A reaction between an acid and a base
- ☐ (e) The breakdown of a compound using electricity

7 What type of reaction occurs when a metal reacts with oxygen?

- ☐ (a) Oxidation
- ☐ (b) Neutralization
- ☐ (c) Reduction
- ☐ (d) Displacement
- ☐ (e) Electrolysis

8 In which of the following situations would an iron nail rust the fastest?

- ☐ (a) In boiled water protected from the air by a layer of oil on top of the water
- ☐ (b) In tap water exposed to the air
- ☐ (c) In dry air in a sealed tube
- ☐ (d) In sea water exposed to the air
- ☐ (e) In boiled water exposed to the air

9 Three iron nails were placed in test tubes and subjected to the following conditions for two weeks:
i. One iron nail was covered in grease
ii. One iron nail was immersed in boiled water and the water covered in a layer of oil
iii. One iron nail was left exposed to the air
Which of the nails would have rusted?

- ☐ (a) i and ii only
- ☐ (b) ii and iii only
- ☐ (c) i and iii only
- ☐ (d) i only
- ☐ (e) iii only

10 Look at the diagram that follows. In which of the tubes would rusting not occur?

- ☐ (a) A only
- ☐ (b) B and C
- ☐ (c) A and C
- ☐ (d) C only
- ☐ (e) B only

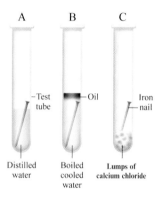

Q10

11 A wad of iron wool is placed in a test tube partly filled with water, as shown in the following diagram. Why does the level of the water in the test tube change as the iron wool rusts?

- ☐ (a) The iron traps the air in the wool thus reducing the volume of air in the test tube
- ☐ (b) The iron reacts with the oxygen thus reducing the volume of air in the test tube
- ☐ (c) The iron breaks down the water into oxygen and hydrogen, thus lowering the level of water in the test tube
- ☐ (d) The iron gives off hydrogen, which increases the volume of air in the test tube
- ☐ (e) None of the above

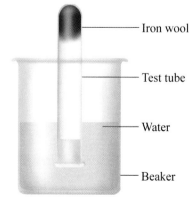

Q11

12 Which one of the following methods of rust prevention will be effective even if oxygen and water come into contact with iron?

- ☐ (a) Grease
- ☐ (b) Painting
- ☐ (c) Sacrificial protection
- ☐ (d) Coat of plastic
- ☐ (e) Tin plating

13 Why does stainless steel not rust, whereas other alloys of iron do?

- ☐ (a) The added chromium prevents the iron on the surface from reacting with the air
- ☐ (b) The mixture of iron and chromium forms an alloy that does not rust
- ☐ (c) The addition of chromium prevents the iron from reaching the water
- ☐ (d) The addition of chromium prevents the iron from reaching the oxygen
- ☐ (e) The chromium will corrode before the iron

14 Which of the following methods could be used to prevent rusting on the moving parts of a car engine?

- ☐ (a) A coat of plastic
- ☐ (b) A coat of grease
- ☐ (c) Painting
- ☐ (d) Galvanizing
- ☐ (e) None of the above

15 Why does a layer of tin only prevent the rusting of iron if the surface is not scratched?

- ☐ (a) The tin is more reactive than iron
- ☐ (b) The tin is less reactive then iron
- ☐ (c) The tin reacts with the iron causing rust
- ☐ (d) The tin will catalyze the rusting of iron
- ☐ (e) None of the above

16 An element, X, is reacted with oxygen to produce a gaseous product that dissolves in water to give an acidic solution. Which of the following could X be?

- ☐ (a) Hydrogen
- ☐ (b) Sulphur
- ☐ (c) Sodium
- ☐ (d) Argon
- ☐ (e) Gold

17 Which gas is formed as a result of the reaction between a metal and an acid, such as the reaction between zinc and hydrochloric acid?

- ☐ (a) Hydrogen
- ☐ (b) Oxygen
- ☐ (c) Chlorine
- ☐ (d) Hydrogen chloride
- ☐ (e) Zinc chloride

18 Iron reacts with the atmosphere to form a new chemical. What is the name of this new chemical?

- ☐ (a) Iron hydride
- ☐ (b) Iron oxide
- ☐ (c) Iron dioxide
- ☐ (d) Iron nitrate
- ☐ (e) Iron hydroxide

19 Iron and sulphur react to form iron sulphide. Iron is silvery grey, sulphur is yellow. What colour is the product of the reaction between these two elements?

- ☐ (a) Black
- ☐ (b) Blue
- ☐ (c) Silver
- ☐ (d) Yellow
- ☐ (e) Grey

20 In the equation that follows, two solutions react together to produce an insoluble substance. What is the name of this type of reaction?

- ☐ (a) Neutralization
- ☐ (b) Displacement
- ☐ (c) Precipitation
- ☐ (d) Electrolysis
- ☐ (e) Oxidation

barium chloride + sodium sulphate → barium sulphate + sodium chloride

$BaCl_2(aq) + Na_2SO_4(aq) \rightarrow BaSO_4(s) + 2NaCl(aq)$

Q20

21 What is polymerization?

- ☐ (a) The process by which large molecules are broken down to form smaller ones
- ☐ (b) The process by which small molecules join up to form a long chain
- ☐ (c) The process by which nitrogen and hydrogen are joined together to form ammonia
- ☐ (d) The process by which copies of molecules are manufactured
- ☐ (e) The process by which the atoms in a molecule are rearranged

22 Which of the following statements are true?
i. Non-metal oxides all dissolve in water to produce acidic solutions

ii. Metal oxides are all soluble in water
iii. Metal chlorides are solids

- ☐ (a) All of them
- ☐ (b) None of them
- ☐ (c) ii only
- ☐ (d) iii only
- ☐ (e) i and ii only

23 Which of the following is not a modern day use of hydrogen?

- ☐ (a) In weather balloons
- ☐ (b) In the manufacture of margarine
- ☐ (c) In the manufacture of ammonia
- ☐ (d) In airships
- ☐ (e) As a fuel in rockets

24 Three elements X, Y, and Z reacted with oxygen in separate gas jars. Which elements could be metals given the following results?
X produced a gas that is acidic.
Y produced a neutral liquid.
Z produced a solid that is basic.

- ☐ (a) X only
- ☐ (b) X and Y only
- ☐ (c) Z only
- ☐ (d) All of them
- ☐ (e) Y only

25 When fresh fruit is left uncooked for a long period of time it starts to rot. What type of reaction is this?

- ☐ (a) Physical
- ☐ (b) Reduction
- ☐ (c) Oxidation
- ☐ (d) Thermal decomposition
- ☐ (e) Precipitation

26 When an apple is freshly cut, the flesh is white. If the flesh is left exposed to the air it turns brown. Which gas in the air is causing this reaction?

- ☐ (a) Oxygen
- ☐ (b) Nitrogen
- ☐ (c) Carbon dioxide
- ☐ (d) Argon
- ☐ (e) Sulphur dioxide

27 Why does covering an apple in toffee prevent the apple from turning brown?

- ☐ (a) It protects the apple from bruising
- ☐ (b) It stops oxygen reaching the flesh of the apple
- ☐ (c) It stops naturally occurring radiation from damaging the flesh
- ☐ (d) It reacts with the apple to form a compound which does not react with oxygen

61

(e) It stops nitrogen reaching the flesh of the apple

28 What is common to all metal oxides?

- (a) They are all gases
- (b) They are all solids
- (c) They are all liquids
- (d) They are all shiny
- (e) They can all be reduced to the metal by heating with carbon

29 Which of the following statements about a scientific theory are true?
i. A scientific theory is the truth
ii. A scientific theory does not change
iii. A scientific theory is always discovered by doing experiments in a laboratory

- (a) i and ii only
- (b) i and iii only
- (c) i only
- (d) iii only
- (e) None of them

30 Which of the following elements, when reacted with oxygen and then dissolved in water, would not produce an acidic solution?

- (a) Sulphur
- (b) Sodium
- (c) Carbon
- (d) Phosphorus
- (e) Nitrogen

31 Which of the following is a synthetic substance?

- (a) Nylon
- (b) Cotton
- (c) Silk
- (d) Wool
- (e) Cashmere

32 A pupil mixes two substances in a test tube. Which of the following would suggest that a chemical reaction has taken place?

- (a) The mixture changes in colour
- (b) The mixture changes in temperature
- (c) The mixture changes in volume
- (d) The mixture changes in density
- (e) The mixture changes in shape

33 Which one of the following is not a manufactured substance?

- (a) Brass
- (b) Bronze
- (c) Gold

(d) Paper
(e) Perspex

34 Which one of the following is a manufactured substance?

- (a) Bronze
- (b) Gold
- (c) Mercury
- (d) Silver
- (e) Sodium

35 What happens if an iron object that has been galvanized (plated with zinc) has its zinc surface scratched?

- (a) The iron underneath starts to rust
- (b) The iron underneath does not rust
- (c) The zinc reacts with the iron and refills the scratch
- (d) The zinc expands to fill the scratch
- (e) A zinc alloy is formed

36 What type of reaction takes place when magnesium is heated in a Bunsen burner flame?

- (a) Chemical
- (b) Physical
- (c) Biological
- (d) Nuclear
- (e) Thermal decomposition

37 Metals that are found in the Earth's crust either as native metals or as compounds. If the metals are found as compounds they have to be extracted. The type of method used to extract a metal depends upon which one of the following properties?

- (a) The melting point of the metal
- (b) The reactivity of the metal
- (c) The area of the world where the ore is found
- (d) The electrical conductivity of the metal
- (e) The malleability of the metal

38 Which of the following is a large scale use of sodium chloride?

- (a) The manufacture of iron
- (b) As a catalyst in the cracking of large hydrocarbon molecules
- (c) The purification of copper
- (d) De-icing roads in winter
- (e) As a weed killer

39 Which of the following is a substance that occurs naturally?

- (a) Salt (sodium chloride)
- (b) PVC (polyvinyl chloride)
- (c) Porcelain

(d) Paper
(e) Steel

40 An element is reacted with chlorine to produce a gas that dissolves in water to give an acidic solution. Which of the following could the element be?

- (a) Sodium
- (b) Carbon
- (c) Argon
- (d) Gold
- (e) Hydrogen

41 Sodium is a metal with all the usual properties of metals and it also floats on water. Most modern ships are made out of metals. Why are ships not made from sodium?

- (a) It absorbs water easily
- (b) It is not very strong
- (c) It is a good conductor of heat
- (d) It is too reactive
- (e) It is not very hard

42 Which of the following will produce a displacement reaction?

- (a) Chlorine and potassium bromide
- (b) Chlorine and sodium fluoride
- (c) Iodine and lithium chloride
- (d) Bromine and sodium chloride
- (e) Iodine and potassium chloride

43 How is ammonia converted into the fertilizer, ammonium sulphate?

- (a) It is reacted with sodium sulphate
- (b) It is reacted with nitric acid
- (c) It is reacted with sulphuric acid
- (d) It is reacted with calcium sulphate
- (e) It is reacted with phosphoric acid

44 What is the name of the process, crucial to the wine-making and brewing industries, which produces ethanol from simple sugars?

- (a) Respiration
- (b) Fermentation
- (c) Photosynthesis
- (d) Esterification
- (e) Alcoholism

QUESTIONS

Higher Level only

45 Which of the following is one definition of an oxidation reaction?

- ☐ (a) A reaction in which an atom reacts with hydrogen
- ☐ (b) A reaction in which an atom reacts with oxygen
- ☐ (c) A reaction in which an atom or ion gains an electron
- ☐ (d) A reaction in which oxygen is produced
- ☐ (e) A reaction in which an atom changes into an oxygen atom

46 Which of the following underlined substances is undergoing an oxidation reaction?

- ☐ (a) $\underline{Li} \rightarrow Li^+ + e^-$
- ☐ (b) $\underline{Cl} + e^- \rightarrow Cl^-$
- ☐ (c) $2Mg + \underline{CO_2} \rightarrow 2MgO + C$
- ☐ (d) $2HCl + \underline{ZnO} \rightarrow ZnCl_2 + H_2O$
- ☐ (e) $\underline{Cu^{2+}} + Zn \rightarrow Cu + Zn^{2+}$

47 Which of the following is one definition of a reduction reaction?

- ☐ (a) A reaction in which there is a loss of electrons
- ☐ (b) A reaction in which there is a loss of oxygen or gain of hydrogen
- ☐ (c) A reaction in which hydrogen is produced
- ☐ (d) A reaction in which there is a loss of mass
- ☐ (e) A reaction in which an atom is changed into a smaller atom of the same group

48 Which of the following is one definition of a reduction reaction?

- ☐ (a) A reaction in which hydrogen is produced
- ☐ (b) A reaction in which an atom reacts with oxygen
- ☐ (c) A reaction in which a substance loses mass
- ☐ (d) A reaction in which an atom or an ion gains an electron or electrons
- ☐ (e) A reaction in which an oxygen atom changes into a hydrogen atom

49 Which of the following is an example of an oxidation reaction?

- ☐ (a) The formation of copper metal during the electrolysis of copper sulphate solution
- ☐ (b) The formation of iron in the blast furnace
- ☐ (c) The formation of sodium ions when sodium reacts with water
- ☐ (d) The formation of ammonia
- ☐ (e) The formation of hydrogen when a metal reacts with an acid

50 Which of the following is an oxidation reaction?

- ☐ (a) The formation of carbon when magnesium is burnt in carbon dioxide
- ☐ (b) The formation of aluminium during the electrolysis of molten aluminium oxide
- ☐ (c) The formation of carbon when magnesium is burnt in carbon monoxide
- ☐ (d) The formation of hydrogen when an alkali metal reacts with water
- ☐ (e) The formation of chlorine during the electrolysis of brine solution (sodium chloride solution)

51 Which of the following statements describing an oxidation reaction, are true?
i. When a substance is oxidized, it loses oxygen
ii. When a substance is oxidized, it gains hydrogen
iii. When a substance is oxidized, the products are always acidic

- ☐ (a) i and iii only
- ☐ (b) ii and iii only
- ☐ (c) iii only
- ☐ (d) i only
- ☐ (e) None of the statements are true

Acids and alkalis – indicators *(Single and Double Awards)*

Most people associate acids and alkalis with chemistry, but few know much about the properties and importance of these substances in everyday life. The idea that acids are extremely dangerous and burn the skin is common, but many people are not aware that acids and alkalis come into contact with their bodies daily. The following questions test ideas that are associated with acids and alkalis.

QUESTIONS

Foundation and Higher Levels

1 What colour would be seen when universal indicator is added to a colourless solution of pH 7?

....

2 Acids turn universal indicator red. Which one of the following would turn universal indicator red?

- ☐ (a) Orangeade
- ☐ (b) Water
- ☐ (c) Oven cleaner
- ☐ (d) A glass of water containing dissolved indigestion tablets
- ☐ (e) Soap

3 What colour is universal indicator in a solution of pH 14?

....

4 What is the colour change seen when a strong acid is added to universal indicator?

- ☐ (a) Purple to green
- ☐ (b) Green to purple
- ☐ (c) Red to purple
- ☐ (d) Red to green
- ☐ (e) Green to red

5 What colour will sodium hydroxide turn universal indicator?

....

6 What is the colour of universal indicator in pure water?

....

7 What colour will potassium hydroxide solution turn universal indicator?

- ☐ (a) Purple
- ☐ (b) Red
- ☐ (c) Yellow
- ☐ (d) Green
- ☐ (e) Brown

8 What colour is universal indicator in a solution of pH 1?

- ☐ (a) Purple
- ☐ (b) Green
- ☐ (c) Yellow
- ☐ (d) Red
- ☐ (e) Orange

9 What colour will the digestive juices from your stomach turn universal indicator?

- ☐ (a) Red
- ☐ (b) Purple
- ☐ (c) Green
- ☐ (d) White
- ☐ (e) Black

10 What colour will oven cleaner turn universal indicator?

- ☐ (a) Brown
- ☐ (b) Black
- ☐ (c) Purple
- ☐ (d) Red
- ☐ (e) Green

11 Use the indicator colour chart that follows to help you answer this question. Which one of the following substances will turn universal indicator orange?

- ☐ (a) Lemon juice
- ☐ (b) Table salt solution
- ☐ (c) Oven cleaner
- ☐ (d) Indigestion tablets dissolved in water
- ☐ (e) Distilled water

Q11

12 Universal indicator was added to liquid X and the mixture was a green colour. Using the list of substances in the previous question, which one of the substances could X be?

....

13 Which one of the following substances would turn universal indicator purple?

- ☐ (a) Grapefruit juice
- ☐ (b) Oven cleaner
- ☐ (c) Water
- ☐ (d) Anti-rust paint
- ☐ (e) Vinegar

14 Three liquids (X, Y, and Z) were mixed together as follows:
i. Universal indicator was added to X and it turned green
ii. Z was added to X and the universal indicator turned violet
iii. Y was added to the mixture of X and Z and the universal indicator turned green
What is the nature of the substances X, Y, and Z respectively?

- ☐ (a) Neutral, alkali, acid
- ☐ (b) Neutral, alkali, neutral
- ☐ (c) Alkali, neutral, acid
- ☐ (d) Neutral, acid, alkali
- ☐ (e) Acid, neutral, alkali

15 A solution of carbon dioxide will turn universal indicator orange. What type of substance is carbon dioxide?

- ☐ (a) A base
- ☐ (b) An alkali
- ☐ (c) An acid
- ☐ (d) A neutral substance
- ☐ (e) An insoluble substance

16 Acids turn universal indicator red. Which of the following will turn universal indicator red?

- ☐ (a) Concrete
- ☐ (b) Milk of magnesia
- ☐ (c) Toothpaste
- ☐ (d) Water
- ☐ (e) Vinegar

17 What colour will sulphuric acid turn universal indicator?

....

18 Which one of the following would turn red litmus paper blue?

- ☐ (a) Sodium chloride solution
- ☐ (b) Sulphuric acid

- ☐ (c) Sodium nitrate solution
- ☐ (d) Sodium hydroxide solution
- ☐ (e) Water

19 Which one of the following would turn red litmus paper blue?

- ☐ (a) Water
- ☐ (b) Magnesium
- ☐ (c) Sulphur dioxide
- ☐ (d) Calcium hydroxide solution
- ☐ (e) Orange juice

20 The pHs of five solutions are given below. Which one of these would change the colour of red litmus paper blue?

- ☐ (a) 4
- ☐ (b) 7
- ☐ (c) 1
- ☐ (d) 11
- ☐ (e) 6

21 Which one of the following would not turn blue litmus paper red?

- ☐ (a) Lemon juice
- ☐ (b) Vitamin C solution
- ☐ (c) Vinegar
- ☐ (d) A solution of indigestion tablets
- ☐ (e) Soda water

22 Which of the following substances, when in solution, would turn U.V.I. blue/purple?
i. Soap flakes
ii. Oven cleaner
iii. Indigestion tablets

- ☐ (a) All of them
- ☐ (b) None of them
- ☐ (c) i only
- ☐ (d) i and ii only
- ☐ (e) ii and iii only

23 Which one of the following is a suitable pH for a weakly acidic solution?

- ☐ (a) 7
- ☐ (b) 1
- ☐ (c) 8
- ☐ (d) 5
- ☐ (e) 14

24 Which one of the following is a suitable pH for a neutral solution?

- ☐ (a) 7
- ☐ (b) 1
- ☐ (c) 5
- ☐ (d) 10
- ☐ (e) 14

25 Which of the following is a suitable pH for a strong alkali?

☐ (a) 5
☐ (b) 1
☐ (c) 14
☐ (d) 7
☐ (e) 8

26 A few drops of universal indicator are added to a strong acid solution. A strong alkali is added in order to neutralize the solution, and then more alkali is added. What would be the colour change of universal indicator?

☐ (a) Green to red to purple
☐ (b) Green to red to green
☐ (c) Green to red
☐ (d) Green to red to green to purple
☐ (e) Green to violet to green to red

27 A pupil carries out an investigation on three solutions (X, Y, and Z), using different indicators as shown in the following diagram. The results obtained are as follows:
X: Phenolphthalein remains colourless and litmus turns red
Y: Phenolphthalein turns pink and litmus turns blue

Z: Phenolphthalein remains colourless and universal indicator solution turns green
Which solutions are acidic?

☐ (a) All of them
☐ (b) None of them
☐ (c) X only
☐ (d) X and Z only
☐ (e) Y only

Table of Results			
Indicator	Acid Colour	Neutral Colour	Alkaline Colour
Phenolphthalein	colourless	colourless	pink
Litmus	red	purple	blue
Universal	red	green	violet purple

Q27

28 Calcium carbonate is an insoluble solid that reacts with acids to form neutral solutions. What colour would universal indicator added to a solution of excess calcium carbonate and hydrochloric acid be?

☐ (a) Red
☐ (b) Blue
☐ (c) Violet
☐ (d) Yellow/green
☐ (e) Orange

29 Indigestion is caused by excess acid in the stomach. What would the pH of a liquid used to treat this excess acid most likely be?

☐ (a) 1
☐ (b) 5
☐ (c) 7
☐ (d) 8
☐ (e) 6

Acids and alkalis – salts *(Single and Double Awards)*

QUESTIONS

Foundation and Higher Levels

1 What is formed when any acid is reacted with any alkali?

....

2 What type of reaction occurs when an acid is reacted with an alkali?

☐ (a) Precipitation
☐ (b) Displacement
☐ (c) Neutralization
☐ (d) Reversible
☐ (e) Esterification

3 What is the name for the group of salts formed when sulphuric acid is reacted with an alkali?

....

4 In the equation that follows, which word would correctly fill in the blank?

☐ (a) Alcohol
☐ (b) Alkane
☐ (c) Alkene
☐ (d) Alkali
☐ (e) Indicator

Reaction with hydrogen equation
Acid + ? → salt + water

Q4

5 What type of reaction would take place between an acid and a metal carbonate? What are the products?

☐ (a) Displacement; carbon dioxide, a salt, and water
☐ (b) Neutralization; hydrogen, a salt, and water
☐ (c) Thermal decomposition; carbon dioxide, a salt, and steam
☐ (d) Neutralization; carbon dioxide, a salt, and water
☐ (e) Neutralization; a salt and water

6 What is the name of the salt produced when sulphuric acid is neutralized by zinc oxide?

....

7 A farmer needs to reduce the acidity of the soil in a field. Which would be the most suitable substance to put onto the field?

☐ (a) Calcium oxide
☐ (b) Salt
☐ (c) Phosphates
☐ (d) Water
☐ (e) Nitrates

8 What is the name of the salt produced when hydrochloric acid and sodium hydroxide are reacted together?

....

9 What is the name of the salt formed when nitric acid is neutralized by calcium hydroxide solution (lime water)?

....

10 Ammonia is used to produce a number of fertilizers by reactions with other substances. To produce the fertilizer ammonium nitrate, what would you react ammonia with?

☐ (a) Calcium phosphate
☐ (b) Sulphuric acid
☐ (c) Sodium nitrate
☐ (d) Nitric acid
☐ (e) Calcium nitrate

11 What is the name of the salt formed when sulphuric acid is neutralized by potassium hydroxide solution?

☐ (a) Potassium sulphite
☐ (b) Potassium nitrate
☐ (c) Potassium sulphate
☐ (d) Ammonium sulphate
☐ (e) Ammonium sulphite

12 What is the name of the salt that is formed when copper(II) oxide reacts with dilute sulphuric acid?

☐ (a) Copper chloride
☐ (b) Copper sulphide
☐ (c) Copper sulphite
☐ (d) Copper sulphate
☐ (e) Copper nitrate

13 What is the name of the salt formed in the reaction between potassium hydroxide and nitric acid?

....

14 Sodium chloride is a naturally occurring salt which can easily be produced in the laboratory. Which one of the following neutralization reactions will produce sodium chloride?

☐ (a) Potassium hydroxide and hydrochloric acid
☐ (b) Sodium hydroxide and hydrochloric acid
☐ (c) Sodium hydroxide and sulphuric acid
☐ (d) Sodium carbonate and nitric acid
☐ (e) Sodium hydroxide and nitric acid

15 When magnesium burns in oxygen it forms magnesium oxide (a white solid) which does not dissolve in water, but which will react with an acid to give a salt and water. What type of substance is magnesium oxide?

☐ (a) A base
☐ (b) An alkali
☐ (c) An acid
☐ (d) A neutral substance
☐ (e) Both an acid and a base

16 Stinging nettles contain an acid (methanoic or formic acid). Which one of the following could best be used to treat a sting from a stinging nettle?

☐ (a) Vinegar
☐ (b) Salt solution
☐ (c) Water
☐ (d) Sodium hydroxide solution
☐ (e) Sodium carbonate solution

QUESTIONS
Higher Level only

17 In the reaction between sodium hydroxide and sulphuric acid, a salt and water are produced. Which of the following ionic equations represents the formation of water during neutralization?

☐ (a) $H^-(aq) + OH^+(aq) \rightarrow H_2O(l)$
☐ (b) $H(aq) + OH(aq) \rightarrow 2H_2O(l)$
☐ (c) $H^{2+}(aq) + OH^{2-}(aq) \rightarrow H_2O(l)$
☐ (d) $H_2(aq) + OH(aq) \rightarrow 4H_2O(l)$
☐ (e) $H^+(aq) + OH^-(aq) \rightarrow H_2O(l)$

18 Which one of the following ions is responsible for acidity?

☐ (a) $OH^-(aq)$
☐ (b) $O_{2-}(aq)$
☐ (c) $H^+(aq)$
☐ (d) $Cl^-(aq)$
☐ (e) $SO_4^{2-}(aq)$

19 Which one of the following ions is present in alkaline solution?

☐ (a) $OH^-(aq)$
☐ (b) $O^{2-}(aq)$
☐ (c) $H^+(aq)$
☐ (d) $Cl^-(aq)$
☐ (e) $SO_4^{2-}(aq)$

Burning and changes to the atmosphere *(Single and Double Awards)*

Burning is a very well known chemical change. Many substances burn, and chemists study these types of reactions for a number of reasons. These burning reactions are a source of heat energy and some of them are a source of new substances. The questions in this section discuss changes that take place during a chemical reaction.

QUESTIONS

Foundation and Higher Levels

1 All combustion reactions involve which of the following?

- ☐ (a) A flame
- ☐ (b) The burning of a fossil fuel
- ☐ (c) The release of energy
- ☐ (d) An explosion
- ☐ (e) None of the above

2 Which of the following statements about combustion are false?
i. Combustion produces energy
ii. Combustion produces waste gases
iii. Combustion is always accompanied by a flame

- ☐ (a) i and ii only
- ☐ (b) ii and iii only
- ☐ (c) i only
- ☐ (d) ii only
- ☐ (e) iii only

3 What type of reaction is respiration?

- ☐ (a) Oxidation
- ☐ (b) Reduction
- ☐ (c) Displacement
- ☐ (d) Decomposition
- ☐ (e) Precipitation

4 What type of compound is formed when oxygen is reacted with an element?

- ☐ (a) Chloride
- ☐ (b) Oxide
- ☐ (c) Hydroxide
- ☐ (d) Sulphate
- ☐ (e) Carbohydrate

5 What is the name for the reaction between an element and oxygen?

- ☐ (a) Displacement
- ☐ (b) Reduction
- ☐ (c) Electrolysis
- ☐ (d) Oxidation
- ☐ (e) Precipitation

6 What is the name of the substance produced when sodium is burnt in air?

- ☐ (a) Sodium nitride
- ☐ (b) Sodium hydroxide
- ☐ (c) Sodium carbonate
- ☐ (d) Sodium hydride
- ☐ (e) Sodium oxide

7 What is the name of the substance that is produced when magnesium is heated in air?

- ☐ (a) Magnesium carbonate
- ☐ (b) Magnesium nitrate
- ☐ (c) Magnesium oxide
- ☐ (d) Magnesium sulphate
- ☐ (e) Magnesium hydroxide

8 What is the name of the substance produced when potassium is burnt in air?

- ☐ (a) Potassium nitride
- ☐ (b) Potassium chloride
- ☐ (c) Potassium oxide
- ☐ (d) Potassium hydride
- ☐ (e) Potassium hydroxide

9 What are all the products of respiration?

- ☐ (a) Carbon dioxide and water
- ☐ (b) Water and energy
- ☐ (c) Carbon dioxide and energy
- ☐ (d) Carbon dioxide, energy, and water
- ☐ (e) Carbon dioxide only

10 In the following equation, what is the name of the missing element?
Calcium + ? → calcium oxide

- ☐ (a) Nitrogen
- ☐ (b) Hydrogen
- ☐ (c) Sulphur
- ☐ (d) Oxygen
- ☐ (e) Chlorine

11 The cells of your body need two reactants in order to respire. One is a sugar, what is the other?

- ☐ (a) Oxygen
- ☐ (b) Carbon dioxide
- ☐ (c) Water
- ☐ (d) Carbon monoxide
- ☐ (e) Nitrogen

12 What are the missing words in this word equation?
fuel + ? → carbon dioxide + ? + water

- ☐ (a) Carbon and oxygen
- ☐ (b) Oxygen and energy
- ☐ (c) Oxygen and flames
- ☐ (d) Energy and oxygen
- ☐ (e) Oxygen and carbon

13 What is the major source of the pollutant carbon monoxide, which is found in the air?

- ☐ (a) Incomplete combustion of fossil fuel
- ☐ (b) Sewage
- ☐ (c) Nuclear power stations
- ☐ (d) Manufacture of steel
- ☐ (e) The extraction of oil

14 What is the percentage of nitrogen in the air?

- ☐ (a) 30%
- ☐ (b) 20%
- ☐ (c) 50%
- ☐ (d) 78%
- ☐ (e) 4%

15 Which of the following is a major pollutant in the air?

- ☐ (a) Carbon monoxide
- ☐ (b) Oxygen
- ☐ (c) Nitrogen
- ☐ (d) Hydrogen
- ☐ (e) Helium

16 Acid rain causes great damage to trees and forests. Which of the following is the cause of acid rain?

- ☐ (a) Sewage
- ☐ (b) Oxygen in the air
- ☐ (c) Carbon monoxide in the air
- ☐ (d) Sulphur dioxide in the air
- ☐ (e) The manufacture of steel

17 What volume of air would remain if 100 cm^3 of air was passed over heated copper metal until no further change in volume occurred?

- ☐ (a) 79 cm^3
- ☐ (b) 84 cm^3
- ☐ (c) 20 cm^3
- ☐ (d) 50 cm^3
- ☐ (e) 99 cm^3

ANSWERS

Chemical changes

Foundation and Higher Levels

1
D is the mixture. A mixture contains two or more elements and/or compounds that have not undergone a chemical reaction and are therefore not bonded together. Of the suggestions A, C, and E are all elements because they only contain one type of atom. B is a compound because the two different atoms have a chemical bond between them.

2 *(b)*
The corrosion of iron is known as rusting. Iron reacts with oxygen in the presence of water.

3 *(d)*
Iron reacts with the oxygen in the atmosphere to form iron oxide, commonly known as rust.

4 *(b)*
The red-brown substance known as rust is the chemically hydrated iron oxide. The conditions required for rust to form are therefore oxygen, iron, and water. Although the presence of dissolved substances, such as salt, will speed up the rusting process, they are not essential.

5 *(a)*
When iron is exposed to the air it undergoes a corrosion reaction. Corrosion is where a metal reacts to form a less useful compound. This corrosion reaction, produced by the reaction of iron with oxygen in the presence of water, is known as rusting

6 *(b)*
Corrosion is the name given to the process in which metals react to form less useful compounds. A good example of this is rusting. The metal iron reacts with oxygen, in the presence of water, to form the less useful compound, rust.

7 *(a)*
The reaction between a metal and oxygen is known as oxidation. The rusting of iron is an example of an oxidation reaction. The iron and oxygen react together in the presence of water.

8 *(d)*
For rusting to take place the nail needs to be in contact with oxygen and water. However, the rate of rusting is increased by the presence of salt, which acts as a catalyst. Therefore, the nail would rust fastest when in contact with sea water (which contains salt) and the air.

9 *(e)*
Rusting of iron will only occur in the presence of both oxygen and water. In the first test tube the grease prevents the water from reaching the surface of the iron and therefore the nail does not rust. In the second tube the nail is exposed to water, but it is protected from the air by the oil. Rusting only takes place in the third tube, because it is exposed to both water and oxygen from the air.

10 *(b)*
For rusting to take place the iron nail must come into contact with both water and oxygen. In test tube B the water does not contain any dissolved oxygen, and the oil on the surface prevents any oxygen entering the water. In test tube C the iron nail is in contact with oxygen from the air, but the presence of the drying agent calcium chloride means that any water is absorbed. This prevents water coming into contact with the nail and so no rusting takes place. Therefore, rusting only takes place in test tube A, as the nail is exposed to both water and oxygen.

11 *(b)*
As the iron rusts it reacts with the oxygen and the water vapour in the air, reducing the volume of air. Hence, the level of water rises to fill the tube. The reaction takes a number of days.

12 *(c)*
Sacrificial protection works by corroding one metal in preference to another. A metal that is more reactive than iron, such as zinc, is placed onto the surface of the iron. The zinc corrodes in preference to the iron and hence prevents rusting. This method is often used on the hull of ships. See following diagram.

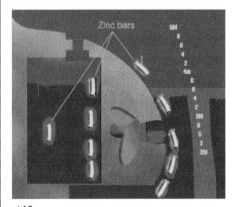

A12

13 *(b)*
Providing the amount of chromium in the alloy exceeds 10%, one of the properties of the alloy is that it will not rust.

14 *(b)*
All the suggestions are methods of preventing rusting. However, all of them, except the use of grease, would be removed by the movement of the engine parts. This would result in the loss of their protective surfaces and so rusting would take place.

15 *(b)*
Tin is less reactive than iron. If the surface of the iron is completely covered by the tin it will prevent the water and oxygen in the air coming into contact with the iron and so there will be no rusting. However, if the tin is scratched, the iron comes into contact with the air, and being more reactive than tin, the iron will rust.

16 *(b)*
Non-metals (except group 0) react with oxygen to give either gaseous or liquid products, which when dissolved in water usually give an acid solution. Therefore, element X could only be sulphur.

17 *(a)*
If a metal reacts with an acid the products of the reaction will be hydrogen and a salt. In the example given in the question, zinc reacts with hydrochloric acid to produce hydrogen and zinc chloride. See equations that follow.

Metal + acid → salt + hydrogen

Zinc + hydrochloric → zinc + hydrogen
acid chloride

A17

18 *(b)*
Iron reacts with the oxygen in the atmosphere to form iron oxide, commonly known as rust.

19 *(a)*
It is impossible to predict the colour of a compound from the colours of the elements that combined to form it, you either know it or you don't!

20 *(c)*
When two solutions are mixed together so that an insoluble substance is formed, the reaction is known as a precipitation

reaction. The insoluble solid is known as a precipitate.

21 *(b)*
Polymerization is the process whereby small molecules join together to form large, long chain molecules. The graphic that follows shows how the double bond in ethene opens up and many molecules join together to form a long chain. The polymer formed by this process is called polyethene, or polythene. See diagram that follows.

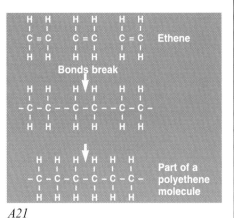

A21

22 *(d)*
The oxides of non-metals are usually acidic when dissolved in water, but some are not. For example, water is an oxide of hydrogen which is neutral. All metal chlorides are solids. Hence, only statement iii is true and therefore *(d)* is the correct answer.

23 *(d)*
Hydrogen has the lowest density of all gases and so can carry weather balloons into the atmosphere. It reacts explosively with oxygen so, if this property is paired with its density, it makes an ideal rocket fuel. It is also used in the manufacture of ammonia and margarine. It was once used in airships due to its density but the gas is very flammable, as was shown in the 1937 Hindenburg disaster, when a spark caused the airship to explode. The inert gas helium is now used in airships.

24 *(c)*
When metals react with oxygen they always produce solid oxides that are basic or amphoteric in nature. Therefore, only Z could be a metal.

25 *(c)*
The fruit is reacting with the oxygen in the air to form a new product that is not useful (the rotting fruit). As oxygen is being added, this is an oxidation reaction. Fruits can be prevented from being oxidized by storing them in an oxygen-free environment.

26 *(a)*
The gas that causes the flesh of an apple to go brown after it is exposed to the air is oxygen. Hence, an oxidation reaction is taking place.

27 *(b)*
The browning of an apple is caused by the flesh reacting with oxygen in the air. The layer of toffee on a toffee apple prevents oxygen from reaching the flesh.

28 *(b)*
One of the similarities of metal oxides is that they are all solids.

29 *(e)*
A scientific theory is only a set of ideas that have been put together using known facts to try to explain something, and it is always changing as new discoveries are made. For example, in the 16th century scientists believed that the earth was the centre of the universe, but we now know that this is not true.

30 *(b)*
Metals react with oxygen to produce a solid oxide which, if soluble, will dissolve in water to produce an alkaline solution. Therefore sodium oxide would produce an alkaline solution when dissolved in water.

31 *(a)*
Nylon is a synthetic substance, whereas cashmere, wool, and silk are naturally produced by animals, and cotton is grown on cotton plants. A naturally occurring substance is one that does not have to undergo any chemical reaction before it can be used.

32 *(b)*
When a chemical reaction takes place bonds are both broken and made, and usually a change in temperature is associated with these processes. Hence, a change in temperature indicates that a chemical reaction has taken place.

33 *(c)*
Gold is a metal that occurs in its pure form, and cannot be made by man, whereas all the other substances have to undergo a manufacturing process.

34 *(a)*
Bronze is manufactured by mixing together copper and tin (and sometimes zinc and lead). All the other substances are metals that cannot be manufactured.

35 *(b)*
As zinc is higher in the reactivity series

than iron, the zinc will corrode in preference to the iron, even if the surface is scratched. Hence, the iron does not rust.

36 *(a)*
When magnesium is heated in air it burns with a bright flame to produce a white powder (magnesium oxide). The magnesium has reacted with the oxygen to produce a new substance and therefore this is a chemical reaction.

37 *(b)*
When a metal is found in the form of a compound, such as an oxide, it has to be reduced to produce the pure metal. The type of extraction method used depends upon the reactivity of the metal. Very reactive metals have to be extracted by electrolysis, but less reactive ones, such as iron, can be extracted by heating with carbon. It is therefore the reactivity of the metal that determines the type of extraction method used. See following table.

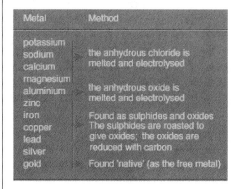

Metal	Method
potassium sodium calcium magnesium	the anhydrous chloride is melted and electrolysed
aluminium zinc	the anhydrous oxide is melted and electrolysed
iron copper lead	Found as sulphides and oxides. The sulphides are roasted to give oxides; the oxides are reduced with carbon
silver gold	Found 'native' (as the free metal)

A37

38 *(d)*
Sodium chloride in the form of rock salt is used in winter to de-ice the roads. The sodium chloride lowers the freezing point of water so that it remains liquid at temperatures well below 0°C, therefore preventing the roads from becoming icy.

39 *(a)*
Sodium chloride occurs naturally, particularly in the ocean as salt water. All of the other substances have to be manufactured.

40 *(e)*
Hydrogen reacts with chlorine to produce hydrogen chloride gas. This will dissolve in water to give an acidic solution of hydrochloric acid:
$H_2 + Cl_2 \rightarrow 2HCl$
$HCl(g) + (aq) \rightarrow H^+(aq) + Cl^-(aq)$

41 *(d)*
Sodium is a low density metal that floats on water. It is not a very strong or hard

metal and this would limit its use in construction. However, the most important reason why it would not be a very good metal to use as a building material for boats is because, like all group I metals, it is highly reactive. It reacts with water to produce hydrogen and sodium hydroxide.

□ **42** *(a)*
A displacement reaction will only take place when a more reactive element is placed into a salt solution of a less reactive element. The halogens become more reactive as the group is descended. As chlorine is above bromine, it will displace bromine from solutions of its salts.

□ **43** *(c)*
Ammonium sulphate is a soluble salt that is produced by reacting ammonia with sulphuric acid. As ammonia is a soluble base it will dissolve in water to produce ammonia solution (NH_4OH) which will neutralize the sulphuric acid and produce ammonium sulphate.
$2NH_4OH + H_2SO_4 \rightarrow (NH_4)_2SO_4 + 2H_2O$
Ammonia + sulphuric acid →
ammonium sulphate + water

□ **44** *(b)*
Fermentation occurs when yeast is added to a solution of simple sugars (fruit juice provides a good sugar solution) in a controlled environment. Enzymes in the yeast then catalyze the conversion of the simple sugars to ethanol and carbon dioxide. The carbon dioxide is a waste product but the ethanol combined with the original solution produces an alcoholic solution. This is the basis of the wine-making and brewing industries.

Chemical changes

Higher Level only

□ **45** *(b)*
An oxidation reaction is one in which an atom reacts with oxygen to form an oxide, for example, when a substance is burnt in air. An oxidation reaction can also be defined as a reaction in which an atom or an ion loses an electron or electrons, as well as a reaction in which a compound loses hydrogen.

□ **46** *(a)*
An oxidation reaction is one in which the substance underlined either loses an electron or electrons, loses hydrogen, or gains oxygen. When a metal ion is formed, the outer shell electrons are lost

and hence this is an oxidation reaction. Lithium will form lithium ions, for example, when it reacts with water.

□ **47** *(b)*
A reduction reaction is one in which there is a loss of oxygen or a gain of hydrogen. The formation of metal from their ores is an example of this type of reaction. A reduction reaction can also be defined as one in which there is a gain of electrons.

□ **48** *(d)*
A reduction reaction is one in which an atom or ion gains an electron or electrons. The formation of copper metal during the electrolysis of copper(II) sulphate is an example of this type of reaction. A reduction reaction can also be defined as a reaction in which there is a loss of oxygen or a gain of hydrogen.

□ **49** *(c)*
An oxidation reaction is defined as one in which an atom or ion loses an electron or electrons. In the formation of metal ions the metal atoms lose their outer shell electrons, hence this is an oxidation reaction.

□ **50** *(e)*
An oxidation reaction is one in which an atom or ion loses an electron or electrons. During the electrolysis of sodium chloride solution the chloride ions lose an electron to form chlorine molecules as shown by the equation:
$2Cl^- \rightarrow Cl_2 + 2e^-$
See diagram that follows.

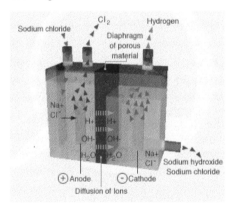

A50

□ **51** *(e)*
Oxidation is the addition of oxygen to a substance, or the removal of hydrogen, and it can also mean the loss of electrons. When oxygen has reacted with a substance to form an oxide, it may be either acidic or basic. The burning of carbon to form carbon dioxide is an example of an oxidation reaction.

Acids and alkalis – indicators

Foundation and Higher Levels

□ **1**
A solution with a pH of 7 is neutral and would therefore turn universal indicator yellow/green.

□ **2** *(a)*
Fizzy drinks, such as orangeade, contain carbonic acid. Therefore they will turn universal indicator red.

□ **3**
A solution with a pH of 14 is a strong alkali and, therefore, would turn universal indicator from green to purple.

□ **4** *(e)*
When universal indicator is added to the strongly acidic solution the indicator changes colour from green (pH 7) to red (pH 1–3).

□ **5**
Sodium hydroxide is an alkaline solution and it will therefore turn universal indicator solution purple (violet).

□ **6**
Pure water is neutral and therefore the universal indicator solution will be yellow/green.

□ **7** *(a)*
Potassium hydroxide solution is an alkali solution and it will therefore turn universal indicator purple.

□ **8** *(d)*
A solution with a pH of 1 is a strong acid and, therefore, would turn universal indicator from green to red.

□ **9** *(a)*
The digestive juices from your stomach contain hydrochloric acid, making them acidic, and they will therefore turn universal indicator solution red.

□ **10** *(c)*
Oven cleaner will make an alkaline solution and it will therefore turn universal indicator solution purple.

□ **11** *(a)*
Lemon juice contains an acid known as citric acid, and this has a pH of about 2–3, so the indicator will turn orange. Of the other suggestions, distilled water and salt solution are neutral and the oven cleaner and indigestion tablets are alkali.

□ **12**
When the universal indicator is added to X it turns green which means it must be a neutral liquid. The only neutral liquid in the suggested list is distilled water. Therefore X could be distilled water.

□ **13** *(b)*
Oven cleaner contains alkalis such as sodium hydroxide solution or ammonia solution, and therefore will turn universal indicator purple.

□ **14** *(d)*
The universal indicator colour is green in X which means that this liquid is neutral. When Z is added to X, it turns violet which tells us that liquid Z must be an alkali. When Y is added to this mixture of X and Z, the universal indicator turns back to green, which means that the final mixture is neutral. The liquid Y must have neutralized the alkali mixture of Z and X, and therefore Y must be an acid. X is neutral, Y is an acid, and Z is an alkali.

□ **15** *(c)*
The orange colour produced with universal indicator means that the solution has a pH of 3–4 and so is weakly acidic. As the solution was formed by dissolving carbon dioxide in water it means that carbon dioxide is an acidic substance. As a general rule, non-metal oxides (such as carbon dioxide) are usually acidic.

□ **16** *(e)*
Vinegar contains ethanoic acid and therefore turns universal indicator red.

□ **17**
Sulphuric acid is an acidic solution and it will therefore turn universal indicator solution red.

□ **18** *(d)*
Alkalis turn red litmus paper blue and sodium hydroxide solution is the only alkali listed.

□ **19** *(d)*
Alkalis turn red litmus paper blue and calcium hydroxide solution is the only alkali listed.

□ **20** *(d)*
As suggestion *(d)* is the only alkali, only this solution would turn the litmus blue.

□ **21** *(d)*
All the suggestions apart from indigestion tablets contain acids, eg. lemon juice contains citric acid; vitamin C is ascorbic acid; vinegar contains ethanoic acid; and soda water contains carbonic acid.

□ **22** *(a)*
All the solutions of the substances listed are alkaline. U.V.I. is an indicator which is blue/purple in alkaline solutions. Therefore all the solutions would turn U.V.I. blue/purple.

□ **23** *(d)*
As can be seen from the diagram below, weak acids, such as soda water, have a pH of less than 7. The diagram also shows that the solution would go yellow if universal indicator were added to it.

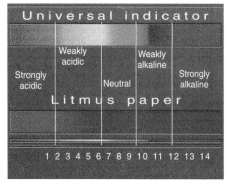

A23, 24, 25

□ **24** *(a)*
As can be seen from the diagram above, neutral solutions, such as pure water, have a pH of about 7. The diagram also shows that the solution would turn to green if universal indicator were added to it.

□ **25***(c)*
As can be seen from the diagram above, strong alkalis, such as sodium hydroxide solution, have a pH of just less than 14. The diagram also shows that the solution would go purple if universal indicator were added to it.

□ **26** *(d)*
The universal indicator in the acid would have turned red. The addition of alkali neutralizes the acid, turning the universal indicator green. The addition of more alkali would turn the indicator to purple.

□ **27** *(c)*
X must be an acid because it is the only one that turns the litmus red and it has no effect on the phenolphthalein.

□ **28** *(d)*
The addition of calcium carbonate would neutralize the acid and produce a neutral solution, in which the universal indicator would turn yellow/green.

□ **29** *(d)*
To reduce the amount of acid in the stomach, it has to be neutralized by an alkali. Alkalis have pH of 7 or above, therefore *(d)* is the correct answer.

Acids and alkalis – salts

Foundation and Higher Levels

□ **1**
When an acid and an alkali are reacted together, salt and water are formed. The salt formed depends on the acid and alkali reacted. For example:
Hydrochloric acid + sodium hydroxide → sodium chloride + water

□ **2** *(c)*
A base is the opposite of an acid, and an alkali is a base that is soluble in water. Hence, when an acid and an alkali react together, they cancel each other out and the reaction is known as neutralization.

□ **3**
When sulphuric acid is reacted with an alkali the salt formed is known as a sulphate because it contains the SO_4^{2-} group. See equation that follows:
$2NaOH + H_2SO_4 \rightarrow Na_2SO_4 + 2H_2O$
Sodium hydroxide + sulphuric acid → sodium sulphate + water

□ **4** *(d)*
When an acid and alkali are reacted together a salt and some water is formed. The salt formed depends on which acid and alkali reacted.

□ **5** *(d)*
The reaction between a metal carbonate and a dilute acid results in the formation of carbon dioxide, a salt, and water. This type of reaction is known as a neutralization reaction because carbonates are basic compounds.

□ **6**
When an acid is neutralized by a base, a reaction takes place that produces salt and water. The name of the salt depends on the acid and base used to form it. When sulphuric acid is used the salts are called sulphates, and the base always gives the first part of the name to the salt. Hence the salt formed when zinc oxide neutralizes sulphuric acid is zinc sulphate.

□ **7** *(a)*
Calcium oxide (quicklime) is a basic compound. It dissolves slowly in water to produce calcium hydroxide which is an alkali and so neutralizes the acidity of the soil.

□ **8**
When an acid and an alkali are reacted together they form a salt and water. The salt formed in the reaction of hydrochloric acid and sodium hydroxide

is sodium chloride. The salt gets part of its name from the alkali, and part from the acid. The sodium comes from the sodium hydroxide, and the chloride from the hydrochloric acid.

☐ 9

The salt formed when calcium hydroxide neutralizes nitric acid is calcium nitrate. When an acid is neutralized by a base, a reaction takes place that produces a salt and water. The name of the salt depends on the acid and base used to form it. When nitric acid is used the salts are called nitrates and the base always gives the first part of the name to the salt.

☐ 10 (d)

Ammonia is a base and will therefore react with an acid to produce a salt. Ammonium nitrate is a salt and is produced by reacting ammonia with nitric acid.
$NH_3 + HNO_3 \rightarrow NH_4NO_3$
Ammonia + nitric acid → ammonium nitrate

☐ 11 (c)

When an acid is neutralized by a base, the reaction that takes place produces a salt and water. The name of the salt depends on the acid and base used to form it. When sulphuric acid is used, the salts are called sulphates, and the base always gives the first part of the name to the salt. Hence, the salt formed when potassium hydroxide neutralizes sulphuric acid is potassium sulphate.

☐ 12 (d)

As copper(II) oxide is a base it will neutralize the acid to form a salt and water. The name of the salt depends on the acid and the base that are used. When sulphuric acid is neutralized the salts formed are sulphates. Hence, the name of this salt is copper sulphate.

☐ 13

In the reaction between potassium hydroxide and nitric acid, the salt formed is potassium nitrate.
$KOH + HNO_3 \rightarrow KNO_3 + H_2O$
The type of salt produced when an acid and an alkali react together will depend upon the acid and the alkali that were used for the neutralization. The salts of nitric acid are called nitrates.

☐ 14 (b)

A neutralization reaction is one that occurs between an acid and a base (alkali). To produce sodium chloride in the laboratory, sodium hydroxide and hydrochloric acid need to be reacted together:

$NaOH + HCl \rightarrow NaCl + H_2O$
Sodium hydroxide + hydrochloric acid → sodium chloride + water

☐ 15 (a)

A base is a substance that will neutralize an acid to form a salt and water, and therefore magnesium oxide is a base. Some bases are soluble in water and these are known as alkalis.

☐ 16 (e)

To treat the sting from a stinging nettle you need to remove the acid. This can be done by neutralizing the acid using an alkali or base. Sodium hydroxide is a very strong alkali and could burn the skin if placed on it. Sodium carbonate solution is a weaker alkali and would react with the acid to produce salt, carbon dioxide, and water thus removing the acid. Hence this solution is the best one to use.

Acids and alkalis – salts

Higher Level only

☐ 17 (e)

When sodium hydroxide and sulphuric acid react together, the hydroxide ions from the sodium hydroxide and the hydrogen ions from the sulphuric acid form water. See equation that follows:

Neutralization reaction equation

$$H^+ \quad + \quad OH^- \rightarrow H_2O$$

Hydrogen ions + hydroxide ions → water

A17

☐ 18 (c)

When an acid dissolves in water it produces hydrogen ions $H^+(aq)$. For example, when hydrogen chloride gas dissolves in water, the molecules break up to form hydrogen and chloride ions.
$HCl(g) + (aq) \rightarrow H^+(aq) + Cl^-(aq)$

☐ 19 (a)

When a solid alkali dissolves in water it produces hydroxide ions, which make the solution alkaline. For example, when sodium hydroxide dissolves in water the crystal lattice breaks up releasing sodium ions and hydroxide ions.
$NaOH(s) \rightarrow Na^+(aq) + OH^-(aq)$

Burning and changes to the atmosphere

Foundation and Higher Levels

☐ 1 (c)

All combustion reactions involve the reaction of a fuel with oxygen and always produce energy. Some combustion reactions involve a flame, but this is not always the case. The process of respiration (which is the conversion of sugar to energy in the body) does not produce a flame.

☐ 2 (e)

The process of combustion happens when a fuel is reacted with oxygen so that it produces energy and waste gases. However, it is not always accompanied by a flame. The process of combustion actually takes place inside the body during respiration.

☐ 3 (a)

Respiration is an example of an oxidation reaction in which a fuel is reacted with oxygen to produce carbon dioxide, water, and energy, with no flame. Respiration is used in your body to release energy from the food you have eaten. See equation that follows:
$C_6H_{12}O_6 + 6O_2 \rightarrow 6CO_2 + 6H_2O$ + energy
Sugar + oxygen → carbon dioxide + water + energy

☐ 4 (b)

When an element is reacted with oxygen, the compound produced is known as an oxide. See equations that follow:
Carbon + oxygen → carbon dioxide
Magnesium + oxygen → magnesium oxide

☐ 5 (d)

The name for the reaction that occurs between oxygen and an element is oxidation. An example of an oxidation reaction is combustion. During the reaction, the oxygen combines with the element to produce an oxide. See equations that follow:
Carbon + oxygen → carbon dioxide
Magnesium + oxygen → magnesium oxide

☐ 6 (e)

When an element is reacted with oxygen it produces an oxide, therefore when sodium reacts with oxygen (when a substance burns in air it is reacting with the oxygen in the air) it forms sodium oxide. See equation that follows:
Sodium + oxygen → sodium oxide
It is a distinctive reaction because the sodium burns with a yellow flame.

☐ **7** *(c)*
When magnesium is heated in the air, it burns brightly and a chemical reaction takes place. The magnesium combines with the oxygen in the air to form magnesium oxide. See equation that follows:
Magnesium + oxygen → magnesium oxide

☐ **8** *(c)*
When an element is reacted with oxygen it produces an oxide. Therefore, when potassium reacts with oxygen (when a substance burns in air it is reacting with the oxygen in the air) it forms potassium oxide. See equation that follows:
Potassium + oxygen → potassium oxide
It is a distinctive reaction because the potassium burns with a lilac flame.

☐ **9** *(d)*
When respiration takes place in the body, sugars in the blood react with oxygen to give carbon dioxide, water, and energy. See equation that follows:
$C_6H_{12}O_6 + 6O_2 \rightarrow 6CO_2 + 6H_2O +$ energy
Sugar + oxygen → carbon dioxide + water + energy

☐ **10** *(d)*
When an element undergoes a chemical reaction to produce an oxide, it has to react with oxygen, therefore the name of the missing element is oxygen.

☐ **11** *(a)*
Respiration is a type of combustion reaction in which fuel (a sugar) is reacted with oxygen to produce carbon dioxide, water, and energy (with no flame). Respiration produces all the energy the body needs for all the activities it undertakes, whether it be digesting lunch or climbing a mountain.

☐ **12** *(b)*
The word equation represents a general combustion reaction. The missing words in the equation are oxygen and energy. The full equation reads:
Fuel + oxygen → carbon dioxide + water + energy
An example of this type of reaction is respiration. See equation that follows:
$C_6H_{12}O_6 + 6O_2 \rightarrow 6CO_2 + 6H_2O +$ energy
Sugar + oxygen → carbon dioxide + water + energy

☐ **13** *(a)*
The source of the pollutant carbon monoxide in the air is the incomplete combustion of fossil fuels. This is caused by the burning of fuels, such as petrol, in a limited supply of air. This can happen in a car engine.

☐ **14** *(d)*
The composition of the air is 78% nitrogen, 21% oxygen, the remainder being noble gases and variable amounts of carbon dioxide and water vapour.

☐ **15** *(a)*
Carbon monoxide is a major pollutant, which is found in the air. It is produced by the incomplete combustion of fossil fuels, such as petrol in cars. Oxygen and nitrogen form about 99% of clean air, while hydrogen and helium are gases that do not pollute the air.

☐ **16** *(d)*
The cause of acid rain is the sulphur dioxide that is present in the air. This sulphur dioxide is a pollutant and is produced by the burning of fossil fuels, such as coal, which contains some sulphur.

☐ **17** *(a)*
If 100 cm³ of air was passed over heated copper metal until no further change in volume occured, then the volume of air left would be 79 cm³. This is because the air contains 21% oxygen and only oxygen will react with the heated copper metal. See the following diagram.

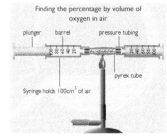

A17

Chemical Formulae

Chemical equations *(Single and Double Awards)*

A knowledge of chemical formulae and chemical equations is essential when a chemist is asked to calculate the amount of chemicals required to make a particular amount of a product. This is not a very difficult task, once the basic ideas are understood and practised. The following questions deal with the key aspects of this part of the subject.

KEY FACTS

• **Word equations:** Chemical reactions can be represented by a word equation. A word equation states in words the names of the reacting substances and the names of the products of the reaction. For example, the reaction of sodium with water can be represented as follows:
sodium + water → sodium hydroxide + hydrogen

• **Chemical symbols:** A chemical reaction can be represented by the symbols or formulae of the reacting substances as well as the symbols and formulae of the products of the reaction. All the elements have symbols, eg. the symbol for hydrogen is H. Chemical substances have formulae that are made up of symbols. For example, the formula of water is H_2O and is composed of the symbols for hydrogen, H, and oxygen, O. The equation must always balance, i.e. there must be the same number of atoms on either side of the equation. The symbol equation shows the ratio of the reacting substances and products, and also the states of the substances. For example, the reaction of sodium and water can be represented as follows:
$2Na(s) + 2H_2O(l) → 2NaOH(aq) + H_2(g)$

• **Using chemical equations:** Equations can be used to help in calculating the mass of a substance needed to react with a given mass of a reactant, and in calculating the masses of products formed. When calculating the masses of substances involved the following rules should be applied:
i. Write a balanced equation for the reaction, eg. $2Na(s) + 2H_2O(l) → 2NaOH(aq) + H_2(g)$
ii. State in words what the equation tells you about the substances concerned, eg. two moles of sodium react with two moles of water to give two moles of sodium hydroxide and one mole of hydrogen.
iii. Convert moles to masses, eg. the relative atomic masses for the elements involved are as follows:
Na = 23, H = 1, O = 16
$(2 \times 23) + 2[(2 \times 1) + 16] →$
$2(23 + 16 + 1) + (2 \times 1)$
46 g of sodium reacts with 36 g of water to give 80 g of sodium hydroxide and 2 g of hydrogen.
iv. Scale the masses to those in the question by using ratios. For example, 4.6 g of sodium would react with 3.6 g of water to give 8.0 g of sodium hydroxide and 0.2 g of hydrogen.

• **Finding chemical formulae:** The formula of a compound can be calculated from the mass composition of a sample of the compound. When calculating the formula of a compound the following rules should be applied:
i. Write down the masses of the combining elements.
ii. Write down the mass of one mole of each element.
iii. Work out the number of moles of each element.
iv. Work out the simplest ratio between the moles of each element.
v. Write down the simplest formula.

 QUESTIONS

Foundation and Higher Levels

1 What is the formula of water?

....

2 Which of the following is the formula of carbon dioxide?

☐ (a) CH_4
☐ (b) H_2O
☐ (c) CO_2
☐ (d) NaCl
☐ (e) $CaCl_2$

3 Which of the following is the formula of hydrogen gas?

☐ (a) H_2O
☐ (b) H
☐ (c) H_2
☐ (d) H_3
☐ (e) Cl_2

4 Which of the following is the formula of hydrochloric acid?

☐ (a) CH_4
☐ (b) H_2O
☐ (c) NaCl
☐ (d) $CaCO_3$
☐ (e) HCl

5 Which of the following is the formula of sodium chloride?

☐ (a) NaCl
☐ (b) H_2O
☐ (c) CH_4
☐ (d) HCl
☐ (e) $CaCl_2$

6 What is the formula of limestone (calcium carbonate)?

....

7 Which of the following is the formula of calcium chloride?

☐ (a) $CaCl_2$
☐ (b) $NaCl_2$
☐ (c) $CaCO_2$
☐ (d) H_2O
☐ (e) CH_4

8 Which of the following is the formula of helium gas?

☐ (a) H
☐ (b) H_2
☐ (c) He
☐ (d) He_2
☐ (e) Hm

9 Which of the following is the formula of chlorine gas?

☐ (a) H_2O
☐ (b) Br_2
☐ (c) Na
☐ (d) Cl_2
☐ (e) CH_4

10 Which of the following is the formula of a compound that contains sulphur and oxygen in the ratio of 1:2?

- ☐ (a) SO_2
- ☐ (b) NaO_2
- ☐ (c) S_2O
- ☐ (d) SlO_2
- ☐ (e) SuO_2

11 What is the correct chemical formula for iron(II) sulphate?

- ☐ (a) $FeSO_3$
- ☐ (b) SFe
- ☐ (c) $FeSO_4$
- ☐ (d) $FeSO_2$
- ☐ (e) FeS

12 When you react calcium with oxygen, what is the chemical formula of the product?

- ☐ (a) Ca_2O
- ☐ (b) CaO
- ☐ (c) CaO_2
- ☐ (d) CaO_3
- ☐ (e) Ca_3O

13 Which of the following is the formula of a compound that contains Mg^{2+} and F^- ions?

- ☐ (a) MgF_2
- ☐ (b) MgF
- ☐ (c) $2MgF$
- ☐ (d) Mg_2F
- ☐ (e) MgF_4

14 Which of the following is the formula of an ionic compound that contains Fe^{3+} and SO_4^{2-} ions?

- ☐ (a) $Fe_2(SO_4)_2$
- ☐ (b) Fe_3SO_4
- ☐ (c) $FeSO_4$
- ☐ (d) $Fe(SO_4)_3$
- ☐ (e) $Fe_2(SO_4)_3$

15 What is the formula of a compound that contains Na^+ and CO_3^{2-} ions?

- ☐ (a) $NaCO_3$
- ☐ (b) Na_2CO_3
- ☐ (c) $Na(CO_3)_2$
- ☐ (d) $Na_2(CO_3)_2$
- ☐ (e) $Na_3(CO_3)_2$

16 Which one of the following is the formula of methane?

- ☐ (a) CH_4
- ☐ (b) CO_2
- ☐ (c) H_2O
- ☐ (d) $NaCl$
- ☐ (e) $CaCO_3$

17 Which one of the following represents the formula of nitric acid?

- ☐ (a) HNO
- ☐ (b) HNO_2
- ☐ (c) HNO_3
- ☐ (d) HNO_4
- ☐ (e) HNO_5

18 Which of the following is the formula of the compound that contains the elements nitrogen and hydrogen in the ratio of 1:3?

- ☐ (a) AmH_3
- ☐ (b) N_3H
- ☐ (c) NH_3
- ☐ (d) NiH_3
- ☐ (e) Am_3H

19 Which of the following is the formula of the compound that contains copper, sulphur, and oxygen in the ratio of 1:1:4?

- ☐ (a) $CpSO_4$
- ☐ (b) CuS_2O_4
- ☐ (c) CSO_4
- ☐ (d) $CuSO_4$
- ☐ (e) $CoSO_4$

20 In the equation below, which of the substances is a liquid?

- ☐ (a) Iron(II) sulphate
- ☐ (b) Sodium hydroxide
- ☐ (c) Iron(II) hydroxide
- ☐ (d) Sodium sulphate
- ☐ (e) None of the substances

Iron(II) sulphate (solution) + Sodium hydroxide (solution) → Iron(II) hydroxide (precipate) + Sodium sulphate (solution)

$FeSO_4(aq) + 2NaOH(aq) \rightarrow Fe(OH)_2(s) + Na_2SO_4(aq)$

Q20

21 In the following equation, which of the substances is a solution?

- ☐ (a) Calcium carbonate
- ☐ (b) Carbon dioxide
- ☐ (c) Calcium oxide
- ☐ (d) Calcium hydroxide
- ☐ (e) None of the substances

Carbon dioxide + Calcium hydroxide → Calcium carbonate + Water

$CO_2(g) + Ca(OH)_2(aq) \rightarrow CaCO_3(s) + H_2O(l)$

Q21

22 Which one of the following word equations represents the reaction between hydrogen and oxygen?

- ☐ (a) Hydrogen + oxygen → water

- ☐ (b) Hydrogen + oxygen → hydrogen carbonate
- ☐ (c) Hydrogen + oxygen → oxygen chloride
- ☐ (d) Hydrogen + oxygen → rust
- ☐ (e) Hydrogen + oxygen → salt

23 Which one of the following word equations represents the reaction between hydrochloric acid and zinc?

- ☐ (a) Hydrochloric acid + zinc → zinc oxide + water
- ☐ (b) Hydrochloric acid + zinc → zinc chloride + hydrogen
- ☐ (c) Hydrochloric acid + zinc → zinc chloride + water
- ☐ (d) Hydrochloric acid + zinc → zinc carbonate + hydrogen
- ☐ (e) Hydrochloric acid + zinc → zinc oxide + hydrogen

24 Which one of the following word equations represents the reaction between zinc and silver nitrate solution?

- ☐ (a) Zinc + silver nitrate → copper nitrate + silver
- ☐ (b) Zinc + silver nitrate → zinc sulphate + silver
- ☐ (c) Zinc + silver nitrate → zinc nitrate + copper
- ☐ (d) Zinc + silver nitrate → zinc nitrate + silver
- ☐ (e) Zinc + silver nitrate → zinc chloride + silver

25 Which of the following word equations represents the reaction between sodium and chlorine?

- ☐ (a) Sodium + chlorine → chlorine sodide
- ☐ (b) Sodium + chlorine → sodium carbonate
- ☐ (c) Sodium + chlorine → sodium chloride
- ☐ (d) Sodium + chlorine → chlorine oxide
- ☐ (e) Sodium + chlorine → sodium oxide

26 Which one of the following word equations represents the reaction between calcium oxide and carbon dioxide?

- ☐ (a) Calcium oxide + carbon dioxide → calcium hydrogen carbonate
- ☐ (b) Calcium oxide + carbon dioxide → calcium carbonate
- ☐ (c) Calcium oxide + carbon dioxide → calcium chloride
- ☐ (d) Calcium oxide + carbon dioxide → calcium dioxide + carbon oxide
- ☐ (e) Calcium oxide + carbon dioxide → calcium oxide + carbon monoxide

Group																		0
I	II							1 H 1				III	IV	V	VI	VII		4 He 2
7 Li 3	9 Be 4											11 B 5	12 C 6	14 N 7	16 O 8	19 F 9		20 Ne 10
23 Na 11	24 Mg 12											27 Al 13	28 Si 14	30 P 15	32 S 16	35 Cl 17		40 Ar 18
39 K 19	40 Ca 20	45 Sc 21	48 Ti 22	51 V 23	52 Cr 24	55 Mn 25	56 Fe 26	59 Co 27	59 Ni 28	63 Cu 29	64 Zn 30	70 Ga 31	73 Ge 32	75 As 33	79 Se 34	80 Br 35		84 Kr 36
85 Rb 37	88 Sr 38	89 Y 39	91 Zr 40	93 Nb 41	96 Mo 42	Tc 43	101 Ru 44	103 Rh 45	106 Pd 46	108 Ag 47	112 Cd 48	115 In 49	119 Sn 50	122 Sb 51	128 Te 52	127 I 53		131 Xe 54
133 Cs 55	137 Ba 56	139 La 57	178 Hf 72	181 Ta 73	184 W 74	186 Re 75	190 Os 76	192 Ir 77	195 Pt 78	197 Au 79	201 Hg 80	204 Tl 81	207 Pb 82	209 Bi 83	Po 84	At 85		Rn 86
Fr 87	226 Ra 88	277 Ac 89																

Q31

27 Which one of the following word equations represents the reaction between sodium hydroxide and sulphuric acid?

- ☐ (a) Sodium hydroxide + sulphuric acid → sodium chloride + water
- ☐ (b) Sodium hydroxide + sulphuric acid → sodium sulphite + water
- ☐ (c) Sodium hydroxide + sulphuric acid → sodium sulphate + hydrogen
- ☐ (d) Sodium hydroxide + sulphuric acid → sodium oxide and hydrogen
- ☐ (e) Sodium hydroxide + sulphuric acid → sodium sulphate + water

28 Which one of the following word equations represents the reaction between copper oxide and nitric acid?

- ☐ (a) Copper oxide + nitric acid → copper sulphate + hydrogen
- ☐ (b) Copper oxide + nitric acid → copper chloride + water
- ☐ (c) Copper oxide + nitric acid → copper hydroxide + oxygen
- ☐ (d) Copper oxide + nitric acid → copper carbonate + water
- ☐ (e) Copper oxide + nitric acid → copper nitrate + water

29 Which of the following equations represents the reaction between zinc and sulphuric acid?

- ☐ (a) $Zn + H_2SO_4 → ZnSO_4 + H_2 + H_2O$
- ☐ (b) $Zn + H_2SO_4 → ZnSO_4 + H_2$
- ☐ (c) $Zn + H_2SO_4 → ZnCl_2 + H_2$
- ☐ (d) $Zn + H_2SO_4 → ZnNH_4 + H_2$
- ☐ (e) $Zn + H_2SO_4 → ZnNO_3 + H_2$

30 Which one of the following equations represents the reaction between potassium hydroxide and sulphuric acid?

- ☐ (a) $2KOH + H_2SO_4 → K_2SO_4 + 2H_2O$
- ☐ (b) $2KOH + H_2CO_3 → K_2CO_3 + H_2O$
- ☐ (c) $KOH + HCl → KCl + H_2O$
- ☐ (d) $KOH + HNO_3 → KNO_3 + H_2O$
- ☐ (e) $KOH + CH_3COOH → CH_3COOK + H_2O$

31 Using the periodic table above, what is the charge on an iron ion in FeS?

- ☐ (a) +2
- ☐ (b) –2
- ☐ (c) –1
- ☐ (d) +1
- ☐ (e) 0

32 Using the following table, calculate the relative formula mass of the compound Na_2SO_4?

- ☐ (a) 132
- ☐ (b) 94
- ☐ (c) 142
- ☐ (d) 119
- ☐ (e) 35

Element	A$_r$
Sodium	23
Sulphur	32
Oxygen	16

Q32

33 Using the following table, calculate the relative formula mass of the compound $Ca(OH)_2$?

....

Element	A$_r$
Calcium	40
Oxygen	16
Hydrogen	1

Q33

QUESTIONS

Higher Level only

34 A metal, M, reacts with chlorine to form the metal chloride. When the chloride was analyzed, it was found to contain 44.1% metal. Given that the relative atomic mass of the metal M is 56, what is the formula of the chloride?
[A$_r$ Cl = 35.5]

- ☐ (a) MCl_3
- ☐ (b) MCl
- ☐ (c) MCl_4
- ☐ (d) MCl_2
- ☐ (e) M_2Cl

35 What is the formula of a compound that is found to contain 1.30 g of zinc, 0.24 g of carbon, and 0.96 g of oxygen?
[A$_r$ Zn = 65, C = 12, O = 16]

- ☐ (a) ZnCO
- ☐ (b) $ZnCO_2$
- ☐ (c) $ZnCO_4$
- ☐ (d) Zn_2CO_3
- ☐ (e) $ZnCO_3$

36 What is the formula of a compound that on analysis is found to contain 34.6% copper, 30.5% iron, and 34.9% sulphur by mass?
[A$_r$ S = 32, Fe = 56, Cu = 64]

- ☐ (a) Cu_2FeS_2
- ☐ (b) $CuFe_3S_2$
- ☐ (c) $CuFeS_2$
- ☐ (d) CuFeS
- ☐ (e) $CuFeS_3$

37 An acid was analyzed and found to contain 2.04% hydrogen, 32.65% sulphur, and 65.31% oxygen by mass. What is the chemical formula of this acid?
[A$_r$ H = 1, S = 32, O = 16]

- ☐ (a) HSO
- ☐ (b) H_2SO_4
- ☐ (c) H_4SO_2
- ☐ (d) H_2SO_3
- ☐ (e) H_3SO_2

38 6 g of an oxide is found to contain 5.2 g of lead. What is the formula of this compound?
[A$_r$ Pb = 207, O = 16]

- ☐ (a) PbO
- ☐ (b) Pb_2O
- ☐ (c) PbO_2
- ☐ (d) PbO_3
- ☐ (e) PbO_4

39 2.6 g of an oxide of mercury is heated and it decomposes to give 2.5 g of the metal. What is the formula of the oxide?
[A_r Hg = 201, O = 16]

- ☐ (a) HgO
- ☐ (b) Hg_2O
- ☐ (c) HgO_2
- ☐ (d) HgO_4
- ☐ (e) Hg_3O

40 1.6 g of an oxide of iron was found to contain 0.48 g of oxygen. What is the formula of the oxide?
[A_r O = 16, Fe = 56]

- ☐ (a) Fe_3O_4
- ☐ (b) FeO
- ☐ (c) Fe_2O_3
- ☐ (d) FeO_2
- ☐ (e) Fe_2O

41 Which of the values of X and Y will balance the equation below:
$CuO + xHCl \rightarrow CuCly + H_2O$

	X	Y
☐ (a)	3	2
☐ (b)	2	2
☐ (c)	1	1
☐ (d)	1	2
☐ (e)	4	6

42 What values of X and Y will balance the following equation?
$Zn + 2HCl \rightarrow ZnCl_x + H_y$

	X	Y
☐ (a)	1	2
☐ (b)	2	3
☐ (c)	1	3
☐ (d)	2	2
☐ (e)	2	1

43 What values of X and Y will balance the following equation?
$xKOH + H_2SO_4 \rightarrow yK_2SO_4 + 2H_2O$

	X	Y
☐ (a)	2	1
☐ (b)	3	3
☐ (c)	4	4
☐ (d)	1	2
☐ (e)	5	6

44 What values of X and Y will balance the following equation?
$Na_xO + H_2SO_4 \rightarrow Na_2SO_4 + yH_2O$

	X	Y
☐ (a)	1	2
☐ (b)	3	6
☐ (c)	2	1
☐ (d)	6	3
☐ (e)	2	2

45 Which of the following equations represents the reaction between hydrochloric acid and copper oxide?

- ☐ (a) $HCl + CuO \rightarrow CuCO_3 + H_2O$
- ☐ (b) $2HCl + Cu \rightarrow CuCl + H_2O$
- ☐ (c) $2HCl + CuO \rightarrow CuCl_2 + H_2O$
- ☐ (d) $HCl + CuO \rightarrow CuSO_4 + HO$
- ☐ (e) $HCl + CuO \rightarrow CuNO_3 + HO$

46 Which one of the following equations represents the reaction between hydrochloric acid and sodium carbonate?

- ☐ (a) $HCl + Na_2CO_3 \rightarrow NaCl + H_2O$
- ☐ (b) $2HCl + Na_2CO_3 \rightarrow NaSO_4 + H_2O + CO_2$
- ☐ (c) $HCl + Na_2CO_3 \rightarrow NaO + H_2O + CO_2$
- ☐ (d) $2HCl + Na_2CO_3 \rightarrow 2NaCl + H_2O + CO_2$
- ☐ (e) $HCl + Na_2CO_3 \rightarrow NaCl + H_2O + CO_2$

47 Which of the following equations represents the reaction between magnesium and silver nitrate?

- ☐ (a) $Mg + 2AgNO_3 \rightarrow Mg(NO_3)_2 + 2Ag$
- ☐ (b) $Mg + AgNO_3 \rightarrow MgNO_3 + Ag$
- ☐ (c) $Mg + AgNO_3 \rightarrow MgNO_3 + AgNO_3$
- ☐ (d) $Mg + AgNO_3 \rightarrow MgSO + Ag$
- ☐ (e) $Mg + AgNO_3 \rightarrow$ no reaction

48 Which of the following equations represents the reaction between zinc and lead nitrate solution?

- ☐ (a) No reaction
- ☐ (b) $Zn + Pb(NO_3)_2 \rightarrow ZnNO_3 + PbNO_3$
- ☐ (c) $Zn + Pb(NO_3)_2 \rightarrow ZnO + PbNO_4$
- ☐ (d) $Zn + Pb(NO_3)_2 \rightarrow Zn(NO_3)_2 + Pb$
- ☐ (e) $Zn + Pb(NO_3)_2 \rightarrow ZnNO_3 + Pb$

49 Which one of the following equations represents the reaction between sodium carbonate and sulphuric acid?

- ☐ (a) $Na_2CO_3 + H_2SO_4 \rightarrow Na_2SO_4 + 4H_2O$
- ☐ (b) $Na_2CO_3 + H_2SO_4 \rightarrow Na_2SO_4 + H_2O$
- ☐ (c) $Na_2CO_3 + 2H_2SO_4 \rightarrow Na_2SO_4 + H_2O$
- ☐ (d) $Na_2CO_3 + H_2SO_4 \rightarrow 3Na_2SO_4 + H_2O$
- ☐ (e) None of the above

50 Which one of the following equations represents the reaction between sodium hydroxide and hydrochloric acid?

- ☐ (a) $2NaOH + H_2SO_4 \rightarrow Na_2SO_4 + H_2O$
- ☐ (b) $2NaOH + HCl \rightarrow Na_2SO_4 + H_2O$
- ☐ (c) $NaOH + HCl \rightarrow NaCl + H_2O$
- ☐ (d) $NaOH + HNO_3 \rightarrow NaNO_3 + H_2O$
- ☐ (e) $2NaOH + H_2 + CO_3 \rightarrow NaCO_3 + H_2O$

51 Which of the following equations represents the reaction between magnesium and hydrochloric acid?

- ☐ (a) $Mg + 2HCl \rightarrow MgCl_2 + H_2$
- ☐ (b) $Mg + HCl \rightarrow MgCl_2 + H_2$
- ☐ (c) $Mg + HCl \rightarrow MgCl_2 + H_2 + H_2O$
- ☐ (d) $Mg + HCl \rightarrow MgCl + H$
- ☐ (e) $Mg + HCl \rightarrow MgSO_4 + H_2$

52 Which of the following equations represents the reaction between nitric acid and magnesium oxide?

- ☐ (a) $HNO_3 + MgO \rightarrow MgNO_3 + H_2O$
- ☐ (b) $2HNO_3 + MgO \rightarrow Mg(NO_3)_2 + H_2O$
- ☐ (c) $HNO_3 + MgO \rightarrow MgSO_4 + H_2O$
- ☐ (d) $HNO_3 + MgO \rightarrow MgHNO_3 + O$
- ☐ (e) $HNO_3 + MgO \rightarrow MgH + NO_4$

53 Which one of the following is the correct balanced equation for the reaction between calcium carbonate and hydrochloric acid?

- ☐ (a) $CaCO_3 + HCl \rightarrow CaCl_2 + CO_2 + 2H_2O$
- ☐ (b) $CaCO_3 + HCl \rightarrow CaCl_2 + CO_2 + 3H_2O$
- ☐ (c) $2CaCO_3 + 2HCl \rightarrow CaCl_2 + CO_2 + 2H_2O$
- ☐ (d) $CaCO_3 + 2HCl \rightarrow CaCl_2 + CO_2 + H_2O$
- ☐ (e) $CaCO_3 + 2HCl \rightarrow CaCl_2 + 2CO_2 + H_2O$

54 Which one of the following equations represents the reaction that takes place at the anode during the electrolysis of molten lead bromide with carbon electrodes?

- ☐ (a) $Pb^+ + 2e^- \rightarrow Pb^{2-}$
- ☐ (b) $Pb^{2+} + 2e^- \rightarrow Cu$
- ☐ (c) $2Br^- \rightarrow Br_2 + 2e^-$
- ☐ (d) No reaction
- ☐ (e) $Pb^{2-} \rightarrow Pb + 2e^-$

55 From the equation below, calculate the number of moles of water produced when 0.5 moles of calcium carbonate is reacted with excess hydrochloric acid.
$CaCO_3 + 2HCl \rightarrow CaCl_2 + CO_2 + H_2O$

- ☐ (a) 2.0

☐ (b) 3.0
☐ (c) 1.0
☐ (d) 0.5
☐ (e) 1.5

56 Using the equation below, if five moles of calcium carbonate are reacted with four moles of hydrochloric acid, how many moles of calcium carbonate are left?
$CaCO_3 + 2HCl \rightarrow CaCl_2 + CO_2 + H_2O$

....

57 Using the equation below, work out how many moles of hydrochloric acid are needed to produce four moles of carbon dioxide.
$CaCO_3 + 2HCl \rightarrow CaCl_2 + CO_2 + H_2O$

☐ (a) 2
☐ (b) 4
☐ (c) 5
☐ (d) 6
☐ (e) 8

58 Using the following equation, work out the number of moles of calcium carbonate that are needed to produce one mole of calcium chloride.
$CaCO_3 + 2HCl \rightarrow CaCl_2 + CO_2 + H_2O$

☐ (a) 1
☐ (b) 2
☐ (c) 6
☐ (d) 3
☐ (e) 4

59 What is the volume, in dm^3, of one mole of any gas at room temperature and pressure?

....

60 What volume would two moles of oxygen occupy at room temperature and pressure?

☐ (a) 64 dm^3
☐ (b) 24 dm^3
☐ (c) 12 dm^3
☐ (d) 48 dm^3
☐ (e) 32 dm^3

61 What volume would 16 g of oxygen occupy at room temperature and pressure?

☐ (a) 24 dm^3
☐ (b) 12 dm^3
☐ (c) 48 dm^3
☐ (d) 32 dm^3
☐ (e) 6 dm^3

62 What volume would 8 g of helium occupy at room temperature and pressure?

☐ (a) 48.0 dm^3
☐ (b) 23.0 dm^3
☐ (c) 12.0 dm^3
☐ (d) 2.4 dm^3
☐ (e) 32.0 dm^3

63 The electrolysis of hydrochloric acid produces hydrogen and chlorine. Calculate the volume of chlorine in litres that is produced for every 48 litres of hydrogen formed (one mole of any gas occupies 24 litres at 25°C and one atm pressure).
$2H^+ + 2e^- \rightarrow H_2 \quad 2Cl^- \rightarrow Cl_2 + 2e^-$

☐ (a) 12
☐ (b) 24
☐ (c) 36
☐ (d) 48
☐ (e) 60

64 What volume of carbon dioxide would be produced if 1 g of carbon is burnt in an excess of air, as shown in the equation below?
$C + O_2 \rightarrow CO_2$
$[A_r C = 12]$
One mole of gas (at RTP) occupies 24 dm^3.

☐ (a) 24 dm^3
☐ (b) 20 dm^3
☐ (c) 2 dm^3
☐ (d) 4 dm^3
☐ (e) 6 dm^3

65 Using the equation below, calculate the mass of zinc needed to produce 12 cm^3 of hydrogen.
$Zn + 2HCl \rightarrow ZnCl_2 + H_2$
$[A_r Zn = 65, Cl = 35.5, H = 1]$
One mole of gas (at RTP) occupies 24000 cm^3.

☐ (a) 0.0275 g
☐ (b) 2.0284 g
☐ (c) 0.0295 g
☐ (d) 0.0310 g
☐ (e) 0.0325 g

66 Using the following equation, calculate the mass of calcium carbonate needed to produce 11.1 g of calcium chloride.
$CaCO_3 + 2HCl \rightarrow CaCl_2 + CO_2 + H_2O$
$[A_r H = 1, C = 12, O = 16, Cl = 35.5, Ca = 40]$

☐ (a) 1.0 g
☐ (b) 10.0 g
☐ (c) 11.1 g
☐ (d) 12.0 g
☐ (e) 100.0 g

67 Using the following equation, calculate the volume of gas produced when 6.5 g of zinc is reacted completely with excess hydrochloric acid.
$Zn + 2HCl \rightarrow ZnCl_2 + H_2$
$[A_r H = 1, Cl = 35.5, Zn = 65]$
One mole of gas (at RTP) occupies 24000 cm^3.

☐ (a) 2250 cm^3
☐ (b) 2500 cm^3
☐ (c) 2300 cm^3
☐ (d) 2635 cm^3
☐ (e) 2400 cm^3

68 A blast furnace uses 160 tonnes of iron(III) oxide every hour. If all the oxide is converted to pure iron, what mass, in tonnes, will be produced every hour?
$[A_r O = 16, Fe = 56]$
[Formula mass $Fe_2O_3 = 160$]

☐ (a) 56
☐ (b) 80
☐ (c) 160
☐ (d) 98
☐ (e) 112

69 What mass of calcium carbonate would be needed to produce 12 cm^3 of carbon dioxide when reacted with excess hydrochloric acid?
$CaCO_3 + 2HCl \rightarrow CaCl_2 + CO_2 + H_2O$
$[A_r H = 1, O = 16, C = 12, Cl = 35.5, Ca = 40]$
One mole of gas (at RTP) occupies 24000 cm^3.

☐ (a) 5.00 g
☐ (b) 50.00 g
☐ (c) 0.50 g
☐ (d) 500.00g
☐ (e) 0.05 g

70 What volume of hydrogen would be needed to react with 56 g of nitrogen to form ammonia, as shown in the equation below?
$N_2 + 3H_2 \rightarrow 2NH_3$
$[A_r H = 1, N = 14]$

☐ (a) 144 dm^3
☐ (b) 96 dm^3
☐ (c) 72 dm^3
☐ (d) 108 dm^3
☐ (e) 60 dm^3

71 1.6 g of an oxide of copper was heated in a stream of hydrogen. The copper oxide was heated until only copper metal remained. The mass of copper left at the end was 1.28 g. What was the formula of the starting oxide?

$[A_r O = 16, Cu = 64]$

- ☐ (a) CuO_3
- ☐ (b) CuO
- ☐ (c) Cu_2O_3
- ☐ (d) Cu_2O_2
- ☐ (e) Cu_2O

72 Calculate the mass of sodium chloride produced when 4 g of sodium hydroxide is reacted with an excess hydrochloric acid.
$NaOH + HCl \rightarrow NaCl + H_2O$
$[A_r H = 1, O = 16, Na = 23, Cl = 35.5]$

- ☐ (a) 5.85 g
- ☐ (b) 58.50 g
- ☐ (c) 4.00 g
- ☐ (d) 2.95 g
- ☐ (e) 4.85 g

73 What mass of copper metal is liberated when 0.250 moles of electrons passes through a solution of copper sulphate?
$[A_r Cu = 64]$

- ☐ (a) 64 g
- ☐ (b) 32 g
- ☐ (c) 8 g
- ☐ (d) 16 g
- ☐ (e) 4 g

74 Calculate the volume of hydrogen produced when 1.2 g of magnesium is reacted with sulphuric acid.
$Mg + H_2SO_4 \rightarrow MgSO_4 + H_2$
$[A_r H = 1, O = 16, Mg = 24, S = 32]$
One mole of gas (at RTP) occupies 24000 cm³.

- ☐ (a) 120.0 cm³
- ☐ (b) 12.0 cm³
- ☐ (c) 1200.0 cm³
- ☐ (d) 1.2 cm³
- ☐ (e) 12000.0 cm³

75 What would the concentration, in mol/dm³, of a solution be if 24.5 g of sulphuric acid was dissolved in one dm³ of water?
$[A_r H = 1, O = 16, S = 32]$

- ☐ (a) 5.00 dm³
- ☐ (b) 0.50 dm³
- ☐ (c) 2.50 dm³
- ☐ (d) 0.25 dm³
- ☐ (e) 0.40 dm³

76 What would the concentration, in mol/dm³, of a sodium hydroxide solution that contains 4 g sodium hydroxide per dm³ be?
$[A_r H = 1, O = 16, Na = 23]$

- ☐ (a) 0.10 mol/dm³

- ☐ (b) 1.00 mol/dm³
- ☐ (c) 10.00 mol/dm³
- ☐ (d) 0.50 mol/dm³
- ☐ (e) 0.01 mol/dm³

77 What mass of sodium chloride would have to be dissolved in 1 dm³ of water to produce a solution with a concentration of 0.5 mol/dm³?
$[A_r Na = 23, Cl = 35.5]$

- ☐ (a) 11.70 g
- ☐ (b) 117.00 g
- ☐ (c) 29.25 g
- ☐ (d) 292.50 g
- ☐ (e) 58.50 g

78 Which of the following equations represents the reaction that takes place at the cathode during the electrolysis of copper sulphate using carbon electrodes?

- ☐ (a) $Cu^{2+} + 2e^- \rightarrow Cu$
- ☐ (b) $Cu^{2+} + e \rightarrow Cu^+$
- ☐ (c) $Cu^+ + e^- \rightarrow Cu$
- ☐ (d) $Cu \rightarrow Cu^{2+} + 2e^-$
- ☐ (e) $Cu^{3+} + 3e^- \rightarrow Cu$

79 How many moles of electrons are given up when one mole of chlorine molecules is liberated during the electrolysis of sodium chloride solution?

- ☐ (a) 1.0
- ☐ (b) 2.0
- ☐ (c) 0.5
- ☐ (d) 3.0
- ☐ (e) 4.0

80 During the electrolysis of copper sulphate solution (see following diagram) how many moles of electrons are needed to liberate four moles of copper metal?

- ☐ (a) 1
- ☐ (b) 2
- ☐ (c) 4
- ☐ (d) 8
- ☐ (e) 6

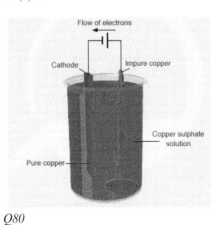

Q80

81 What mass of aluminium would be deposited if 96500 coulombs of electricity are passed through molten aluminium oxide during the extraction of aluminium?
$[A_r Al = 27]$
1 mole of electrons = 1 Faraday = 96500 coulombs.

- ☐ (a) 3 g
- ☐ (b) 6 g
- ☐ (c) 9 g
- ☐ (d) 4 g
- ☐ (e) 5 g

82 What mass of lead will be formed during the electrolysis of molten lead bromide when 16 g of bromine is produced? See diagram that follows.
$[A_r Br = 80, Pb = 207]$
$Pb^{2+} + 2e^- \rightarrow Pb \quad 2Br^- \rightarrow Br_2 + 2e^-$

- ☐ (a) 207.00 g
- ☐ (b) 10.35 g
- ☐ (c) 20.70 g
- ☐ (d) 41.40 g
- ☐ (e) 103.50 g

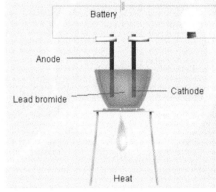

Q82

ANSWERS

Chemical equations

Foundation and Higher Levels

☐ **1**
The formula of water is H_2O.

☐ **2** *(c)*
The formula of carbon dioxide is CO_2.

☐ **3** *(c)*
The formula of hydrogen gas is H_2. A molecule of hydrogen gas is made up of two hydrogen atoms bonded together.

☐ **4** *(e)*
The formula of hydrochloric acid is HCl. An aqueous solution of hydrogen chloride is known as hydrochloric acid.

☐ **5** *(a)*
The formula of sodium chloride is NaCl.

☐ **6**
The formula of limestone (calcium carbonate) is $CaCO_3$.

☐ **7** *(a)*
The formula of calcium chloride is $CaCl_2$.

☐ **8** *(c)*
The formula for helium gas is He. Helium is inert and, unlike hydrogen, atoms of helium do not pair together to make molecules.

☐ **9** *(d)*
The formula of chlorine gas is Cl_2. A molecule of chlorine gas is made up of two chlorine atoms bonded together.

☐ **10** *(a)*
The formula of the compound that contains sulphur and oxygen in the ratio of 1:2 is SO_2 (sulphur dioxide).

☐ **11** *(c)*
The correct formula of iron(II) sulphate is $FeSO_4$.

☐ **12** *(b)*
Calcium forms +2 ions (Ca^{2+}) and oxygen forms –2 ions (O^{2-}) in many reactions. Hence, the chemical formula of the product calcium oxide is CaO.

☐ **13** *(a)*
An ionic compound contains ions of different charges but the compound itself has no overall charge. Therefore, the ratio of the ions must be such that the compound has no overall charge.

For this to happen the ratio of the magnesium to fluoride ions has to be 1:2, and so the formula is MgF_2 (magnesium fluoride).

☐ **14** *(e)*
An ionic compound contains ions of different charges but the compound itself has no overall charge. Therefore, the ratio of the ions must be such that the compound has no overall charge. The iron ion has a +3 charge and the sulphate ion has a –2 charge so, to balance the charges, the ratio of iron to sulphate has to be 2:3 and hence the formula is $Fe_2(SO_4)_3$ (iron(III) sulphate).

☐ **15** *(b)*
An ionic compound contains ions of different charges but the compound itself has no overall charge. Therefore, the ratio of the ions must be such that the compound has no overall charge. For this to happen the ratio of sodium to carbonate ions has to be 2:1 and hence the formula is Na_2CO_3.

☐ **16** *(a)*
The formula of methane is CH_4.

☐ **17** *(c)*
The formula of nitric acid is HNO_3.

☐ **18** *(c)*
The formula of the compound that contains the elements nitrogen and hydrogen in the ratio of 1:3 is NH_3 (ammonia).

☐ **19** *(d)*
The formula of a compound that contains copper (Cu), sulphur (S), and oxygen (O) in a ratio of 1:1:4 is $CuSO_4$ (copper sulphate).

☐ **20** *(e)*
None of the substances in the equation are in the form of a liquid. The state symbols for the substances in the equation show them to be either in solution (aq) or solid (s).

☐ **21** *(d)*
Calcium hydroxide is a solution in the equation. This can be seen by the fact that the formula for calcium hydroxide is followed by the state symbol (aq), which indicates that the substance is in solution with water.

☐ **22** *(a)*
The word equation for the reaction between hydrogen and oxygen is as follows:

Hydrogen + oxygen → water

☐ **23** *(b)*
When a reactive metal reacts with an acid it produces a salt and hydrogen. The word equation that represents the reaction between hydrochloric acid and zinc is as follows:
Hydrochloric acid + zinc → zinc chloride + hydrogen

☐ **24** *(d)*
When a reactive metal is placed into a solution of a less reactive metal, the less reactive metal is displaced. Zinc is more reactive than silver and therefore the silver is displaced and the zinc goes into solution. The word equation is as follows:
Zinc + silver nitrate → zinc nitrate + silver

☐ **25** *(c)*
The word equation for the reaction between sodium and chlorine is as follows:
Sodium + chlorine → sodium chloride

☐ **26** *(b)*
The reaction between calcium oxide (a base) and carbon dioxide (an acidic gas) produces calcium carbonate. The word equation for the reaction between calcium oxide and carbon dioxide is as follows:
Calcium oxide + carbon dioxide → calcium carbonate

☐ **27** *(e)*
The reaction between an acid and an alkali produces a salt and water. The word equation for the reaction between sulphuric acid and sodium hydroxide is as follows:
Sodium hydroxide + sulphuric acid → sodium sulphate + water

☐ **28** *(e)*
The reaction between an acid and a base produces a salt and water, as shown in the following diagram. The reaction between nitric acid and a base produces a nitrate salt and water. The word equation for the reaction between copper oxide (a base) and nitric acid is as follows:
Copper oxide + nitric acid → copper nitrate + water

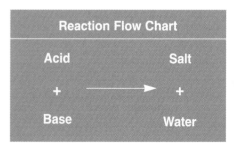

Reaction Flow Chart		
Acid		**Salt**
+	→	**+**
Base		**Water**

☐ 29 *(b)*
The reaction between an acid and a reactive metal produces a salt and hydrogen gas. The reaction between sulphuric acid and zinc produces zinc sulphate and hydrogen. The equation for the reaction is as follows:
$Zn + H_2SO_4 \rightarrow ZnSO_4 + H_2$

☐ 30 *(a)*
The reaction between an acid and an alkali produces a salt and water. The reaction between sulphuric acid and potassium hydroxide produces the salt, potassium sulphate. The equation for this reaction is as follows:
$2KOH + H_2SO_4 \rightarrow K_2SO_4 + 2H_2O$

☐ 31 *(a)*
Sulphur is in Group VI, so it always has a valency of –2. Compounds have a combined valency of 0, and so iron must be +2 because +2 + –2 = 0. (Iron, being a transition metal, has a variable valency, and it can either be +2 or +3.)

☐ 32 *(c)*
To calculate the relative formula mass of a compound, add the relative atomic masses of the atoms in the formula.
Sodium (23 x 2) + sulphur (32) + oxygen (16 x 4) = 142

☐ 33
To calculate the relative formula mass of a compound, add the relative atomic masses of the atoms in the formula.
Calcium (40) + oxygen (16 x 2) + hydrogen (1 x 2) = 74

Chemical equations

Higher Level only

☐ 34 *(d)*

	Metal M	Cl
Mass in 100 g	44.1 g	55.9g
Mass of 1 mole	56 g	35.5 g
No. of moles	0.79	1.57
Simplest ratio	1 :	2

The formula of the chlorine formed is therefore MCl_2.

☐ 35 *(e)*

	Zn	C	O
Mass	1.30g	0.24 g	0.96 g
Mass of 1 mole	65 g	12 g	16 g
No. of moles	1.30÷65	0.24÷12	0.96÷16
	= 0.02	= 0.02	= 0.06
Simplest ratio	1 :	1 :	3

The formula is therefore $ZnCO_3$.

☐ 36 *(c)*

	Cu	Fe	S
Mass in 100 g	34.6 g	30.5 g	34.9 g
Mass of 1 mole	64 g	56 g	32 g
No. of moles	34.6÷64	30.5÷56	34.9÷32
	= 0.54	= 0.54	= 1.09
Simplest ratio	1 :	1 :	2

The formula is therefore $CuFeS_2$.

☐ 37 *(b)*

	H	S	O
Mass in 100 g	2.04 g	32.65 g	65.31 g
Mass of 1 mole	1 g	32 g	16 g
No. of moles	2.04÷1	32.65÷32	65.31÷16
	= 2.04	= 0.54	= 1.09
Simplest ratio	2 :	1 :	4

Hence, the chemical formula of the acid is H_2SO_4.

☐ 38 *(c)*

	Pb	O
Mass	5.2 g	0.8 g
Mass of 1 mole	207 g	16 g
No. of moles	5.2÷207	0.8÷16
	= 0.025	= 0.050
Simplest ratio	1 :	2

Hence, the formula of the oxide is PbO_2.

☐ 39 *(b)*

	Hg	O
Mass	2.5 g	0.1 g
Mass of 1 mole	201 g	16 g
No. of moles	2.5÷201	0.1÷16
	= 0.0124	= 0.0062
Simplest ratio	2 :	1

Hence, the formula of the mercury oxide is Hg_2O.

☐ 40 *(c)*

	Fe	O
Mass	1.12 g	0.48 g
Mass of 1 mole	56 g	16 g
No. of moles	1.12÷56	0.48÷16
	= 0.02	= 0.03
Simplest ratio	2 :	3

Therefore, the formula of the iron oxide is Fe_2O_3.

☐ 41 *(b)*
For the equation to balance, the value of X has to be 2 and the value of Y has to be 2 also. The balanced equation is as follows:
$CuO + 2HCl \rightarrow CuCl_2 + H_2O$

☐ 42 *(d)*
In order to balance the above equation the number of atoms on each side of the equation must be equal. To balance the equation, X has to have a value of 2 and Y has to have a value of 2 also. The balanced equation for the reaction is as follows:
$Zn + 2HCl \rightarrow ZnCl_2 + H_2$

☐ 43 *(a)*
For a chemical equation to balance there must be the same number of atoms on both sides of the equation. The values of X and Y that balance the equation are 2 and 1. The balanced equation is as follows:
$2KOH + H_2SO_4 \rightarrow K_2SO_4 + 2H_2O$

☐ 44 *(c)*
For the equation to balance, the number of atoms on each side of the equation has to be equal and the formulae must be correct. In order for this equation to balance, the value of X has to be 2 and the value of Y has to be 1. The balanced equation is as follows:
$Na_2O + H_2SO_4 \rightarrow Na_2SO_4 + H_2O$

☐ 45 *(c)*
The reaction between an acid and base produces a salt and water. In the reaction that takes place between hydrochloric acid and copper oxide, the salt copper chloride is produced. The equation for the reaction is as follows:
$2HCl + CuO \rightarrow CuCl_2 + H_2O$

☐ 46 *(d)*
The reaction between an acid and a carbonate produces a neutral salt, carbon dioxide, and water. The reaction between hydrochloric acid and sodium carbonate produces sodium chloride, carbon dioxide, and water. The equation for the reaction is as follows:
$2HCl + Na_2CO_3 \rightarrow 2NaCl + H_2O + CO_2$

☐ 47 *(a)*
When a reactive metal is placed into a solution of a less reactive metal, the less reactive metal is displaced and the reactive metal goes into solution. In this reaction, the magnesium is more reactive than silver and therefore the silver is displaced and the magnesium goes into solution as magnesium nitrate. The equation for the reaction is as follows:
$Mg + 2AgNO_3 \rightarrow Mg(NO_3)_2 + 2Ag$

☐ 48 *(d)*
If a reactive metal is placed into a salt solution of a less reactive metal, the less reactive metal is displaced and the reactive metal goes into solution. In this reaction zinc, which is more reactive than lead, displaces the lead and goes into solution to form zinc nitrate. The equation for the reaction is as follows:
$Zn + Pb(NO_3)_2 \rightarrow Zn(NO_3)_2 + Pb$

☐ 49 *(e)*
The reaction between sulphuric acid and sodium carbonate produces sodium sulphate, water, and carbon dioxide. None of the equations show the production of carbon dioxide, and therefore none of them are balanced. The correct equation is as follows:
$Na_2CO_3 + H_2SO_4 \rightarrow H_2O + CO_2 + Na_2SO_4$

☐ **50** (c)
The reaction between an acid and a base produces a salt and water. In the reaction between sodium hydroxide and hydrochloric acid, the salt formed is sodium chloride. The equation for this reaction is as follows:
$NaOH + HCl \rightarrow NaCl + H_2O$

☐ **51** (a)
The reaction between an acid and a reactive metal produces a salt and hydrogen gas. The reaction between hydrochloric acid and magnesium produces magnesium chloride and hydrogen. Hence, the equation for this reaction is as follows:
$Mg + 2HCl \rightarrow MgCl_2 + H_2$

☐ **52** (b)
The reaction between an acid and a base produces a salt and water. The neutralization of nitric acid will give a salt known as a nitrate. The correct equation for the reaction between nitric acid and magnesium oxide is (b). Suggestion (a) is not correct because the formula for magnesium nitrate is $Mg(NO_3)_2$. The equation for this reaction is as follows:
$2HNO_3 + MgO \rightarrow Mg(NO_3)_2 + H_2O$

☐ **53** (d)
The reaction between an acid and a carbonate produces a salt, carbon dioxide, and water. In this reaction, the products are calcium carbonate, carbon dioxide, and water. For the equation to balance there must be the same number of atoms on each side of the equation, and all the formulae must be correct. Hence, the balanced equation for this reaction is as follows:
$CaCO_3 + 2HCl \rightarrow CaCl_2 + CO_2 + H_2O$

☐ **54** (c)
During the electrolysis of lead bromide solution, the anode (positive electrode) attracts the negative bromide ions. At the electrode these ions each lose an electron and become bromine atoms, which pair up to form bromine molecules.
$2Br^- \rightarrow Br_2 + 2e^-$

☐ **55** (d)
As can be seen from the equation, the ratio of calcium carbonate to water is 1:1. Therefore, if 0.5 moles of calcium carbonate are reacted, 0.5 moles of water will be formed.

☐ **56**
From the equation it can be seen that the ratio of calcium carbonate to hydrochloric acid is 1:2. If four moles of hydrochloric acid are used, then two moles of calcium carbonate will react, leaving three moles unreacted.

☐ **57** (e)
From the equation it can be seen that the ratio of hydrochloric acid to carbon dioxide is 2:1. In order to produce four moles of carbon dioxide, eight moles of hydrochloric acid will be needed.

☐ **58** (a)
From the equation it can be seen that the ratio of calcium carbonate to calcium chloride is 1:1. Therefore, one mole of calcium carbonate is needed to produce one mole of calcium chloride.

☐ **59**
The volume of one mole of any gas at room temperature and pressure is 24 dm^3.

☐ **60** (d)
One mole of any gas at room temperature and pressure has a volume of 24 dm^3. Therefore, two moles of oxygen would have a volume of 48 dm^3.

☐ **61** (b)
One mole of any gas occupies a volume of 24 dm^3. Oxygen has a formula of O_2 and so has a molecular mass of 32 g/mol. Therefore 16 g is 0.5 moles. Thus, the volume that 16 g of oxygen would occupy is 12 dm^3.

☐ **62** (a)
One mole of any gas occupies a volume of 24 dm^3. Helium has molecular mass of 4 g/mol and therefore 8 g is two moles of helium. Thus, two moles of helium will occupy a volume of 48 dm^3.

☐ **63** (d)
The overall reaction is as follows:
$2H^+ + 2Cl^- \rightarrow H_2 + Cl_2$
When one mole of hydrogen is formed, one mole of chlorine is formed also. 48 litres of hydrogen is two moles. Hence two moles of chlorine will be formed which will occupy a volume of 48 litres.

☐ **64** (c)
By using the equation it can be seen that one mole of carbon produces one mole of carbon dioxide. One gram of carbon is $1/12$ of a mole and will therefore produce $1/12$ of a mole of carbon dioxide. One mole of any gas will occupy 24 dm^3, therefore $1/12$ of a mole will produce 2 dm^3 of carbon dioxide.

☐ **65** (e)
As can be seen from the equation, the ratio of zinc to hydrogen is 1:1, i.e. one mole of hydrogen is produced from one mole of zinc. One mole of any gas occupies a volume of 24000 cm^3. Therefore 12 cm^3 is 12/24000 moles of hydrogen. The mass of zinc needed is 12 ÷ 24000 x the relative atomic mass of zinc (65) = 0.0325 g.

☐ **66** (b)
It can be seen from the equation that the ratio of calcium carbonate to calcium chloride is 1:1. The relative formula mass of calcium chloride is 111 (Ca = 40, Cl = 35.5, so 40 + 35.5 + 35.5 = 111). The relative formula mass of calcium carbonate is 100 (Ca = 40, C = 12, O = 16, so 40 + 12 + 16 + 16 + 16 = 100). 100 g of calcium carbonate would produce 111 g of calcium chloride, and therefore 10 g of calcium carbonate would produce 11.1 g of calcium chloride.

☐ **67** (e)
As can be seen from the equation, the ratio of zinc to hydrogen is 1:1, i.e. one mole of zinc would produce one mole of hydrogen. One mole of any gas occupies a volume of 24000 cm^3 or 24 dm^3. The relative atomic mass of zinc is 65. 6.5 g is therefore 0.1 moles, and if this amount is reacted with hydrochloric acid it will produce 0.1 moles of hydrogen molecules. 0.1 moles would have a volume of 2400 cm^3 (0.1 x 24000).

☐ **68** (e)
Each Fe_2O_3 will be reduced in the blast furnace and produce 2Fe. The relative formula mass of Fe_2O_3 = 160 and the relative atomic mass of Fe = 56. Therefore, 160 g of Fe_2O_3 will produce 112 g of Fe (2 x 56), and 160 tonnes of Fe_2O_3 will produce 112 tonnes of Fe.

☐ **69** (e)
As can be seen from the equation, the ratio between calcium carbonate and carbon dioxide is 1:1, i.e. one mole of calcium carbonate, when reacted with acid, will produce one mole of carbon dioxide. One mole of any gas occupies a volume of 24000 cm^3. Therefore, 12 cm^3 is 12/24000 moles, and hence 12 ÷ 24000 x 100 g of calcium carbonate will be needed to produce this volume. (The relative formula mass of calcium carbonate is 100; Ca = 40, C = 12, O = 16, so 40 + 12 + 16 + 16 + 16 = 100.) The mass of calcium carbonate is therefore equal to 0.05 g.

☐ **70** (a)
The equation shows that one mole of nitrogen reacts with three moles of hydrogen. One mole of nitrogen has a

mass of 28 g/mol, and so 56 g is two moles of nitrogen. Two moles of nitrogen will react with six moles of hydrogen. One mole of any gas occupies a volume of 24 dm³ and therefore six moles of hydrogen will occupy a volume of 144 dm³ (6 x 24 dm³).

☐ **71** *(b)*

	Cu	O
Mass	1.28 g	1.6 – 1.28 = 0.32 g
Mass of 1 mole	64 g	16 g
No. of moles	1.28÷64 = 0.02	0.32÷16 = 0.02

The formula of copper oxide is CuO.

☐ **72** *(a)*
As can be seen from the equation, the ratio of sodium hydroxide to sodium chloride is 1:1, i.e. one mole of sodium hydroxide when neutralized will produce one mole of sodium chloride. The relative formula mass of sodium chloride is 40 [A_r Na = 23, O = 16, H = 1, so 23 + 16 + 1 = 40]. 4 g is equal to 0.1 moles of sodium hydroxide. This will therefore produce 0.1 moles of sodium chloride. 0.1 moles of sodium chloride is equal to 5.85 g (relative formula mass of sodium chloride = 58.5).

☐ **73** *(c)*
Two moles of electrons will liberate one mole of copper metal: $Cu^{2+} + 2e^- = Cu$. Therefore, one mole of electrons will liberate 0.5 moles of copper, which is equal to 32 g. Hence 0.250 moles of electrons will liberate 8 g (0.250 x 32).

☐ **74** *(c)*
As can be seen from the equation, the ratio of magnesium to hydrogen is 1:1, i.e. one mole of magnesium will produce one mole of hydrogen. One mole of any gas occupies a volume of 24000 cm³. The relative atomic mass of magnesium is 24. Therefore, 1.2 g is 1.2/24 moles of magnesium. The volume of gas produced is 1200 cm³ ([1.2 ÷ 24] x 24000).

☐ **75** *(d)*
One mole of sulphuric acid has a mass of 98 g. Therefore, 24.5 g is 0.25 moles. If this mass of sulphuric acid is dissolved in 1 dm³ of water, the concentration will be 0.25 mol/dm³.

☐ **76** *(a)*
One mole of sodium hydroxide (NaOH) has a mass of 40 g. Therefore, 4 g is 0.1 moles. The concentration of the solution is therefore 0.1 mol/dm³.

☐ **77** *(c)*
To produce a concentration of 0.5 mol/dm³, 0.5 moles of sodium chloride would have to be dissolved in 1 dm³ of water. One mole of sodium chloride has a mass of 58.5 g. Therefore, a mass of 58.5 x 0.5 = 29.25 g would have to be dissolved to produce a solution of 0.5 mol/dm³.

☐ **78** *(a)*
During the electrolysis of copper sulphate solution, the cathode (negative electrode) attracts the positive copper ions. At the electrode these ions gain two electrons and become copper atoms, and the electrode is coated with a red/brown covering of copper. The equation for the reaction is as follows: $Cu^{2+} + 2e^- \rightarrow Cu$

☐ **79** *(b)*
One mole of electrons is given up by one mole of chloride ions at the anode ($Cl^- = Cl + e^-$) but two moles of atoms are needed to produce one mole of chlorine molecules Cl_2. Therefore, two moles of electrons are needed to produce one mole of chlorine molecules. See diagram that follows.

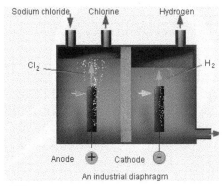

A79

☐ **80** *(d)*
Two moles of electrons are needed to liberate one mole of copper ions ($Cu^{2+} + 2e^- = Cu$). Therefore, to liberate four moles of copper ions, eight moles of electrons are needed.

☐ **81** *(c)*
Three moles of electrons are needed to liberate one mole of aluminium from molten aluminium oxide : $Al^{3+} + 3e^- = Al$. One mole of electrons is equal to 96500 coulombs of charge (the Faraday constant). Therefore, one mole of electrons would liberate 0.33 moles of aluminium. The mass of 0.33 moles of aluminium is RAM x number of moles = 27 x 0.33 = 9 g.

☐ **82** *(c)*
The overall reaction is as follows: $Pb^{2+} + 2Br^- \rightarrow Pb + Br_2$ When one mole of bromine is formed, one mole of lead is formed also. The relative formula mass of bromine is 2 x 80 = 160. When 160 g of bromine is formed, 207 g of lead is formed. Therefore, when 16 g of bromine is formed, 20.7 g of lead will be formed.

Patterns of Behaviour

Metals and non-metals *(Single and Double Awards)*

Most people can name a number of metallic elements, but few can name any non-metallic elements. A knowledge and understanding of the differences between these two main classes of elements is essential for students to grasp the ideas behind the formation of many compounds, and the following questions test these ideas.

 KEY FACTS

• **Alkali metals:** The elements in group I, for example, lithium, sodium, and potassium, are known as the alkali metals. They are all soft, silvery white, reactive metals with low melting points. They are all stored in oil to protect them from the oxygen and water vapour in the atmosphere. The alkali metals will react vigorously with cold water to produce the metal hydroxide and hydrogen. The reactivity of the metals increases as the group is descended, with lithium being the least reactive and potassium the most reactive (the other metals below potassium are too reactive to use in school laboratories). The alkali metals will burn in oxygen with coloured flames to produce a white solid oxide, which when dissolved in water will produce an alkaline solution. All the compounds of the group I metals are soluble in water and are white ionic crystalline solids. The oxides and hydroxides are strongly alkaline. The compounds of group I metals have many uses: sodium hydroxide is used as oven cleaner and in the manufacture of soap; sodium chloride is used to de-ice roads and as a flavouring in foods. It is also used in the manufacture of chlorine and sodium hydroxide. Sodium itself is used in sodium vapour lamps, which are used for street lighting. Sodium is also used as a coolant in nuclear reactors.

• **Halogens:** The elements in group VII, for example, chlorine, bromine, and iodine, are known as the halogens. They are all very reactive, coloured, non-metallic elements that exist as covalent molecules. For example, chlorine (Cl_2), bromine (Br_2), and iodine (I_2) form diatomic molecules. They are not found free in nature because they are so reactive. They are found in combination with metals as salts. The melting point of the elements increases down the group: chlorine is a green gas, bromine a brown/red liquid, and iodine a purple/black solid. The elements are moderately soluble in water and are soluble in organic solvents such as hexane. They will react with metals, such as the group I metals, to produce white ionic crystalline solids, although the reactions get less vigorous as the group is descended. They will react with hydrogen to produce fuming colourless gases, such as hydrogen chloride or hydrogen bromide, which when dissolved in water produce a strongly acidic solution. The halogens, chlorine in particular, are very important raw materials for the chemical industry. Chlorine is used in the manufacture of the following: bleach, weedkiller, antiseptics, chloroform, dry cleaning solvents, plastic (PVC), and pesticides. Chlorine is also used to sterilize drinking water. Bromine is used in the manufacture of dyestuffs, fire extinguishers, and additives for petrol.

• **Transition metals:** The transition metals are the block of metallic elements found between groups II and III of the periodic table. They all have very similar properties. The elements such as iron, copper, and nickel are all hard, dense metals with high melting points (with the exception of mercury, which is a liquid at room temperature). They are less reactive than group I and II

Group

Mass number	1	
	H	Chemical symbol
Atomic number	1	

Key	
	Alkali metals
	Transition metals
	Halogens

I	II										III	IV	V	VI	VII	0
																4 He 2
7 Li 3	9 Be 4										11 B 5	12 C 6	14 N 7	16 O 8	19 F 9	20 Ne 10
23 Na 11	24 Mg 12										27 Al 13	28 Si 14	30 P 15	32 S 16	35 Cl 17	40 Ar 18
39 K 19	40 Ca 20	45 Sc 21	48 Ti 22	51 V 23	52 Cr 24	55 Mn 25	56 Fe 26	59 Co 27	59 Ni 28	63 Cu 29	64 Zn 30	70 Ga 31	73 Ge 32	75 As 33	79 Se 34	80 Br 35	84 Kr 36
85 Rb 37	88 Sr 38	89 Y 39	91 Zr 40	93 Nb 41	96 Mo 42	Tc 43	101 Ru 44	103 Rh 45	106 Pd 46	108 Ag 47	112 Cd 48	115 In 49	119 Sn 50	122 Sb 51	128 Te 52	127 I 53	131 Xe 54
133 Cs 55	137 Ba 56	139 La 57	178 Hf 72	181 Ta 73	184 W 74	186 Re 75	190 Os 76	192 Ir 77	195 Pt 78	197 Au 79	201 Hg 80	204 Tl 81	207 Pb 82	209 Bi 83	Po 84	At 85	Rn 86
Fr 87	226 Ra 88	277 Ac 89														

The periodic table

metals, and can form coloured compounds and ions with different charges. For example, iron forms ions of formulae Fe^{2+} and Fe^{3+}. The metals and their compounds are used in industry as catalysts. For example, iron or iron(III) oxide is used as the catalyst in the manufacture of ammonia.

QUESTIONS

Foundation and Higher Levels

1 Which one of the following is a metal?

- ☐ (a) Zinc
- ☐ (b) Carbon
- ☐ (c) Silicon
- ☐ (d) Sulphur
- ☐ (e) Chlorine

2 Which one of the following is not a metal?

- ☐ (a) Sodium
- ☐ (b) Silicon
- ☐ (c) Iron
- ☐ (d) Copper
- ☐ (e) Uranium

3 Which of the following is a property of all non-metallic elements?

- ☐ (a) They do not conduct electricity
- ☐ (b) They are all gases
- ☐ (c) They all have very high melting points
- ☐ (d) They cannot be hammered or bent into shape
- ☐ (e) They react only with other non-metals

4 Which of the following statements are true for properties of non-metals?
i. They all form basic oxides
ii. They are all non-conductors of electricity
iii. They all react readily with oxygen

- ☐ (a) i only
- ☐ (b) i and ii only
- ☐ (c) ii only
- ☐ (d) None of them
- ☐ (e) All of them

5 Which of the following properties are true for all pure metals?
i. They all conduct electricity
ii. They are all solids
iii. They are all shiny

- ☐ (a) i and ii only

- ☐ (b) iii only
- ☐ (c) i and iii only
- ☐ (d) All of the above
- ☐ (e) i only

6 Tungsten metal has all the following properties, but which one is an important reason for its use in light bulbs?

- ☐ (a) It is shiny
- ☐ (b) It forms compounds with non-metals
- ☐ (c) It has a high melting point
- ☐ (d) It is malleable
- ☐ (e) It can easily be made into alloys

7 What is iron?

- ☐ (a) An ion
- ☐ (b) A compound
- ☐ (c) A mixture
- ☐ (d) An element
- ☐ (e) An alloy

8 What colour is pure iron?

- ☐ (a) Silver/grey
- ☐ (b) White/yellow
- ☐ (c) Black/brown
- ☐ (d) Blue
- ☐ (e) Orange

9 Iron and sulphur are two elements. Which of the following statements are true?
i. They have the same melting point
ii. They could react together to form a compound
iii. A mixture of them could be separated using a magnet

- ☐ (a) i only
- ☐ (b) i and ii only
- ☐ (c) All of them
- ☐ (d) None of them
- ☐ (e) ii and iii only

10 Which one of the following is a property of all metal elements?

- ☐ (a) They are solid
- ☐ (b) They float on water
- ☐ (c) They are very dense
- ☐ (d) They conduct electricity
- ☐ (e) They are dull

11 Which one of the following could be used as a conclusive test for a metal?

- ☐ (a) Test the substance to see if it floats on water
- ☐ (b) Test the substance to see if it is solid at room temperature
- ☐ (c) Test the substance to see if it conducts electricity

- ☐ (d) Test the substance to see if it is shiny
- ☐ (e) None of these tests is conclusive

12 Which of the following elements would be shiny?

- ☐ (a) Bromine
- ☐ (b) Chlorine
- ☐ (c) Zinc
- ☐ (d) Sulphur
- ☐ (e) Neon

13 Which of the following would not light the bulb if it were to be placed inside the circuit shown below?

- ☐ (a) Carbon (graphite)
- ☐ (b) Sodium
- ☐ (c) Sulphur
- ☐ (d) Copper
- ☐ (e) Gold

Q13

14 Which one of the metals listed below has the following properties:
i Low melting point
ii Can be cut with a knife
iii Produces an alkaline solution when reacted with water

- ☐ (a) Copper
- ☐ (b) Iron
- ☐ (c) Sodium
- ☐ (d) Magnesium
- ☐ (e) Aluminium

15 Where are metal ores found?

- ☐ (a) In the atmosphere
- ☐ (b) In the sea
- ☐ (c) In the earth's crust
- ☐ (d) In outer space
- ☐ (e) All of the above

16 Which one of the following will be reduced by carbon monoxide?

- ☐ (a) Magnesium oxide
- ☐ (b) Sodium oxide
- ☐ (c) Lead oxide
- ☐ (d) Calcium oxide
- ☐ (e) Potassium chloride

17 What information is used to decide how a metal is extracted from its ore?

☐ (a) Its position in the reactivity series
☐ (b) Its position in the periodic table
☐ (c) Its position in the earth's crust
☐ (d) The composition of its ore
☐ (e) The melting point of its ore

18 What method is used to extract aluminium from its compounds?

☐ (a) Aluminium is found native and does not have to be extracted from compounds
☐ (b) By electrolysis of its molten oxide
☐ (c) By reaction of the oxide with carbon
☐ (d) By electrolysis of the molten chloride
☐ (e) By reaction of the chloride with concentrated sulphuric acid

19 What is the name of the ore from which aluminium is extracted?

☐ (a) Aluminite
☐ (b) Magnetite
☐ (c) Bauxite
☐ (d) Cumintonite
☐ (e) Spodumine

20 Which of the following methods would you use to extract the metal lead from its ore?

☐ (a) Heating the oxide with carbon
☐ (b) Electrolysis of the molten chloride
☐ (c) Lead is found native
☐ (d) Electrolysis of the melted oxide
☐ (e) None of the above

21 Which of the following methods is used to extract iron from its ore?

☐ (a) Heating the oxide with carbon
☐ (b) Electrolysis of the molten chloride
☐ (c) Iron is found native
☐ (d) Electrolysis of the melted oxide
☐ (e) None of the above

22 Which element is extracted from the ore haematite?

....

23 Metals such as copper are used to make wires. Which one of the following properties allows metals to be used for this purpose?

☐ (a) They are shiny
☐ (b) They are malleable
☐ (c) They have a high melting point

☐ (d) They are ductile
☐ (e) They are solids

24 Which one of the following elements would be the least suitable for making overhead power cables?

☐ (a) Copper
☐ (b) Nickel
☐ (c) Silicon
☐ (d) Iron
☐ (e) Aluminium

25 Iron is extracted from its ore by the use of a blast furnace. Along with the iron ore, two other solid materials are added. What are these two substances?

☐ (a) Salt and sulphuric acid
☐ (b) Limestone and coke
☐ (c) Coke and salt
☐ (d) Coke and sulphuric acid
☐ (e) Coke and sodium nitrate

26 What is the main purpose of the coke in the extraction of iron in the blast furnace?

☐ (a) It is used to remove the impurities
☐ (b) It contains a large amount of iron
☐ (c) It reacts to produce the carbon monoxide that acts as a reducing agent
☐ (d) It supplies the energy needed in the blast furnace
☐ (e) None of the above

27 How is the metal iron extracted from iron ores such as haematite?

☐ (a) By heating its oxides until they decompose to give the metal
☐ (b) By electrolysis of molten iron oxide
☐ (c) By reacting iron oxides with carbon
☐ (d) By electrolysis of molten iron chloride
☐ (e) By reacting iron chloride with concentrated sulphuric acid

28 What is the slag product in the blast furnace often used as? (See diagram that follows.)

....

Q28

29 Iron is extracted from its ores in a blast furnace by reducing the ores with carbon. The iron ore contains impurities that could clog up the blast furnace. What is added to the blast furnace to remove these impurities?

☐ (a) Limestone
☐ (b) Salt
☐ (c) Sodium nitrate
☐ (d) Sulphuric acid
☐ (e) Scrap steel

30 What is bauxite an ore of?

....

31 What are the anode and cathode made from in the extraction of aluminium?

☐ (a) Carbon (graphite)
☐ (b) Ceramic
☐ (c) Sodium
☐ (d) Iron
☐ (e) High density polythene

32 In the extraction of aluminium what is produced at the anode (positive electrode) by ionic discharge?

☐ (a) Carbon dioxide
☐ (b) Sodium
☐ (c) Aluminium
☐ (d) Oxygen
☐ (e) Hydrogen

33 What is produced at the cathode (negative electrode) during the electrolysis of aluminium oxide?

....

34 Why do the anodes (positive electrodes) have to be replaced at regular intervals during the extraction of aluminium?

☐ (a) They get coated in a layer of aluminium oxide that prevents them from conducting

☐ (b) They are corroded by the
cryolite in the melt
☐ (c) They melt because of the very
high temperatures in the process
☐ (d) They react with the oxygen
produced at the anode and form
carbon dioxide
☐ (e) None of these

35 What needs to be added to
purified bauxite before aluminium
can be extracted from it?

☐ (a) Rock salt
☐ (b) Cryolite
☐ (c) Iron oxide
☐ (d) Water
☐ (e) Scrap aluminium

QUESTIONS

Higher Level only

36 Metals and ionic compounds
are both crystalline materials.
Why can metals change shape
without breaking, whereas ionic
compounds are very brittle?

☐ (a) The bonds in metals are
stronger than in ionic compounds

☐ (b) Metals have covalent bonding
☐ (c) The bonds in metals are
weaker than in ionic compounds
☐ (d) Ionic compounds contain ions
☐ (e) The bonds of ionic compounds
are directed in shape, and therefore
more rigid

37 When metals are extracted
from their ore they are said to
have undergone "reduction".
What does reduction mean?

☐ (a) Loss of hydrogen
☐ (b) Change in size
☐ (c) Loss of electrons
☐ (d) Gain of electrons
☐ (e) Gain of oxygen

38 Which one of the following
statements explains why graphite
is able to conduct electricity?

☐ (a) It is a metal
☐ (b) It is an ionic compound
☐ (c) It contains delocalized electrons
☐ (d) It is a covalent compound
☐ (e) It contains only carbon ions

39 Why can metal be shaped
without breaking?

☐ (a) The atoms are held together
very strongly
☐ (b) The free electrons hold the
metal ions together
☐ (c) The bonds between the ions
are very weak
☐ (d) The bonds between the metal
molecules are very strong
☐ (e) The bonds between the atoms
are very weak

40 Which of the following is the
reason why copper is a good
conductor of electricity?

☐ (a) Electrons in copper are
free to move
☐ (b) Copper contains ions
☐ (c) Electrons in copper are
fixed in position
☐ (d) Protons in copper are
fixed in position
☐ (e) Atoms in copper are
fixed in position

The periodic table *(Single and Double Awards)*

Some students see chemistry as a huge list of unrelated facts.
An understanding of the arrangement of the elements in the periodic
table helps students to see the clear patterns present and helps them
to appreciate that there is a way to arrange chemical knowledge in a
sensible order. These ideas are tested in the questions that follow.

Helium airship

KEY FACTS

• **Arrangement of elements in the
periodic table:** The elements in
the periodic table are arranged in
order of increasing atomic number
(see table on page 84). The table
is arranged into horizontal rows
known as periods, and vertical
columns known as groups. The
metals are found on the left-hand
side of the table and the non-metals
on the right-hand side. There are
only 22 non-metal elements.

• **Groups of elements in the
periodic table:** The groups of the
periodic table contain elements
with similar physical and chemical
properties. The elements in group 0,
for example, are all very unreactive

gases. For this reason these
elements are referred to as the
noble gases. The uses of the noble
gases include the filling of airships
(in the case of helium) and for
coloured lighting. The noble gases
will produce coloured light if a
current of electricity is passed
through them. For example, neon
produces red light, argon gives blue
light, and xenon produces an intense
white light. The elements within a
group also have the same number
of electrons in their outer shell.
The group number corresponds to
the number of electrons in the outer
shell. For example, the elements
in group I have one electron in the
outer shell, group VII have seven
and group 0 (or group VIII) have
a full outer shell.

QUESTIONS

Foundation and Higher Levels

1 What is a group in the
periodic table?

☐ (a) It is a type of element
☐ (b) It is a vertical column
☐ (c) It is a horizontal row
☐ (d) It contains only
three elements
☐ (e) None of the above

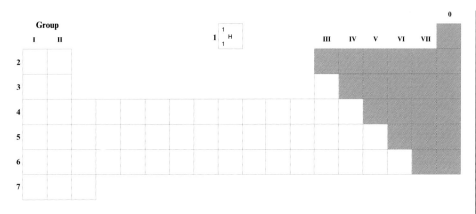

Q2, 3, 4

Q10, 11

9 Potassium is in group I of the periodic table. How many electrons would it have in its outer shell?

....

10 What is the name given to the elements in group 0 of the periodic table? (See table on the left.)

☐ (a) Alkaline earth metals
☐ (b) Alkali metals
☐ (c) Noble gases
☐ (d) Halogens
☐ (e) Transition metals

11 Which of the following is a use for the noble gases? (See table on the left.)

☐ (a) As solvents
☐ (b) In the extraction of metals
☐ (c) As fuels
☐ (d) In producing an inert atmosphere
☐ (e) As indicators

12 From which group in the periodic table does iron come?

☐ (a) Halogens
☐ (b) Alkali metal
☐ (c) Transition metals
☐ (d) Noble gases
☐ (e) Alkaline earth metals

13 What is the symbol for iron?

....

14 What is the symbol for the element lead?

....

15 What is the symbol for the element silver?

....

16 What is the symbol for the element potassium?

....

17 Which of the following is a non-metal?

☐ (a) Aluminium
☐ (b) Sulphur
☐ (c) Mercury
☐ (d) Sodium
☐ (e) Calcium

2 The periodic table is arranged into a series of horizontal rows and vertical columns as shown in the table above. What are the vertical columns known as?

☐ (a) Periods
☐ (b) Chemical columns
☐ (c) Groups
☐ (d) Series
☐ (e) Metals

3 What are the horizontal rows in the periodic table known as? (See table above.)

☐ (a) Triads
☐ (b) Families
☐ (c) Octets
☐ (d) Periods
☐ (e) Groups

4 In the periodic table above, what does the shaded area represent?

☐ (a) Metals
☐ (b) Liquids
☐ (c) Solids
☐ (d) Non-metals
☐ (e) Reactive elements

5 What type of elements are those in group II of the periodic table?

☐ (a) Non-metals
☐ (b) Transition metals
☐ (c) Semi-metals (metalloids)
☐ (d) Metals
☐ (e) Liquids

6 Sodium is in group I of the periodic table. How many electrons does it have in its outer shell?

☐ (a) 6
☐ (b) 4
☐ (c) 1
☐ (d) 8
☐ (e) 10

7 Boron is in group III of the periodic table. How many electrons does it have in its outer shell?

....

8 Why are sodium, lithium, and potassium placed into the same group of the periodic table?

☐ (a) They are all metals
☐ (b) They all react with water
☐ (c) They all have the same number of electrons in the outer shell
☐ (d) They are all solids
☐ (e) None of the above

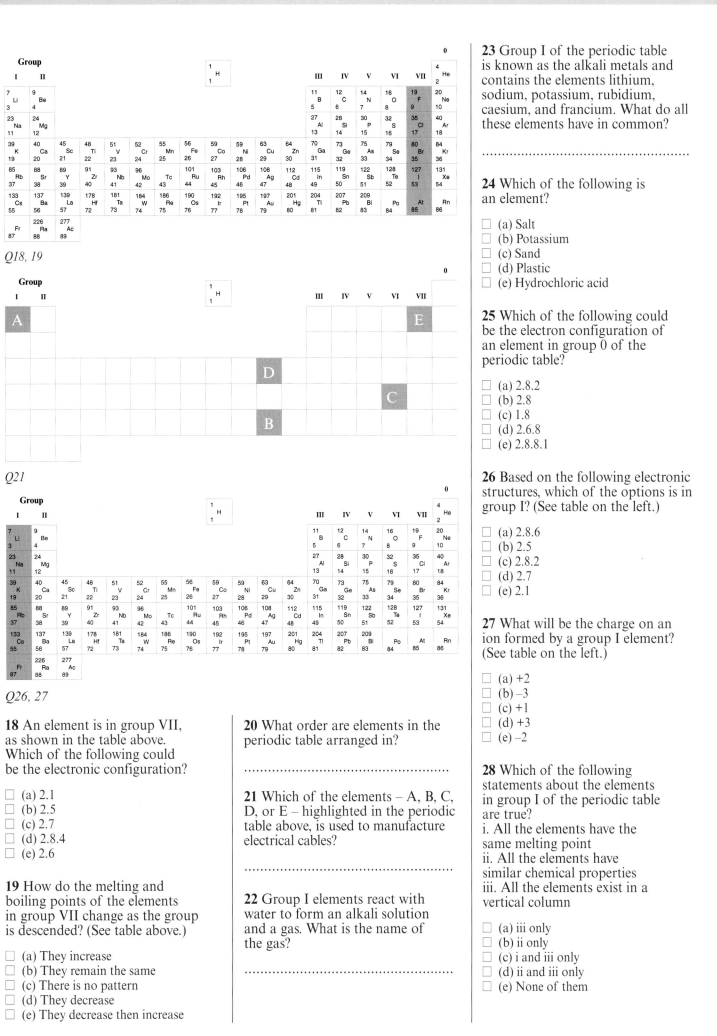

Q18, 19

Q21

Q26, 27

18 An element is in group VII, as shown in the table above. Which of the following could be the electronic configuration?

☐ (a) 2.1
☐ (b) 2.5
☐ (c) 2.7
☐ (d) 2.8.4
☐ (e) 2.6

19 How do the melting and boiling points of the elements in group VII change as the group is descended? (See table above.)

☐ (a) They increase
☐ (b) They remain the same
☐ (c) There is no pattern
☐ (d) They decrease
☐ (e) They decrease then increase

20 What order are elements in the periodic table arranged in?

....

21 Which of the elements – A, B, C, D, or E – highlighted in the periodic table above, is used to manufacture electrical cables?

....

22 Group I elements react with water to form an alkali solution and a gas. What is the name of the gas?

....

23 Group I of the periodic table is known as the alkali metals and contains the elements lithium, sodium, potassium, rubidium, caesium, and francium. What do all these elements have in common?

....

24 Which of the following is an element?

☐ (a) Salt
☐ (b) Potassium
☐ (c) Sand
☐ (d) Plastic
☐ (e) Hydrochloric acid

25 Which of the following could be the electron configuration of an element in group 0 of the periodic table?

☐ (a) 2.8.2
☐ (b) 2.8
☐ (c) 1.8
☐ (d) 2.6.8
☐ (e) 2.8.8.1

26 Based on the following electronic structures, which of the options is in group I? (See table on the left.)

☐ (a) 2.8.6
☐ (b) 2.5
☐ (c) 2.8.2
☐ (d) 2.7
☐ (e) 2.1

27 What will be the charge on an ion formed by a group I element? (See table on the left.)

☐ (a) +2
☐ (b) –3
☐ (c) +1
☐ (d) +3
☐ (e) –2

28 Which of the following statements about the elements in group I of the periodic table are true?
i. All the elements have the same melting point
ii. All the elements have similar chemical properties
iii. All the elements exist in a vertical column

☐ (a) iii only
☐ (b) ii only
☐ (c) i and iii only
☐ (d) ii and iii only
☐ (e) None of them

29 Which of the following is not an element?

- ☐ (a) Air
- ☐ (b) Oxygen
- ☐ (c) Nitrogen
- ☐ (d) Argon
- ☐ (e) Neon

30 What is produced when a group I metal reacts with water?

- ☐ (a) A salt and water
- ☐ (b) The metal hydroxide and hydrogen
- ☐ (c) Metal oxide and oxygen
- ☐ (d) The metal hydride and oxygen
- ☐ (e) An acidic solution

31 What will be the charge on an ion formed by an element in group III?

- ☐ (a) +3
- ☐ (b) +5
- ☐ (c) +1
- ☐ (d) –3
- ☐ (e) –5

32 The elements of group II form ionic compounds with non-metals. What is the charge of the group II ions in these compounds?

- ☐ (a) –2
- ☐ (b) –1
- ☐ (c) +3
- ☐ (d) +2
- ☐ (e) +1

33 An element X has an electron structure of 2.8.5. Which group of the periodic table is it in?

....

34 Group I elements will react with water to produce a gas. Which of the following is the name of the gas?

- ☐ (a) Chlorine
- ☐ (b) Oxygen
- ☐ (c) Hydrogen
- ☐ (d) Nitrogen
- ☐ (e) Carbon dioxide

35 Fluorine is in group VII of the periodic table. How many electrons would it have in its outer shell?

....

36 How many groups are there in the periodic table?

- ☐ (a) 18
- ☐ (b) 7
- ☐ (c) 3
- ☐ (d) 8
- ☐ (e) 6

37 Of the highlighted elements shown in the table on page 91, which one will be the most reactive?

- ☐ (a) A
- ☐ (b) B
- ☐ (c) C
- ☐ (d) D
- ☐ (e) E

38 Which one of the following statements about the elements in group 0 is true? (See table on page 91.)

- ☐ (a) They are all unreactive
- ☐ (b) They are all lighter than air
- ☐ (c) They are all metals
- ☐ (d) They are a mixture of solids and gases
- ☐ (e) They are all radioactive

39 Which one of the following highlighted elements has five electrons in its outer shell? (See table on page 91.)

- ☐ (a) P
- ☐ (c) Q
- ☐ (c) R
- ☐ (d) S
- ☐ (e) T

40 Based on the following electronic structures, which of the options is in group VI?

- ☐ (a) 2.8.5
- ☐ (b) 2.2
- ☐ (c) 2.6
- ☐ (d) 2.8.8
- ☐ (e) 2.8.7

41 Hydrogen is placed on its own in the periodic table, but it could be placed in group I. What property of hydrogen allows it to be placed in group I? (See table on page 91.)

- ☐ (a) It is less dense than water
- ☐ (b) It is a gas
- ☐ (c) It forms a positive ion with a charge of +1
- ☐ (d) It will react with non-metals
- ☐ (e) It consists of molecules made up from two atoms

42 How many electrons does a calcium atom have in its outer shell? (See table on page 91.)

....

43 Which of the following electronic structures is that of an element in group IV (See table on page 91.)

- ☐ (a) 2.8.4
- ☐ (b) 2
- ☐ (c) 2.8
- ☐ (d) 2.6
- ☐ (e) 2.8.3

44 Which one of the following is a property of all hydrogen halides?

- ☐ (a) They are all soluble in water
- ☐ (b) They produce alkaline solutions in water
- ☐ (c) They are insoluble in water
- ☐ (d) They are all solids at room temperature
- ☐ (e) They are non-toxic

45 An element is in group 0 of the periodic table. How many electrons could it have in its outer shell?

....

46 What is the nature of elements that are found in group II of the periodic table?

- ☐ (a) They are all non-metals
- ☐ (b) They are all metals
- ☐ (c) They are all semi-metals (metalloids)
- ☐ (d) They are a mixture of metals and non-metals
- ☐ (e) They are a mixture of metals and semi-metals (metalloids)

47 Which of the following is a metal?

- ☐ (a) Helium
- ☐ (b) Sodium
- ☐ (c) Silicon
- ☐ (d) Boron
- ☐ (e) Iodine

48 Which of the following is a property of all group I metals?

- ☐ (a) They do not react with water
- ☐ (b) They do not conduct electricity
- ☐ (c) They react with noble gases
- ☐ (d) They react with alkalis to produce a salt and water
- ☐ (e) They form hydroxides that dissolve in water to form alkaline solutions

49 Which of the following is a use for the element argon?

- ☐ (a) In weather balloons
- ☐ (b) In light bulbs
- ☐ (c) In the manufacture of margarine
- ☐ (d) To sterilize swimming pool water
- ☐ (e) As a solvent

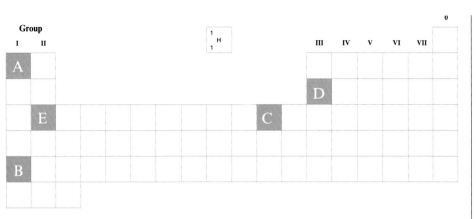

Q37

Q38, 52

Q39

Q41, 42, 43

50 The elements in group VII in the periodic table are known as halogens. How does the reactivity of the elements change as the group is descended?

....

51 Which of the following statements about transition metals are true?
i. They are not very dense metals
ii. They are poor conductors of electricity
iii. They can form coloured compounds

☐ (a) i only
☐ (b) ii and iii
☐ (c) iii only
☐ (d) i and ii
☐ (e) i and iii

⬤ QUESTIONS

Higher Level only

52 Why are the elements in group 0 very unreactive? (See table on the left.)

☐ (a) They all have a full outer shell of electrons
☐ (b) They all have an even number of electrons in their outer shell
☐ (c) They all have a stable nucleus
☐ (d) They all have no electrons
☐ (e) They are all gases

53 Why is sodium more reactive than magnesium?

☐ (a) A magnesium atom has less protons in the nucleus than sodium
☐ (b) It is easier for a sodium atom to lose an electron than it is for a magnesium atom to lose two electrons.
☐ (c) Magnesium has three electrons in its outer shell
☐ (d) Sodium has to gain only one electron to obtain the inert gas electronic structure (configuration)
☐ (e) Magnesium has to gain two electrons to obtain the inert gas electronic structure (configuration)

54 The elements in group I increase in reactivity as the group is descended. Why is this?

....
....

55 Elements in group VII become less reactive as the group is descended. What is the main reason for this?

- ☐ (a) The elements become more dense as the group is descended
- ☐ (b) The electrons become harder to remove as the group is descended
- ☐ (c) The melting point of the elements increases as the group is descended
- ☐ (d) The addition of an electron becomes more difficult as the group is descended
- ☐ (e) The elements become more metallic as the group is descended

Reactivity series *(Single and Double Awards)*

The idea that there is an order in the reactivity of metals is very helpful in explaining the reactions of various metals. Also the reactivity of a metal has a very important influence on the use of that metal. An understanding and knowledge of the reactivity series of metals is examined in the following set of questions.

 QUESTIONS

Foundation and Higher Levels

1 Metals can be put in order of reactivity. What is this order called? (See table below.)

- ☐ (a) The periodic table
- ☐ (b) The reactivity series
- ☐ (c) The reactivity group
- ☐ (d) The reactivity table
- ☐ (e) The displacement series

Metal	Symbol	
Potassium	K	
Sodium	Na	
Calcium	Ca	
Magnesium	Mg	
Aluminium	Al	
Zinc	Zn	Reactivity
Iron	Fe	decreases
Tin	Sn	from top
Lead	Pb	to bottom
(Hydrogen)	(H)	
Copper	Cu	
Silver	Ag	
Gold	Au	
Platinum	Pt	

Q1, 2, 3

2 Magnesium will react with dilute hydrochloric acid to produce hydrogen and magnesium chloride. The metal zinc is not far below magnesium in the reactivity series. How would you expect zinc to react with hydrochloric acid? (See table above.)

- ☐ (a) The same as magnesium
- ☐ (b) More vigorously than magnesium
- ☐ (c) Less vigorously than magnesium
- ☐ (d) Zinc will not react with hydrochloric acid
- ☐ (e) Zinc will produce chlorine, not hydrogen, when it reacted

3 Using the reactivity series, which of the following reactions is not possible? (See table on the left.)

- ☐ (a) Aluminium + iron oxide → aluminium oxide + iron
- ☐ (b) Copper + iron oxide → copper oxide + iron
- ☐ (c) Magnesium + iron oxide → magnesium oxide + iron
- ☐ (d) Zinc + iron oxide → zinc oxide + iron
- ☐ (e) Calcium + iron oxide → calcium oxide + iron

4 A pupil is asked to set up the following experiments. Which one will cause a displacement reaction to take place?

- ☐ (a) Zinc in copper sulphate solution
- ☐ (b) Iron in sodium chloride solution
- ☐ (c) Copper in aluminium sulphate solution
- ☐ (d) Lead in zinc sulphate solution
- ☐ (e) Magnesium in calcium chloride solution

5 Which one of the following oxides can be reduced to a metal by reaction with hydrogen?

- ☐ (a) Na_2O
- ☐ (b) CaO
- ☐ (c) Cu_2O
- ☐ (d) Fe_2O_3
- ☐ (e) K_2O

6 In the reactivity series of metals, which of the following is the correct order of decreasing activity?

- ☐ (a) Iron, potassium, magnesium, gold, copper
- ☐ (b) Potassium, magnesium, iron, copper, gold
- ☐ (c) Magnesium, gold, copper, potassium, iron
- ☐ (d) Magnesium, copper, potassium, iron, gold
- ☐ (e) Magnesium, iron, gold, copper potassium

7 Three metals, X, Y, and Z are reacted with water, as shown in the diagram that follows. X reacted steadily with the water. Y reacted very vigorously, and Z only reacted when heated. What is the order of reactivity of these metals (most reactive first)?

- ☐ (a) X, Y, Z
- ☐ (b) Z, X, Y
- ☐ (c) Y, Z, X
- ☐ (d) Z, Y, X
- ☐ (e) Y, X, Z

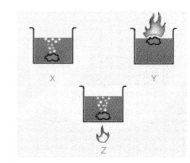

Q7

8 Four metals A, B, C, and D were mixed with an oxide of metal Z and heated. The results were recorded in the table below. Which of the following statements is true?

- ☐ (a) Z is more reactive than B
- ☐ (b) C is less reactive than Z
- ☐ (c) A and C are both more reactive than Z
- ☐ (d) C and D are both more reactive than Z
- ☐ (e) A and D are less reactive than Z

Test Results	
Test 1	A + Z oxide = no reaction
Test 2	B + Z oxide = B oxide + Z
Test 3	C + Z oxide = C oxide + Z
Test 4	D + Z oxide = no reaction

Q8

9 What happens when copper is placed into a solution of zinc sulphate?

- ☐ (a) The copper is displaced
- ☐ (b) There is no reaction
- ☐ (c) The zinc is displaced
- ☐ (d) The solution turns blue
- ☐ (e) The solution gets warm

10 The order of reactivity of three unknown metals is Z, X, and Y (the first being the most reactive). Which of the following statements are true?
i. X metal will displace Z from a solution containing Z
ii. Y metal will not displace X or Z from solutions containing X or Z
iii. Z metal will displace Y from a solution containing Y

- ☐ (a) i only
- ☐ (b) ii only
- ☐ (c) ii and iii only
- ☐ (d) iii only
- ☐ (e) All of them

11 Five metals were added to separate test tubes containing a solution of hydrochloric acid, as shown in the picture that follows. The starting temperature of all the solutions was 20°C. Which of the metals shown is the most reactive?

- ☐ (a) Copper
- ☐ (b) Iron
- ☐ (c) Zinc
- ☐ (d) Aluminium
- ☐ (e) Magnesium

Mg	Zn	Al	Fe	Cu
95°C	65°C	35°C	25°C	20°C

FINISHING TEMPERATURES

Q11

12 Potassium is above sodium in the reactivity series. How would you expect the reactivity of the metals with water to compare?

- ☐ (a) They both react with the same vigour
- ☐ (b) Sodium reacts more vigorously than potassium
- ☐ (c) Potassium reacts more vigorously than sodium
- ☐ (d) They do not react with water
- ☐ (e) They both dissolve quickly with no evolution of gas

13 A student carries out a series of displacement reactions with three metals (X, Y, and Z) and the solution of their salts. The results are shown in the table that follows. What is the order of reactivity of these metals (with the most reactive first)?

- ☐ (a) Z, Y, Z
- ☐ (b) Y, X, Z
- ☐ (c) Z, X, Y
- ☐ (d) X, Z, Y
- ☐ (e) Z, Y, X

Displacement Reaction Test		
Metal	Salt solution	Result
X	Y	no reaction
Y	Z	Z displaced
Y	X	X displaced
Z	X	no reaction

Q13

14 Pieces of zinc, lead, magnesium, and silver were added to separate test tubes of blue copper(II) nitrate solution and left for three days. Using the following order of decreasing reactivity – magnesium, zinc, lead, copper, silver – how many test tubes remained unchanged?

- ☐ (a) All of them
- ☐ (b) 3
- ☐ (c) 2

- ☐ (d) 1
- ☐ (e) 0

15 Why is aluminium used in a displacement reaction (known as the thermite reaction) with iron oxide?

- ☐ (a) Because aluminium is cheap
- ☐ (b) Because aluminium is less reactive than iron
- ☐ (c) Because iron is a very reactive metal
- ☐ (d) Because aluminium is more reactive than iron
- ☐ (e) Because aluminium is not a very dense metal

16 Which is the correct order of reactivity of the reaction of a group I metal with water (most reactive first)? (See table below.)

- ☐ (a) Potassium, sodium, lithium
- ☐ (b) Lithium, sodium, potassium
- ☐ (c) Sodium, potassium, lithium
- ☐ (d) Potassium, lithium, sodium
- ☐ (e) Sodium, lithium, potassium

Methods used for the extraction of metals	
Metal	Method
Potassium, Sodium, Calcium, Magnesium	The anhydrous chloride is melted and electrolyzed.
Aluminium	The anhydrous is melted and electrolyzed.
Zinc, Iron, Copper, Lead	Found as sulphides and oxides. The sulphides are roasted to give oxides; the oxides are reduced with carbon.
Silver, Gold	Found as "native" (as the free metal).

A16, 17

17 Gold is a metal with many of the usual properties of metals. However, it is very rare and is used to make jewellery. What is the main reason for gold being used for this purpose? (See table above.)

- ☐ (a) It is very shiny
- ☐ (b) It is very low in the reactivity series
- ☐ (c) It is a good conductor of heat
- ☐ (d) It is malleable
- ☐ (e) It is very expensive

18 What is seen when zinc metal is placed into a solution of silver nitrate?

- ☐ (a) The zinc becomes coated with silver
- ☐ (b) The zinc is displaced
- ☐ (c) The solution turns blue
- ☐ (d) The zinc is unaffected
- ☐ (e) The solution turns green

ANSWERS

Metals and non-metals

Foundation and Higher Levels

☐ **1** *(a)*
Zinc is the only metal.

☐ **2** *(b)*
Although silicon has some properties of metals it is actually classified as a non-metal. Elements that are situated close to the dividing line between metals and non-metals are also known as metalloids or semi-metals.

☐ **3** *(d)*
Non-metals are insulators, with the exception of carbon in the form of graphite. Generally, they tend to have low melting and boiling points, although some elements are solid, and most will form compounds with both metals and non-metals. However, they are all brittle and so they cannot be hammered.

☐ **4** *(d)*
Non-metals are all non-conductors of electricity with the exception of graphite, an allotrope of carbon. The reactivity of the non-metals varies from element to element and some, such as the inert gases, are very unreactive. Non-metal oxides tend to be acidic or neutral, not basic.

☐ **5** *(c)*
Metals are all good conductors of heat and electricity and they are all shiny. At room temperature all metals, with the exception of mercury, are solids. Mercury is a liquid that is used in thermometers.

☐ **6** *(c)*
When the electric current flows through the wire in a light bulb element, it causes the wire to get so hot that it glows. Therefore, the tungsten must have a high melting point, otherwise it would melt and be unable to glow.

☐ **7** *(d)*
An element is a substance that cannot be broken down to simpler substances by chemical means. Elements are either metals or non-metals. Iron is an element.

☐ **8** *(a)*
Iron filings are silvery grey particles. Many people think that iron is the same colour as rust, but pure iron is of a colour similar to silver – rust is iron oxide that forms on the surface of iron as this is where the oxygen in the air can react with the iron.

☐ **9** *(e)*
All elements have different melting and boiling points, therefore statement i is false. Iron and sulphur do react together to form a compound, therefore statement ii is true. A mixture of iron and sulphur can easily be separated with a magnet, because as iron is magnetic and as no chemical bonds have formed in the mixture, the iron will be attracted to the magnet.

☐ **10** *(d)*
All metal elements will conduct electricity because they have electrons that are free to move. Metals are therefore used in electrical cables.

☐ **11** *(e)*
Although all metals will conduct electricity, the non-metal carbon in the form of graphite will also conduct electricity. All metals with the exception of mercury are solids so this is not conclusive either. The density of both metals and non-metals varies and non-metals such as iodine are shiny. Hence, no one test is conclusive.

☐ **12** *(c)*
As a general rule, metals tend to be shiny and non-metals tend to be dull, although there are exceptions to this such as iodine, a shiny non-metal. But of the suggestions given, only zinc is a shiny metal and the others are either dull or colourless non-metals.

☐ **13** *(c)*
Only solid metals and the non-metal carbon (in graphite form) will conduct electricity. Therefore, sulphur (a non-metal) will not light the bulb.

☐ **14** *(c)*
The metals of group I are the only metals that have all of the properties mentioned. The group I metals include lithium, sodium, and potassium.

☐ **15** *(c)*
Metal ores are found in the earth's crust. The ore is found as a compound in the rock. If the rock contains enough of the metal compound to make it profitable to extract the metal, the rock is called an ore. Some metals, such as copper, are found native (uncombined in the crust).

☐ **16** *(c)*
Carbon and carbon monoxide will only reduce metal oxides of metals that are below carbon in the reactivity series.

☐ **17** *(a)*
The information used to decide the method of extraction is the metal's position in the reactivity series: the more reactive a metal is, the more stable are its compounds. This makes some metals hard to extract.

☐ **18** *(b)*
Aluminium is the most abundant metal in the earth's crust. It is quite a reactive metal, so it is not found native and it has to be extracted from its ores. As carbon is less reactive than aluminium, it has to be extracted by electrolysis of the molten ore, aluminium oxide. (See diagram below.)

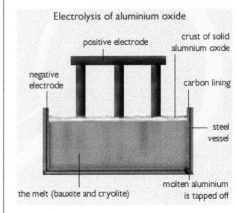

A18, 19

☐ **19** *(c)*
The ore that aluminium is extracted from is known as bauxite. Bauxite contains a large amount of aluminium oxide (Al_2O_3). (See diagram above.)

☐ **20** *(a)*
Lead is less reactive than carbon and therefore its oxides can be reduced to the metal by heat with carbon.

☐ **21** *(a)*
Iron is below carbon in the reactivity series and can therefore be extracted by reduction of its oxide by heat with carbon. This is done on an industrial scale in the blast furnace.

☐ **22**
Haematite is a red, grey, or black ore that can be found either as massive beds or as deposits in igneous rock. It is the main source of iron, with the iron being extracted from it in a blast furnace.

☐ **23** *(d)*
Metals can easily be drawn out into long wires and cables, which means that they are ductile.

☐ **24** *(c)*
Although all the elements suggested will conduct electricity, silicon, being a non-metal, is not very ductile and so cannot be stretched into wires.

☐ **25** *(b)*
The solid raw materials that are added to the blast furnace are iron ore, limestone, and coke. The iron ore is reduced to iron by carbon monoxide, which is produced by the reaction of the coke (carbon) with oxygen. The limestone is added to remove the impurities in the iron ore, which react to form slag.

☐ **26** *(c)*
Coke is put into the blast furnace to produce carbon monoxide, which is the reducing agent. Carbon monoxide is produced by the reaction of the carbon dioxide, produced when the coke first reacts with the air. (See diagram below.)

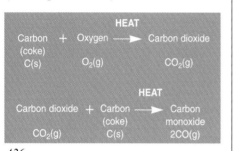

A26

☐ **27** *(c)*
Iron is extracted from its ores iron(III) oxide by heating them in the presence of carbon. As carbon is more reactive than iron, it removes the oxygen from the oxide to form carbon dioxide and molten iron.

☐ **28**
The slag produced in the extraction of iron is mainly used as a road stone.

☐ **29** *(a)*
The main impurity in the iron ore is silicon dioxide (sand). The limestone undergoes thermal decomposition in the blast furnace to form calcium oxide and carbon dioxide. The calcium oxide (a basic metal oxide) will react with the silicon dioxide (an acidic non-metal oxide) to form calcium silicate (slag). This floats on top of the molten iron and so is easily removed.

☐ **30**
Bauxite is and ore of aluminium and its main source. Aluminium is a metal that is very important for it has a low density and is therefore ideal for the construction of such things as aeroplanes.

☐ **31** *(a)*
The electrodes in the extraction of aluminium are made from carbon because it will conduct electricity and it has a very high melting point. Also it will not react with the aluminium.

☐ **32** *(d)*
During the extraction of aluminium from aluminium oxide, oxygen is produced at the anode.

☐ **33**
Aluminium is produced at the cathode during the electrolysis of aluminium oxide.

☐ **34** *(d)*
The carbon anodes have to be replaced at regular intervals in the extraction of aluminium because at a high temperature they will react with the oxygen produced and form carbon dioxide. In other words, they will burn away.

☐ **35** *(b)*
Cryolite is added to the purified aluminium before the aluminium can be extracted to lower the melting point from 2050ºC to 700ºC so that the aluminium oxide can be electrolyzed.

Metals and non-metals

Higher Level only

☐ **36** *(e)*
Metals and ionic compounds are both crystalline substances; differences in their properties arise because of their respective bonding and structure. In a metal, the electrons are free to move between metal ions, allowing one plane of the crystal to move relative to an adjacent plane. In an ionic compound, the ions are fixed in place by rigid bonds. If one plane of the ionic compound crystal moves relative to an adjacent plane, it brings two similarly charged ions opposite each other, and this causes the crystal to break points.

☐ **37** *(d)*
Reduction is the gain of electrons, the gain of hydrogen or the loss of oxygen. For example, in the extraction of aluminium, the Al^{3+} ions gain electrons to become aluminium atoms.

☐ **38** *(c)*
Graphite is a non-metal element that contains only carbon atoms. When a potential difference is applied, it will conduct electricity because it contains delocalized electrons that are free to move. (See diagram that follows.)

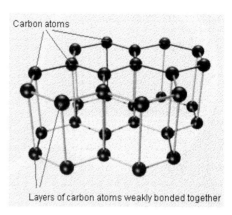

A38

☐ **39** *(b)*
The bonding in metals consists of positive metal ions in a sea of electrons that are free to move between the ions. These electrons act as a kind of cement, holding the ions together. When a metal is bent, the shape changes but the electrons continue to hold the metal ions together.

☐ **40** *(a)*
Copper consists of positive metal ions in a sea of delocalized electrons. These electrons are free to move about between the metal ions. When a potential difference is applied to the metal, these electrons allow electricity to be conducted through it.

The periodic table

Foundation and Higher Levels

☐ **1** *(b)*
A group in the periodic table is a vertical column containing elements with similar properties.

☐ **2** *(c)*
The vertical columns in the periodic table are known as groups.

☐ **3** *(d)*
The horizontal rows in the periodic table are known as periods.

☐ **4** *(d)*
The elements in this area of the periodic table are non-metals.

☐ **5** *(d)*
The elements in group II are all metals. They are known as the alkaline earth metals because most of the elements are found as minerals in the earth's crust. The metals form basic oxides, hence the name alkaline earth metals. (See table on the right.)

☐ **6** *(c)*
The group number tells you how many electrons there are in the outer shell, or sub-shell, of any element within that group. Sodium is in group I and will therefore have one electron in its outer shell.

☐ **7**
Boron is in group III and will therefore have three electrons in its outer shell.

☐ **8** *(c)*
The number of electrons in the outer shell, or sub-shell, determines the group number of that element. Sodium, lithium, and potassium all have one electron in their outer shell and are therefore placed together in group I. The elements hydrogen and helium are exceptions to this rule.

☐ **9**
Potassium is in group I and will therefore have one electron in its outer shell.

☐ **10** *(c)*
The elements in group 0 are known as the noble gases. All these elements are very unreactive gases.

☐ **11** *(d)*
As the noble gases are all unreactive, they can be used to produce an atmosphere that is unreactive. For example, to prevent an element reacting with oxygen when heated to a high temperature in air, the element could be heated in an atmosphere of a noble gas.

☐ **12** *(c)*
Iron is a transition element because it has a variable valency: Fe(II) and Fe(III).

☐ **13**
Fe is the symbol for iron, which comes from ferrum – the Latin name for iron.

☐ **14**
The symbol for the element lead is Pb.

☐ **15**
The symbol for the element silver is Ag.

☐ **16**
The symbol for the element potassium is K.

☐ **17** *(b)*
Sulphur is a non-metal.

☐ **18** *(c)*
Suggestion (c) has seven electrons in its outer shell and is therefore in group VII.

☐ **19** *(a)*
As group VII is descended, the melting and boiling point of the elements increase. Hence, the elements change from gases (fluorine and chlorine) to liquid (bromine) to solid (iodine).

☐ **20**
The elements in the periodic table are arranged in order of increasing atomic number (increasing number of protons).

☐ **21**
Elements to the left of the red dividing line are metals (see table below). All metals conduct electricity and element D (copper) in the table is used to manufacture electrical cables.

☐ **22**
All the elements in group I will react with water to produce hydrogen gas and the metal hydroxide:
$2Na + 2H_2O \rightarrow 2NaOH + H_2$
(sodium + water $\rightarrow$ sodium hydroxide + hydrogen)

☐ **23**
The elements within a group of the periodic table all have similar (but not identical) chemical and physical properties. Therefore, they will have different melting points. They differ in both atomic mass and atomic number. The group I elements all have one electron in their outer shell.

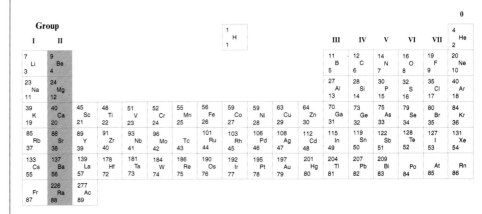

A5

A21

□ **24** *(b)*
An element is a substance that cannot be broken down into simpler substances, whilst a compound is a substance made up of two or more elements chemically bonded together. Potassium is an element (all elements known to man are shown in the periodic table) whereas salt, sand, plastic, and hydrochloric acid are all compounds.

□ **25** *(b)*
All the elements in group 0 of the periodic table have a full outer shell of electrons. This means that they all, with the exception of helium which has only two electrons, have eight electrons in their outer shell. Hence, their outer shell is full and the electron configuration of the noble gases will end with an 8. For example, 2.8, 2.8.8. The electron configuration of helium is 2. This is a full shell because the first shell can only contain two electrons.

□ **26** *(e)*
The group number tells you how many electrons there are in the outer shell for each of the elements in that group. The final number in the electronic structure shows the number of electrons in the outer shell for that particular element. In the options, the element with the electronic structure 2.1 clearly has one electron in its outer shell and therefore would be in group I of the periodic table.

□ **27** *(c)*
The elements in group I have one electron in their outer shell. In order to obtain a noble gas electronic structure (configuration) they need to lose this one electron. As electrons have a negative charge the ion formed will have a charge of +1.

□ **28** *(d)*
Group I in the periodic table is a vertical column of elements with similar (but not identical) chemical and physical properties. They will therefore not have the same melting point.

□ **29** *(a)*
Nitrogen, oxygen, argon, and neon are some of the gases found in air (they are also elements). Therefore, air itself is a mixture of gases, not an element.

□ **30** *(b)*
When a group I metal reacts with water it produces the metal hydroxide and hydrogen.

□ **31** *(a)*
The group number tells us how many electrons are in the outer shell (or sub-

shell) of an atom. For metallic elements it also tells us how many electrons it has to lose to gain a noble gas structure, and hence the charge on the ion.

□ **32** *(d)*
All the elements in group II have two electrons in their outer shell. When they react with non-metals, they lose these two negative electrons and so have a charge of +2.

□ **33**
The number of electrons in the outer shell (or sub-shell) of an element is equal to its group number (with the exception of hydrogen and helium). The element X has five electrons in its outer shell and is therefore in group V.

□ **34** *(c)*
All the elements in group I will react with water to produce hydrogen gas. For example: $2K + 2H_2O \rightarrow 2KOH + H_2$ (potassium + water → potassium hydroxide + hydrogen)

□ **35**
The group number tells you how many electrons there are in the outer shell of any element within that group. Fluorine is in group VII and will therefore have seven electrons in its outer shell.

□ **36** *(d)*
A group in the periodic table is a vertical column containing elements with similar properties. Although the table contains 18 columns only 8 of them are known as groups.

□ **37** *(b)*
Group I metals are the most reactive metals and their reactivity increases as the group is descended. Therefore, element B (near the bottom of group I) will be the most reactive.

□ **38** *(a)*
The elements in group 0 are all very unreactive gases. They can form compounds. For example, xenon reacts with fluorine producing xenon fluorides, but this occurs rarely.

□ **39** *(a)*
P is in group V and will therefore have five electrons in its outer shell.

□ **40** *(c)*
The group number tells you how many electrons there are in the outer shell for each of the elements in that group. The final number in the electronic structure shows the number of electrons in the outer shell for that particular element. In the options, the

element with the electronic structure 2.6 has six electrons in its outer shell and would therefore be in group VI of the periodic table.

□ **41** *(c)*
Hydrogen is a difficult element to classify because it has some properties of both a group I and a group VII element. The reason it can be placed into group I of the periodic table is that it forms positive ions with a charge of +1, as do all the elements in this group.

□ **42**
The group number indicates the number of electrons in the outer shell of any element. As calcium is in group II of the periodic table it means it has two electrons in its outer shell.

□ **43** *(a)*
The electronic structure 2.8.4 clearly has four electrons in its outer shell and therefore would be in group IV of the periodic table.

□ **44** *(a)*
The hydrogen halides such as hydrogen chloride are toxic gases which are all soluble in water and dissolve to produce acid solutions. For example, hydrogen chloride gas will dissolve in water to produce hydrochloric acid.

□ **45**
The elements in group 0 all have a full outer shell of electrons and this makes them very stable. Although helium has only two electrons (as the first shell only contains two electrons), neon will have a full shell of eight electrons.

□ **46** *(b)*
The elements in group II of the periodic table are all metals and they are known collectively as the alkaline earth metals.

□ **47** *(b)*
Sodium is a metal, silicon and boron are semi-metals and helium and iodine are non-metals.

□ **48** *(e)*
The group I metals are very reactive metals, which form soluble hydroxides i.e. alkalis.

□ **49** *(b)*
Argon is a noble gas and as such is very unreactive. When a light bulb is switched on the metal filament inside is heated to a very high temperature. If the light bulb contained any oxygen the filament would burn away very quickly. Argon is used in light bulbs so that the metal filament does not burn away and the bulb lasts longer.

☐ 50
The elements in group VII of the periodic table (see table below) get less reactive as the group is descended. Chlorine, for example, reacts explosively with hydrogen in the presence of sunlight, whereas iodine reacts very slowly with hydrogen.

☐ 51 (c)
Some of the properties of transition metals include:
1. They are dense metals
2. They are very good conductors
3. They can form ions with different charges
4. They have high melting points
5. They can form coloured compounds

The periodic table
Higher Level only

☐ 52 (a)
The elements in group 0 are unreactive because their outer shell of electrons is full. A full outer shell of electrons is a stable structure and therefore the gases do not need to lose, gain, or share electrons in a chemical bond to make themselves stable.

☐ 53 (b)
Sodium is found in group I and therefore only has one electron in its outer shell. An atom of sodium only needs to lose this one electron to obtain the inert gas electronic structure (configuration). Magnesium is in group II and so has to lose two electrons, which is more difficult. Hence, magnesium is less reactive than sodium.

☐ 54
As group I is descended, the atoms get larger and so more electron shells are added. This means that the outer electron is further away from the nucleus. As a result, the attraction between the negatively charged electron and the positively charged nucleus is less, and so the outer electron is more easily lost. The reactivity will therefore increase as the atoms get larger going down the group.

☐ 55 (d)
Group VII elements require only one more electron to have a full outer shell of electrons. Fluorine, at the top of the group, is a small atom and so the nucleus exerts a great attraction on the extra electron needed. This means it is easy for fluorine to gain an extra electron and this makes it very reactive. As the group is descended, the atoms get larger and the outer electron shell is further away from the nucleus and so there is less attraction to gain this extra electron. The elements therefore become less reactive.

Reactivity series
Foundation and Higher Levels

☐ 1 (b)
When the metals are put in order of reactivity it is called the reactivity series.

☐ 2 (c)
As zinc is below magnesium in the reactivity series it will be less reactive than magnesium. The reaction with hydrochloric acid will therefore be less vigorous. Hydrogen gas will still be produced as zinc is more reactive than hydrogen.

☐ 3 (b)
For a metal to displace another metal from its compounds, one metal needs to be more reactive than the other metal. As can be seen from the reactivity series table that follows, copper is less reactive than iron, and will therefore not displace it from iron oxide.

Metal	Symbol	
Potassium	K	
Sodium	Na	
Calcium	Ca	
Magnesium	Mg	
Aluminium	Al	
Zinc	Zn	Reactivity decreases from top to bottom
Iron	Fe	
Tin	Sn	
Lead	Pb	
(Hydrogen)	(H)	
Copper	Cu	
Silver	Ag	
Gold	Au	
Platinum	Pt	

A3, 4, 5

☐ 4 (a)
For a metal to displace another it needs to be above it in the reactivity series. As can be seen from the table above, the only reaction that would produce displacement is the one between zinc and copper sulphate, with the copper being displaced.

☐ 5 (c)
For hydrogen to displace a metal from a compound it needs to be above it in the reactivity series. As can be seen from the table above, hydrogen is less reactive than all of the metals mentioned, except for copper. It will therefore displace copper from its oxide, reducing it to the metal.

☐ 6 (b)
From the vigorousness of the reactions of metals it is possible to draw up a series. The series shown in the table that follows, is based on the metals' reaction with acids. The most reactive metals are in group I, as can be seen from the information in the table below.

Metal	Reaction
Potassium Sodium Lithium Calcium	The reaction is dangerously violent.
Magnesium Aluminium Zinc Iron Tin Lead	Most metals react with dilute hydrochloric acid to produce hydrogen and a solution of the metal chloride. The speed of the reaction decreases from calcium to lead. (The reactions of metals with dilute sulphuric acid give hydrogen and sulphates.)
Copper Silver Gold Platinum	These metals do not react with dilute hydrochloric acid and dilute sulphuric acid.

A6

☐ 7 (e)
The more reactive an element, the more vigorous its reactions. Y reacts vigorously with water and is therefore the most reactive. X reacts steadily with water and does not require heating, whereas Z needs to be heated before it will react. The order of reactivity is then Y, X, Z.

Group																		0
I	II												III	IV	V	VI	VII	4 He 2
								1 H 1										
7 Li 3	9 Be 4												11 B 5	12 C 6	14 N 7	16 O 8	19 F 9	20 Ne 10
23 Na 11	24 Mg 12												27 Al 13	28 Si 14	30 P 15	32 S 16	35 Cl 17	40 Ar 18
39 K 19	40 Ca 20	45 Sc 21	48 Ti 22	51 V 23	52 Cr 24	55 Mn 25	56 Fe 26	59 Co 27	59 Ni 28	63 Cu 29	64 Zn 30	70 Ga 31	73 Ge 32	75 As 33	79 Se 34	80 Br 35	84 Kr 36
85 Rb 37	88 Sr 38	89 Y 39	91 Zr 40	93 Nb 41	96 Mo 42	Tc 43	101 Ru 44	103 Rh 45	106 Pd 46	108 Ag 47	112 Cd 48	115 In 49	119 Sn 50	122 Sb 51	128 Te 52	127 I 53	131 Xe 54
133 Cs 55	137 Ba 56	139 La 57	178 Hf 72	181 Ta 73	184 W 74	186 Re 75	190 Os 76	192 Ir 77	195 Pt 78	197 Au 79	201 Hg 80	204 Tl 81	207 Pb 82	209 Bi 83	Po 84	At 85	Rn 86
Fr 87	226 Ra 88	277 Ac 89															

A50

☐ **8** *(e)*
A more reactive metal will displace a less reactive metal from its compounds. Both B and C displace Z from its oxide and are therefore more reactive than Z. A and D will not displace Z and are therefore less reactive than Z. Hence, statement (e) is correct.

☐ **9** *(b)*
As copper is less reactive than zinc it will not displace zinc from the solution of zinc sulphate and so there will be no reaction.

☐ **10** *(c)*
A metal in the reactivity series will displace metals below it. Z is the most reactive and will therefore displace both X and Y. Hence, statement iii is true. X is below Z and will only displace Y. Hence, statement i is false. Y is the least reactive and will not displace either of the others. Hence, statement ii is true.

☐ **11** *(e)*
The more reactive a metal, the more vigorously it will react. One way of measuring the reactivity is to measure the temperature increase during the reaction. Magnesium has the greatest temperature increase, and is therefore the most reactive.

☐ **12** *(c)*
As potassium is above sodium in the reactivity series it will be more reactive than sodium.

☐ **13** *(b)*
When a reactive metal is placed into a solution of a less reactive metal, the less reactive metal is displaced and the reactive metal goes into a solution. In the above experiment Y displaces both X and Z and is therefore the most reactive. X is not displaced by Z and is therefore more reactive than Z. Hence, the order of reactivity is Y, X, Z.

☐ **14** *(d)*
If a reactive metal is placed into a solution of a less reactive metal, that metal is displaced. Zinc, magnesium, and lead are more reactive than copper and will therefore displace it from its salt solution. As the copper is displaced, the solution loses its blue colour.
Hence, only silver will not displace the copper and so there will be one solution that is still blue and unchanged.

☐ **15** *(d)*
The thermite reaction is a convenient way of producing molten iron. Aluminium is used because it is higher in the reactivity series than iron, and therefore more reactive and will displace the iron from its oxide. The heat produced in the reaction is enough to melt the iron. (See equation below.)

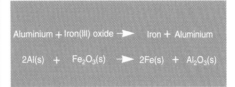

$$\text{Aluminium} + \text{Iron(III) oxide} \longrightarrow \text{Iron} + \text{Aluminium}$$
$$2Al(s) + Fe_2O_3(s) \longrightarrow 2Fe(s) + Al_2O_3(s)$$

A15

☐ **16** *(a)*
The order of reactivity of the group I metal increases as the group is descended. (See table below.) Therefore, the correct order of reactivity is: potassium, sodium, lithium.

☐ **17** *(b)*
As gold is a metal it will conduct heat and electricity. It is also shiny (when polished), malleable, and a rare, expensive metal. But the main reason for it being used to make jewellery is that it is very low in the reactivity series; it does not react with air, water, or dilute acids and will therefore stay shiny for a long time.

☐ **18** *(a)*
Since zinc is more reactive than silver it will displace the silver from its salt solution. As the silver is displaced it coats the zinc with a layer of silver.

Group																		0
I	II								1 H 1			III	IV	V	VI	VII		4 He 2
7 Li 3	9 Be 4											11 B 5	12 C 6	14 N 7	16 O 8	19 F 9		20 Ne 10
23 Na 11	24 Mg 12											27 Al 13	28 Si 14	30 P 15	32 S 16	35 Cl 17		40 Ar 18
39 K 19	40 Ca 20	45 Sc 21	48 Ti 22	51 V 23	52 Cr 24	55 Mn 25	56 Fe 26	59 Co 27	59 Ni 28	63 Cu 29	64 Zn 30	70 Ga 31	73 Ge 32	75 As 33	79 Se 34	80 Br 35		84 Kr 36
85 Rb 37	88 Sr 38	89 Y 39	91 Zr 40	93 Nb 41	96 Mo 42	Tc 43	101 Ru 44	103 Rh 45	106 Pd 46	108 Ag 47	112 Cd 48	115 In 49	119 Sn 50	122 Sb 51	128 Te 52	127 I 53		131 Xe 54
133 Cs 55	137 Ba 56	139 La 57	178 Hf 72	181 Ta 73	184 W 74	186 Re 75	190 Os 76	192 Ir 77	195 Pt 78	197 Au 79	201 Hg 80	204 Tl 81	207 Pb 82	209 Bi 83	Po 84	At 85		Rn 86
Fr 87	226 Ra 88	277 Ac 89																

A16

Rates, Equilibrium, and Energetics

Reaction rates *(Single and Double Awards)*

The rusting of iron is a fairly slow change and the burning of petrol is a fairly fast change. What affects the rate of a chemical reaction? The answer to this question is important in many reactions that occur in our daily lives. The following questions involve the key ideas linked to rates of reaction.

KEY FACTS

• **Rates of reactions:** The rate of a chemical reaction is the speed at which that reaction takes place. Some reactions take place very quickly. For example, the explosive reaction caused when Semtex explosive is detonated. Other reactions take place very slowly, such as the rusting of iron in the presence of water and oxygen. The rate can be measured by following the appearance of the products or the disappearance of the reactants over a certain time period. For example, the rate of the reaction between calcium carbonate and hydrochloric acid can be followed by collecting the carbon dioxide formed in the reaction and noting the time taken for this gas to be produced. The rate of reaction can be calculated by the following equation:
rate of reaction = amount of product ÷ time taken. The rate of a chemical reaction changes as the reaction proceeds. It is fastest at the start and slows down as the reactants are used up.

QUESTIONS

Foundation and Higher Levels

1 What is a catalyst?

☐ (a) A substance that speeds up a chemical reaction
☐ (b) A substance that changes the products of a reaction
☐ (c) A substance that changes the state of the products of a reaction
☐ (d) A substance that causes a reaction to become reversible
☐ (e) A substance that stops a reaction

2 Catalysts are widely used in industrial processes, such as the manufacture of margarine and sulphuric acid. What is the purpose of the use of catalysts in industry?

☐ (a) It increases the yield of the product
☐ (b) It removes impurities from the product
☐ (c) It reduces the time taken to produce the product
☐ (d) It increases the temperature of the reaction
☐ (e) The product can easily be changed into another one

3 Why is it that the speed of a chemical reaction can be increased by raising the temperature?

☐ (a) The particles get larger
☐ (b) The particles move faster
☐ (c) The volume of the particles increases
☐ (d) The surface area increases
☐ (e) The activation energy is lowered

4 In a chemical reaction, a catalyst can be used to increase the rate of reaction. The mass of catalyst is monitored throughout, and the results plotted on a graph as shown below. Which graph represents the results obtained?

....

Table of results

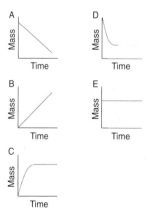

Q4

5 Why would 5 g of small marble chips react faster with 50 cm³ of hydrochloric acid than 5 g of large marble chips?

☐ (a) The small marble chips have a large collective surface area
☐ (b) The small marble chips have more energy
☐ (c) The large marble chips have more energy
☐ (d) The small marble chips contain less particles
☐ (e) There is no difference in the speed of reaction between the marble chips

6 Which of the following statements about chemical reactions are true?
i. The rate of a reaction cannot change
ii. During a chemical reaction, the total mass of reactants and products does not change
iii. Heat is always given out in a chemical reaction

☐ (a) All of them
☐ (b) None of them
☐ (c) i only
☐ (d) ii only
☐ (e) iii only

7 What must happen to the reacting particles before a chemical reaction can take place?

☐ (a) They must collide
☐ (b) They must dissolve
☐ (c) They must be heated
☐ (d) They must be stirred
☐ (e) They must be acidic

8 Why is food kept in the refrigerator?

☐ (a) To make the food cold before you eat it
☐ (b) To slow down the decay of the food
☐ (c) To make it taste better
☐ (d) To keep it away from the air
☐ (e) To kill any bacteria present

9 Five test tubes (A–E) each contained the same volume of hydrochloric acid (but of varying concentration). Into each tube was placed 5 g of calcium carbonate. The volume of carbon dioxide produced was measured every 15 seconds, and the results plotted to produce a graph. Which of the lines on the graph that follows was produced by the least concentrated solution?

....

Table of results

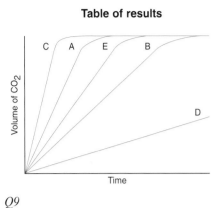

Q9

10 The speed of the reaction between calcium carbonate and hydrochloric acid was to be investigated. This reaction results in the formation of carbon dioxide gas. The apparatus was set up, as shown in the graph that follows, and the experiment performed three times with increasingly large pieces of calcium carbonate (but the same total mass). The calcium carbonate was added to the flask and the cotton wool replaced. The loss in total mass was recorded every 5 seconds. Which of the three experiments would decrease the total mass fastest?

☐ (a) The first experiment using the smallest pieces of calcium carbonate
☐ (b) The second experiment using larger pieces of calcium carbonate
☐ (c) The third experiment using the largest pieces of calcium carbonate
☐ (d) They would all lose weight at the same rate
☐ (e) None of them would lose weight.

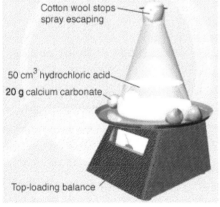

Cotton wool stops spray escaping

50 cm³ hydrochloric acid
20 g calcium carbonate

Top-loading balance

Q10

11 Hydrochloric acid reacts with marble chips to produce the gas carbon dioxide. Why does a more concentrated solution of hydrochloric acid react faster than a more dilute solution?

☐ (a) The higher concentration acid has more energy
☐ (b) The higher concentration acid has a higher surface area
☐ (c) The higher concentration acid has a lower activation energy
☐ (d) The higher concentration acid has faster moving particles
☐ (e) None of the above

12 When calcium carbonate is reacted with hydrochloric acid, the reaction produces carbon dioxide, water, and calcium chloride. The rate of the reaction can be found by measuring the volume of gas produced in a set time. In one such experiment, 50 cm³ of gas was produced in 20 seconds. What is the average rate of this reaction?

☐ (a) 25 cm³/s
☐ (b) 2 cm³/s
☐ (c) 5 cm³/s
☐ (d) 2.5 cm³/s
☐ (e) 50 cm³/s

13 Why does a 5 g lump of sugar dissolve more slowly than 5 g of sugar grains?

☐ (a) The grains of sugar have more energy
☐ (b) The grains of sugar have a larger surface area
☐ (c) The grains of sugar need more energy to dissolve
☐ (d) The sugar lump contains more sugar
☐ (e) The grains of sugar have more energy

14 A series of experiments using 20 cm³ portions of hydrochloric acid and 10 g of zinc was carried out. The volume and concentration of the acid did not change and the mass of zinc used was also kept constant at 10 g. The reaction is as follows:
$Zn + 2HCl \rightarrow ZnCl_2 + H_2$
Which of the following statements are true?
i. The mass of hydrogen will be the same in all conditions
ii. The mass of the zinc chloride ($ZnCl_2$) produced will be the same in all conditions
iii. The speed of the reaction will be the same in all conditions

☐ (a) All of them
☐ (b) None of them
☐ (c) ii and iii only
☐ (d) i and iii only
☐ (e) i and ii only

15 Modern petrol engine motor cars are fitted with catalytic converters to reduce the volume of harmful gases in the exhaust fumes. Why do these only work if the car has been driven for some time?

☐ (a) Not enough gases are produced when the engine is first turned on
☐ (b) The catalyst is not warm enough when the engine is first turned on
☐ (c) The catalyst needs a lot of air to pass through it before it can work
☐ (d) The catalyst only works when the car is moving at more than 50 mph
☐ (e) Very few harmful gases are produced by the engine when the car has just started

16 Three 5 g samples of the same sized marble chips are placed in three separate test tubes. To each of the test tubes is added a 25 cm³ portion of hydrochloric acid of the same concentration. Test tube A is placed in a water bath at 60°C, test tube B is placed in the refrigerator at 4°C, and test tube C is left on the bench in the laboratory (room temperature is 25°C). What is the order of reaction (fastest first)?

☐ (a) B, C, A
☐ (b) C, B, A
☐ (c) A, B, C
☐ (d) B, A, C
☐ (e) A, C, B

17 What would happen to the rate of fermentation if the temperature at which the reaction was taking place was lowered by a few degrees from the optimum?

☐ (a) The rate would speed up
☐ (b) The rate would remain the same
☐ (c) The rate would slow down
☐ (d) The rate would become uncontrollable
☐ (e) Fermentation would stop

18 A series of experiments using 20 cm³ portions of hydrochloric acid and 5 g of zinc was carried out. The volume and concentration of the acid did not change and the mass of zinc used was also kept constant at 5 g. The reaction is as follows: $Zn + 2HCl \rightarrow ZnCl_2 + H_2$
Which of the following can vary?

☐ (a) The mass of $ZnCl_2$ produced
☐ (b) The mass of H_2 produced
☐ (c) The time taken for the reaction to finish
☐ (d) The type of products produced
☐ (e) None of the above

19 The speed of the reaction between calcium carbonate and hydrochloric acid was investigated. The experiment was performed three times with increasingly larger pieces of calcium carbonate (but the same total mass). The calcium carbonate is added to the flask and the mass is recorded every 5 seconds. The results were plotted on a single graph as shown below. Which of the following is the correct shape for the graph?

....

Table of results

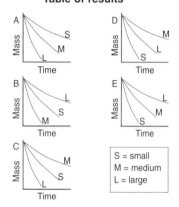

Q19

20 The following results were obtained during the decomposition of hydrogen peroxide using a catalyst:

Time (seconds)
0   5   10   15   20   25
Volume of oxygen produced (cm³)
0   4   8   11   12   13

During the first 20 seconds of the reaction, what is the average rate of oxygen evolution?

☐ (a) 1.6 cm³/s
☐ (b) 60 cm³/s
☐ (c) 6 cm³/s
☐ (d) 0.6 cm³/s
☐ (e) 16 cm³/s

21 Which of the following statements about catalysts are false?
i. They speed up the rate of a reaction
ii. They are chemically unchanged at the end of the reaction
iii. They increase the amount of products produced at the end of the reaction

☐ (a) i and iii only
☐ (b) ii and iii only
☐ (c) iii only
☐ (d) i and ii only
☐ (e) i only

22 Three identical reactions are carried out in three separate test tubes (X, Y, and Z) at different temperatures (100°C, 40°C, and 20°C respectively). The reaction produces a gas. The progress of the reaction is followed by measuring the volume of gas produced every 5 seconds until the reaction has stopped. The results were plotted to produce a graph as shown below. Which graph shows the correct results obtained?

....

Table of results

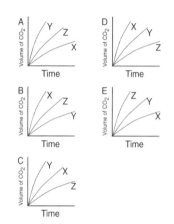

Q22

23 What would happen to the rate of fermentation of a mixture of sugar solution and yeast if the sugar concentration was lowered?

☐ (a) The rate of reaction would get slower
☐ (b) The yeast would die
☐ (c) The rate of reaction would get faster
☐ (d) The reaction would produce methanol
☐ (e) None of the above

24 How does a catalyst speed up the rate of a reaction?

☐ (a) It increases the temperature of the reaction
☐ (b) It lowers the activation energy of the reaction
☐ (c) It increases the surface area of the solid reagents
☐ (d) It increases the concentration of the liquid reactants
☐ (e) It increases the energy of the reactants

25 In the following energy level diagram, what does the question mark refer to?

☐ (a) Ignition energy

☐ (b) Start up energy
☐ (c) Exothermic energy
☐ (d) Catalyst energy
☐ (e) Activation energy

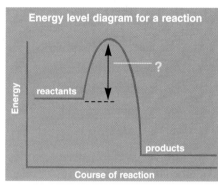

Q25

26 What happens to the fermentation of sugar if the ethanol content in the reaction mixture goes over 15.5%?

☐ (a) The reaction stops because it has no sugar with which to react
☐ (b) It starts to produce methanol instead of ethanol
☐ (c) The rate of reaction gets faster
☐ (d) The reaction stops as the yeast is killed by the ethanol
☐ (e) Spirits are formed

27 In which of the following is fermentation used?
i. Making bread
ii. Making wine
iii. Making beer

☐ (a) i and ii only
☐ (b) i only
☐ (c) ii and iii only
☐ (d) iii only
☐ (e) All of the above

28 Why does the fermenter have to be kept next to a source of heat?

☐ (a) The reaction is endothermic
☐ (b) The heat keeps the reaction near the optimum temperature
☐ (c) The reaction is exothermic
☐ (d) The yeast will die if the temperature drops below 600°C
☐ (e) None of the above

29 To produce spirits why do you need to use both fermentation and distillation?

☐ (a) Both processes make the spirits taste better
☐ (b) Fermentation only produces a 15.5% alcohol solution, distillation produces a higher concentration
☐ (c) Distillation gives a good colour to the spirit

☐ (d) Distillation makes the spirit fizzy
☐ (e) Both processes are needed to remove the yeast

30 The manufacture of spirits such as whisky has an alcohol concentration of approximately 35%. Why does fermentation alone, not produce such a concentration?

☐ (a) The yeast is killed by concentrations of alcohol above 15.5%
☐ (b) The reactants run out before this concentration is reached
☐ (c) The carbon dioxide given off in the reaction kills the yeast before the concentration gets this high
☐ (d) The yeast starts to use the alcohol up
☐ (e) It would take the yeast too long to produce this high concentration of alcohol

31 Ammonia is a base, but it can be converted into nitric acid. How is this conversion carried out?

☐ (a) By catalytic oxidation

☐ (b) By reaction with sulphuric acid
☐ (c) By reaction with hydrogen
☐ (d) By reaction with hydrogen peroxide
☐ (e) By catalytic cracking

32 Enzymes are used in washing powders to improve their performance. What is an enzyme?

☐ (a) A biological catalyst
☐ (b) A bleaching agent
☐ (c) A type of detergent
☐ (d) A type of salt
☐ (e) Something that glows to give clothes a hint of blue

33 What type of substance present in yeast allows fermentation to take place?

☐ (a) An ion
☐ (b) A metal
☐ (c) A base
☐ (d) An enzyme
☐ (e) An acid

34 Which of the following statements about fermentation are true?

i. It is an endothermic reaction
ii. The reaction must not be allowed to reach a temperature over 60°C
iii. The reaction needs oxygen

☐ (a) i and iii only
☐ (b) ii and iii only
☐ (c) iii only
☐ (d) ii only
☐ (e) i only

Reversible reactions and equilibrium *(Double Award only)*

A reversible reaction is one which can go forwards or backwards depending upon the conditions. Many chemical reactions are reversible. In these reactions the reactants and products reach a state of equilibrium. At equilibrium the rate of the forward reaction is equal to the rate of the backward reaction. Both the forward and the backward reactions are taking place at the same rate, and this is known as dynamic equilibrium.

 ## KEY FACTS

• **Reversible reactions:** A reversible reaction is one which can go forwards or backwards depending upon the conditions. All physical reactions are reversible, for example, the melting of ice. There are also a lot of chemical reactions that are reversible. In these reactions the reactants and products reach a state of equilibrium. At equilibrium the rate of the forward reaction is equal to the rate of the backward reaction. The reaction has not stopped, but both reactions take place at the same time. This is known as a dynamic equilibrium.

• **Effect of conditions on reversible reactions:** The position of equilibrium is determined by the conditions of the reaction. We can alter the conditions (temperature, concentration, and pressure) to increase the yield of the products by following Le Chatelier's principle. This states that if a reaction in equilibrium is disturbed, the reaction will oppose any changes enforced upon it. For example, if the product is removed from the reaction mixture, the position of equilibrium will shift so that more of the product is produced, thus increasing the yield.

• **Reversible reactions in industry:** Some important industrial processes, such as the production of ammonia in the Haber Process and the manufacture of sulphuric acid in the Contact Process, are based on reversible reactions. Le Chatelier's principle can be applied to these processes to improve the yield of the products. Often the actual conditions used are not the conditions which would produce the highest yield. The higher yield conditions often require prohibitively expensive

high pressures or be such that the rate of reaction would be too slow to be economic. Therefore, industry uses compromise conditions that strike a balance between the yield and the rate of reaction. For example, the conditions used in the Haber Process only produce a 10% yield, but the rate is sufficient to make this economically viable.

 ## QUESTIONS

Higher Level only

1 What does the following symbol tell us about a reaction?

....

Q1

2 What is meant by a dynamic equilibrium?

- ☐ (a) The reaction has stopped
- ☐ (b) The reaction has reached completion
- ☐ (c) Both the forward and reverse reactions occur simultaneously
- ☐ (d) Only the forward reaction occurs
- ☐ (e) Only the reverse reaction occurs

3 What is the name for a type of reaction that does not go all the way to completion, but reaches an equilibrium?

- ☐ (a) Displacement
- ☐ (b) Neutralization
- ☐ (c) Reversible
- ☐ (d) Oxidation
- ☐ (e) Precipitation

4 Which of the following describes a reversible reaction?

- ☐ (a) One which always returns to the initial concentrations of the reactants
- ☐ (b) One in which the rate of forward reaction becomes equal to the rate of reverse reaction
- ☐ (c) One which always goes all the way to completion
- ☐ (d) One in which only the reverse reaction takes place
- ☐ (e) One in which exactly half the reactants react

5 Which of the following statements about a reaction that has reached equilibrium are true?
i. The rate of the forward reaction is equal to the rate of the reverse reaction
ii. The concentration of the reactants and products is equal
iii. The concentration of the reactants and products is constantly changing

- ☐ (a) i and iii only
- ☐ (b) i only
- ☐ (c) All the statements
- ☐ (d) i and ii only
- ☐ (e) iii only

6 Which of the following is true about the concentration of reactants and products in a reaction that has reached equilibrium?

- ☐ (a) The concentration of the reactants is zero, and the concentration of the products is at a maximum
- ☐ (b) The concentration of the products is zero, and the concentration of the reactants is at a maximum
- ☐ (c) The concentrations of the reactants and the products are equal

- ☐ (d) The concentrations of the reactants and the products are constant, but not necessarily equal
- ☐ (e) The concentrations of the reactants and the products are continually changing

7 The production of ammonia in the Haber Process is exothermic. How is the position of equilibrium changed if there is a decrease in temperature?

- ☐ (a) The equilibrium moves up
- ☐ (b) The equilibrium moves to the left
- ☐ (c) The equilibrium moves to the right
- ☐ (d) The equilibrium moves down
- ☐ (e) The equilibrium is not affected by the decrease in temperature

8 In the following reaction, how is the position of equilibrium affected by an increase in pressure? (See equation below.)

- ☐ (a) It moves to the left
- ☐ (b) It is destroyed
- ☐ (c) It stays the same
- ☐ (d) It goes all the way to completion
- ☐ (e) It moves to the right

Ammonia synthesis equation

$$N_2(g) \quad + \quad 3H_2(g) \quad \rightleftharpoons \quad 2NH_3(g)$$

Nitrogen   hydrogen   ammonia

Q8

9 If ammonia is removed from the reaction vessel as soon as it is produced, what would happen to the position of equilibrium?

- ☐ (a) The equilibrium is unaffected
- ☐ (b) The equilibrium moves to the left
- ☐ (c) The equilibrium no longer exists
- ☐ (d) The equilibrium moves to the right
- ☐ (e) None of the above

10 Which of the following factors will increase the yield of ammonia during the Haber Process? (The formation of ammonia is an exothermic process.)
i. An increase in pressure
ii. The addition of a catalyst
iii. An increase in temperature

- ☐ (a) i only
- ☐ (b) i and ii only
- ☐ (c) All of them
- ☐ (d) iii only
- ☐ (e) ii only

11 During the manufacture of sulphuric acid, sulphur dioxide is reacted with oxygen to produce sulphur trioxide as shown in the equation below. How is the yield of sulphur trioxide affected if a catalyst is used in the reaction?

$$2SO_2(g) + O_2(g) \rightleftharpoons 2SO_3(g)$$

- ☐ (a) The yield is increased
- ☐ (b) The yield is decreased, but is produced more quickly
- ☐ (c) The yield and rate remains the same
- ☐ (d) The yield is increased and it is produced more quickly
- ☐ (e) The yield is unchanged

12 Ethanoic acid ionizes slightly when water is added to it and an equilibrium is set up. In the following equation what happens to the position of equilibrium if a small amount of sodium hydroxide is added?

$$CH_3COOH(aq) \rightleftharpoons CH_3COO^-(aq) + H^+(aq)$$

- ☐ (a) The equilibrium moves to the right
- ☐ (b) The equilibrium moves up
- ☐ (c) The equilibrium moves to the left
- ☐ (d) The equilibrium moves down
- ☐ (e) The equilibrium does not move

Exothermic and endothermic reactions

(Single and Double Awards)

Many chemical reactions are carried out to produce energy. Fuels are chemicals that are used as a source of energy. Everyday, millions of tonnes of petrol, natural gas, and coal are burnt. Do all chemical reactions produce energy? The following questions include the key ideas linked to energy changes in chemical reactions.

 KEY FACTS

• **Exothermic and endothermic reactions:** A chemical reaction which results in an increase in the temperature of the surroundings is known as an exothermic reaction. In an exothermic reaction there is an increase in the temperature of the surroundings because the reactants have more energy than the products. Therefore, energy is released when the products are formed. Examples of exothermic reactions include the combustion of methane, the neutralization of acids, and respiration. A chemical reaction that results in a decrease in the temperature of the surroundings is known as an endothermic reaction. In an endothermic reaction, the products have more energy than the reactants. Therefore, energy is taken from the surroundings in order for the reaction to take place and the temperature decreases. Although in an exothermic reaction energy is released into the surroundings, the reactions do not always happen spontaneously. For example, the reaction of oxygen and methane is very exothermic, but it will not take place without the input of a small amount of energy (in the form of a flame or spark).

 QUESTIONS

Foundation and Higher Levels

1 What is an exothermic reaction?

- ☐ (a) One which requires heat
- ☐ (b) One which gives out heat
- ☐ (c) One which takes in energy
- ☐ (d) One which gives out electricity
- ☐ (e) One in which the products have more energy than the reactants

2 Which of the following reactions is exothermic?

- ☐ (a) The decomposition of copper carbonate by heat
- ☐ (b) The burning of magnesium
- ☐ (c) The dissolving potassium nitrate in water
- ☐ (d) The decomposition of limestone to lime
- ☐ (e) The decomposition of water to hydrogen and oxygen

3 Using the information displayed in the table below, which option shows the exothermic reactions?

- ☐ (a) ii only
- ☐ (b) i, ii, and iv only
- ☐ (c) i and iv only
- ☐ (d) iii and v only
- ☐ (e) ii, iii, and v only

	Starting temp °C	Final temp °C
i	25	73
ii	11	11
iii	32	10
iv	187	762
v	−10	−15

Q3

4 Using the information displayed in the table below, which option shows the exothermic reactions?

- ☐ (a) i and iii only
- ☐ (b) ii, iii, and iv only
- ☐ (c) ii and iii only
- ☐ (d) i and v only
- ☐ (e) i, iv, and v only

	Starting temp °C	Final temp °C
i	4562	721
ii	−100	0
iii	0	1
iv	−32	−213
v	100	0

Q4

5 Which of the following reactions is not exothermic?

- ☐ (a) The burning of petrol
- ☐ (b) The burning of coal
- ☐ (c) Respiration
- ☐ (d) The reaction of sodium and water
- ☐ (e) Dissolving ammonium nitrate in water when the temperature drops by 4°C

6 Using the information displayed in the table below, which option shows all the endothermic reactions?

- ☐ (a) ii and v only
- ☐ (b) i, iii, iv, and v only
- ☐ (c) ii only
- ☐ (d) i, iii, and v only
- ☐ (e) i, iii, and iv only

	Starting temp °C	Final temp °C
i	64	63
ii	10	71
iii	232	110
iv	18	18
v	12	−15

Q6

7 What is an endothermic reaction?

- ☐ (a) One which requires heat to start it
- ☐ (b) One which gives out heat
- ☐ (c) One which takes in energy
- ☐ (d) One which gives out electricity
- ☐ (e) One in which the products have less energy than the reactants

8 Dissolving ammonium nitrate in water is an example of an endothermic reaction. Which one of the following statements, concerning endothermic reactions, is true?

- ☐ (a) The reaction vessel will feel cold to the touch
- ☐ (b) The reaction will give out heat
- ☐ (c) The products will have less energy than the reactants
- ☐ (d) The reactants will have more energy than the products
- ☐ (e) There will be a change in state

9 Which of the reactions shown in the table below are endothermic?

- ☐ (a) i, ii, and iii only
- ☐ (b) i and iii only
- ☐ (c) ii and iv only
- ☐ (d) iv only
- ☐ (e) i, iii, and v only

	Starting temp °C	Final temp °C
i	34	98
ii	10	−15
iii	25	127
iv	567	142
v	1367	1399

Q9

10 Which of the reactions below is endothermic?

- ☐ (a) Fermentation
- ☐ (b) The decomposition of limestone to lime
- ☐ (c) Reaction between sodium and oxygen
- ☐ (d) Burning of wood
- ☐ (e) Reaction between oxygen and hydrogen

11 A test tube that contained two chemicals was placed into a beaker of water at room temperature. A reaction in the test tube caused the water around it to freeze. Which of the following statements about the reaction are true?
i. The reaction took energy from its surroundings
ii. The reactants had more energy than the products
iii. It was an endothermic reaction

- ☐ (a) i and iii only
- ☐ (b) ii and iii only
- ☐ (c) i and ii only
- ☐ (d) i only
- ☐ (e) ii only

12 A test tube that contained two chemicals was placed into a beaker of water at room temperature (25°C). The reaction in the test tube was slightly endothermic. Which of the following could be the final temperature of the water surrounding the test tube?

- ☐ (a) 27°C
- ☐ (b) 5°C
- ☐ (c) 22°C
- ☐ (d) −27°C
- ☐ (e) 107°C

13 Which of the following reactions or processes is endothermic?

- ☐ (a) The burning of natural gas
- ☐ (b) The boiling of water
- ☐ (c) The reaction between potassium and water
- ☐ (d) The reaction between hydrochloric acid and sodium hydroxide
- ☐ (e) The combustion of petrol

14 Two solutions are mixed together in one beaker. Which of the following can occur?
i. A temperature increase
ii. The precipitation of a solid
iii. The release of a gas

- ☐ (a) All of them
- ☐ (b) i and ii only
- ☐ (c) i only
- ☐ (d) ii and iii only
- ☐ (e) i and iii only

QUESTIONS

Higher Level only

15 Which of the following statements about exothermic reactions are false?
i. Heat is given out during the reaction
ii. Activation energy is often needed to start the reaction
iii. The products possess more energy than the reactants

- ☐ (a) i and ii only
- ☐ (b) ii and iii only
- ☐ (c) iii only
- ☐ (d) i only
- ☐ (e) ii only

16 How do the bonds formed in an endothermic reaction compare with the strength of bonds that are broken?

- ☐ (a) The bonds formed are weaker than those broken
- ☐ (b) The bonds are the same strength before and after
- ☐ (c) The bonds broken are weaker than those formed
- ☐ (d) The bonds formed are stronger than those broken
- ☐ (e) The bonds both formed and broken are the same strength

17 Which of the following energy level diagrams represents an exothermic reaction?

....

Q17

18 From the heats of reaction given below, state which would produce the most unstable compound (all values in kJ/mol).

- ☐ (a) 915 given out
- ☐ (b) 538 taken in
- ☐ (c) 7463 given out
- ☐ (d) 1587 taken in
- ☐ (e) 435 taken in

19 Choosing from the heats of reaction, which reaction would produce the weakest bonds? (All values in kJ/mol.)

- ☐ (a) 2778 given out
- ☐ (b) 345 taken in
- ☐ (c) 9875 taken in
- ☐ (d) 49 given out
- ☐ (e) 947532 given out

20 The following are two statements about endothermic reactions. Read them carefully and decide which are true.
i. A product of an endothermic reaction has more energy than its starting materials.
ii. During an endothermic reaction energy is taken in by the reactants.

	Statement i	Statement ii
☐ (a)	True	True
☐ (b)	False	False
☐ (c)	True	False
☐ (d)	False	True
☐ (e)	Not enough information given to answer	

21 What sort of a process is the breaking of chemical bonds in a reaction?

- ☐ (a) Endothermic
- ☐ (b) Displacement
- ☐ (c) Exothermic
- ☐ (d) Neutralization
- ☐ (e) Precipitation

22 What are the correct units for bond energies?

- [ ] (a) kJ mol
- [ ] (b) mol kJ^{-1}
- [ ] (c) kJ mol^{-1}
- [ ] (d) Jmol k^{-1}
- [ ] (e) kmol J^{-1}

23 What does the breaking of chemical bonds in a reaction require?

- [ ] (a) An input of energy
- [ ] (b) A removal of energy
- [ ] (c) A repulsive force
- [ ] (d) An attractive force
- [ ] (e) None of the above

24 If 11g of propane (C_3H_8) burns in air to produce 555 kJ of energy, how much energy would be released by one mole of propane?
RAMs: C = 12, H = 1

- [ ] (a) 555.0 kJ
- [ ] (b) 1110.0 kJ
- [ ] (c) 111.0 kJ
- [ ] (d) 2220.0 kJ
- [ ] (e) 277.5 kJ

25 What type of process is bond formation?

- [ ] (a) Endothermic
- [ ] (b) Displacement
- [ ] (c) Exothermic
- [ ] (d) Neutralization
- [ ] (e) None of these

26 What does the term bond energy represent?

- [ ] (a) The energy contained in a chemical bond
- [ ] (b) The energy given out when the bond is broken
- [ ] (c) The energy needed to break a bond
- [ ] (d) The energy taken in when a bond is formed
- [ ] (e) The total energy given out or taken in during a reaction

27 Bond energies are used in chemistry to calculate the energy given out in a reaction. How are bond energies first worked out?

- [ ] (a) By guesswork
- [ ] (b) By experiment
- [ ] (c) By calculation
- [ ] (d) By stretching a substance until it breaks
- [ ] (e) None of the above

28 Use the bond energy values shown in the table that follows to calculate the energy change for the following reaction:

$$\begin{matrix} H-H \\ H-H \end{matrix} + O=O \longrightarrow \begin{matrix} H-O-H \\ H-O-H \end{matrix}$$

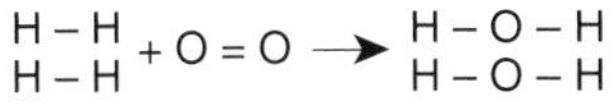

- [ ] (a) 347 kJ given out
- [ ] (b) 764 kJ given out
- [ ] (c) 926 kJ given out
- [ ] (d) 847 kJ taken in
- [ ] (e) 484 kJ given out

Bond	Bond energy (kJ/mol)
H – H	436
O = O	496
C – C	348
C = C	612
C – H	412
C – O	360
C = O	743
H – O	463
Br – Br	193
C – Br	276

Q28, 29, 30, 31, 32

29 Use the bond energies in the table above to calculate the energy change for the following reaction:

$$\begin{matrix} H & O & H \\ | & \| & | \\ H-C-C-C-H \\ | & | & H \\ H & H \end{matrix} + I \longrightarrow \begin{matrix} H \\ | \\ H & O & H \\ | & | & | \\ H-C-C-C-H \\ | & | & | \\ H & H & H \end{matrix}$$

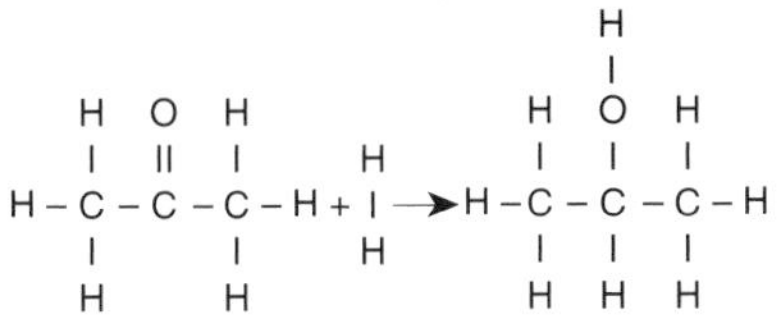

- [ ] (a) 64 kJ taken in
- [ ] (b) 304 kJ taken in
- [ ] (c) 56 kJ given out
- [ ] (d) 304 kJ taken in
- [ ] (e) 436 kJ given out

30 Use the bond energy information in the table above to calculate the energy change for the following reaction:

$$\begin{matrix} H & H \\ | & | \\ C=C \\ | & | \\ H & H \end{matrix} + \begin{matrix} O=O \\ +O=O \\ O=O \end{matrix} \longrightarrow \begin{matrix} O=C=O & H-O-H \\ + \\ O=C=O & H-O-H \end{matrix}$$

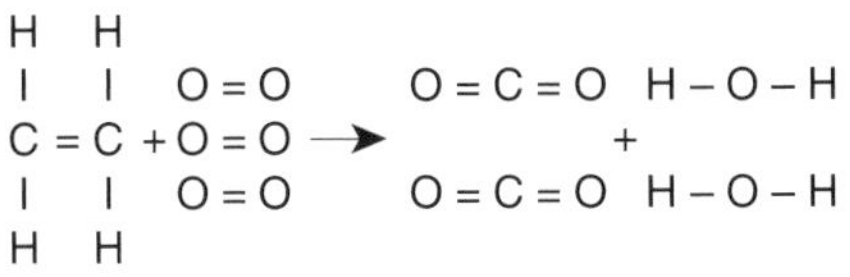

- [ ] (a) 1208 kJ given out
- [ ] (b) 1342 kJ given out
- [ ] (c) 986 kJ given out
- [ ] (d) 1076 kJ given out
- [ ] (e) 1020 kJ taken in

31 Use the bond energy information shown in the table to calculate the energy change for the following reaction: $CH_4 + 2O_2 \rightarrow CO_2 + 2H_2O$

- [ ] (a) 2640 kJ given out
- [ ] (b) 3338 kJ taken in
- [ ] (c) 2640 kJ taken in
- [ ] (d) 3338 kJ given out
- [ ] (e) 698 kJ given out

32 Use the bond energy information given in the previous table to calculate the energy change for the following reaction:
$CH_2 = CHCH_3 + Br_2 \rightarrow CH_2BrCHBrCH_3$

- [ ] (a) 107 kJ given out
- [ ] (b) 288 kJ given out
- [ ] (c) 243 kJ given out
- [ ] (d) 95 kJ given out
- [ ] (e) 89 kJ taken out

33 Why are all bond energies positive?

- [ ] (a) The energy is needed to start the reaction
- [ ] (b) The energy is needed to break the chemical bond
- [ ] (c) The energy is given out when the bond is broken
- [ ] (d) Total energy change of a reaction involving bond breaking is negative
- [ ] (e) The activation energy is negative

34 The bond energy for an oxygen–oxygen bond (O=O) is 496 kJ/mol, and the bond energy for a carbon–oxygen bond (C=O) is 743 kJ/mol. Which of the following statements are true?
i. The carbon–oxygen bond is stronger than the oxygen–oxygen bond
ii. The oxygen–oxygen gives out more energy when it is formed
iii. The carbon–oxygen bond needs less energy to break it

- [ ] (a) i and iii only
- [ ] (b) ii and iii only
- [ ] (c) iii only
- [ ] (d) ii only
- [ ] (e) i only

35 The burning of methane gas is an exothermic reaction, which produces carbon dioxide and water. Each mole of methane produces 890 kJ of energy. How much energy is released by 1200 cm^3 of methane? (One mole of gas = 24000 cm^3.)

- [ ] (a) 44.50 kJ
- [ ] (b) 89.00 kJ
- [ ] (c) 44.00 kJ
- [ ] (d) 22.25 kJ
- [ ] (e) 890.00 kJ

ANSWERS
Reaction rates

Foundation and Higher Levels

□ 1 (a)
A catalyst is a substance that speeds up a chemical reaction without being used up in the reaction. It works by lowering the activation energy and so more particles have sufficient energy to react.

□ 2 (c)
In industry, the use of catalysts reduces the time taken for the product to be produced, and subsequently reduces the running cost of the factory.

□ 3 (b)
A chemical reaction only takes place when the reacting particles collide with each other with sufficient energy to cause a reaction. By increasing the temperature, the energy of the particles is increased and they will move faster and therefore collide more often. These collisions are also more violent as the particles have more energy. Hence, raising the temperature increases both the number and the energy of the collisions and so the reaction will go faster.

□ 4
E is the correct graph. A catalyst speeds up the rate of a chemical reaction, but is chemically unchanged by the reaction. Hence, the mass of the catalyst remains constant throughout the reaction.

□ 5 (a)
A large surface area means that more of the particles of the solid are exposed. Hence, more collisions can take place and therefore the speed of reaction will be faster. The 5 g of small marble chips will have a larger collective surface area than the same mass of larger chips.

□ 6 (d)
In a chemical reaction the total mass of all the substances present does not change. This is the law of mass conservation. Heat is not always given out during a chemical reaction, some reactions will take in heat. The rate of a chemical reaction is dependent on a number of factors (concentration, surface area, temperature, and the use of a catalyst).

□ 7 (a)
Before any reaction can take place between two reactants, they must first come into contact with each other.

□ 8 (b)
Food is kept in the refrigerator to slow down the chemical reactions that cause the food to decay. Chemical reactions are slowed down by lowering the temperature.

□ 9
The correct line is D. In order for a reaction to take place the calcium carbonate and hydrochloric acid have to come into contact with each other. The solution which has the lowest concentration will contain the least acid particles and so there will be less collisions. Hence, a slow reaction, which would produce little carbon dioxide in a set time, and the resulting line would not be very steep.

□ 10 (a)
The smaller the pieces of calcium carbonate the larger the surface area for the same total mass. The larger the surface area, the more collisions with the acid, and so the faster the reaction. Hence, the smallest pieces would react fastest and therefore lose weight more quickly than the other two.

□ 11 (e)
The reason why a solution of higher concentration increases the speed of the reaction is because there are more particles present. Before a reaction can take place there has to be a collision, and a higher concentration will result in more collisions and so the reaction will proceed faster.

□ 12 (d)
The average rate of a reaction is the amount of product divided by the time taken. In this reaction the rate is $50 \div 20 = 2.5 \text{ cm}^3/\text{s}$.

□ 13 (b)
The difference is due to the fact that the surface area of the grains of sugar is much greater than that of the sugar lump. The sugar only dissolves when it comes into contact with the water and if the particle is large (sugar lump) it has a small surface area, so there is little contact with the water. The sugar grains are much smaller and so they have a large surface area in contact with the water and so they dissolve faster.

□ 14 (e)
The mass of the products of a chemical reaction are constant in all conditions as long as the mass of the reactants is constant. This is the law of mass conservation. However, the speed of the reaction can change. For example, if the temperature is increased, the reaction will be faster. So the correct statements are i and ii.

□ 15 (b)
Like most catalysts, the catalytic converter in an exhaust system works more effectively at high temperatures. When the car engine is first turned on, the exhaust fumes warm up the catalyst and only when it has reached its working temperature does it start to convert the harmful gas. Hence, the catalytic converter only works when the engine has been running for some time. (See diagram below.)

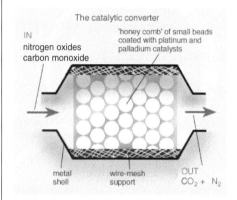

A15

□ 16 (e)
The rate at which a reaction takes place depends on a number of factors, one of which is temperature. The higher the temperature the faster the reaction. Therefore, the test tube at the highest temperature will finish first. Hence, the order is: A (at 60°C), C (at 25°C), and B (4°C).

□ 17 (c)
As the temperature is lowered, the rate of reaction would slow down because the activity of the yeast slows down, reducing the conversion of sugars to ethanol.

□ 18 (c)
The rate or speed of reaction will determine the time taken for a reaction to finish. The rate of reaction is dependent on a number of factors (such as temperature and particle size of the zinc) and can therefore vary. The speed of reaction does not affect the final mass of the products, as this is dependent on the starting mass of the reactants.

□ 19
The correct graph is E. The smaller the pieces of calcium carbonate, the larger the surface area. The larger the surface area, the more collisions with the acid and so the faster the reaction. The smallest pieces would react fastest and therefore lose weight quicker than the other two. Hence, the curve for the smallest particles will be the steepest, and the largest particles the least steep.

☐ **20** *(d)*
The rate of reaction can be calculated by using the following equation:
rate = volume of gas produced/time taken to produce gas. Therefore, the average rate of reaction over the first 20 seconds is 12 ÷ 20 = 0.6 cm³/s

☐ **21** *(c)*
A catalyst is a substance that speeds up a chemical reaction, but does not get used up and so remains unchanged at the end. A catalyst will not alter the amount of product that is formed and so statement iii is false.

☐ **22**
D is the correct answer. The higher the temperature, the faster a reaction takes place. This means that in a given time, the reaction that takes place at a higher temperature will produce more of the gas. Therefore, X will have produced the most gas in a given time and have the steepest gradient.

☐ **23** *(a)*
The rate of a chemical reaction is controlled by a number of factors, one of which is the concentration of the reactants. If the concentration of the sugar is lowered there will be less sugar, and therefore the rate of reaction will be lowered.

☐ **24** *(b)*
A catalyst speeds up the rate of a reaction by lowering the activation energy. This means that more particles have sufficient energy to react and so more of the collisions will be successful.

☐ **25** *(e)*
The initial input of energy required to start a reaction is known as the activation energy. This energy is used to overcome the hurdle at the start of the reaction.

☐ **26** *(d)*
The fermentation of sugar produces ethanol. The ethanol is poisonous to the yeast and if the content reaches 15.5% the reaction stops as the yeast is killed.

☐ **27** *(e)*
Fermentation is used in all of the processes. In the manufacture of wine and beer it is used to produce alcohol, and in the manufacture of bread it is used to produce carbon dioxide, which helps make the bread rise.

☐ **28** *(b)*
Yeast is a living organism and has an optimum temperature at which fermentation will take place. The heat source keeps the reaction near the optimum temperature. If the reaction gets too hot or too cold the yeast will not ferment the sugar as quickly, and the yeast may die.

☐ **29** *(b)*
Fermentation can only produce a solution containing about 15.5% alcohol, because this concentration kills off the yeast and stops fermentation. As spirits have an alcohol concentration of about 35%, they can only be produced by distilling the fermented mixture.

☐ **30** *(a)*
Fermentation can only produce a concentration of about 15.5% alcohol (ethanol) because the yeast is killed off if the concentration gets any higher. Distillation is used to produce a higher concentration.

☐ **31** *(a)*
Ammonia can be converted into nitric acid by oxidation in the presence of a platinum catalyst. The oxidation converts ammonia into nitrogen oxides, which then react with more oxygen and water to form nitric acid. (See diagram below.)

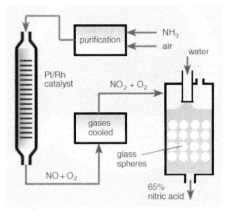

A31

☐ **32** *(a)*
An enzyme is a biological catalyst that improves the performance of washing powders by speeding up the breakdown of protein material, such as food stains and blood.

☐ **33** *(d)*
An enzyme (zymase) within the yeast acts as a catalyst for the breakdown of glucose into ethanol and carbon dioxide.

☐ **34** *(d)*
Fermentation is an exothermic reaction (it gives out heat). It is also an example of anaerobic respiration (it takes place without oxygen). The reaction must not be allowed to reach a temperature over 60°C as the yeast will die and the reaction will stop.

Reversible reactions and equilibrium
Higher Level only

☐ **1**
The symbol means that the reaction is reversible. This means that the forward and reverse reactions take place simultaneously.

☐ **2** *(c)*
When a system has reached dynamic equilibrium the composition of the mixture will appear constant. However, the system is not actually static as the forward and reverse reactions are occurring at the same rate. If liquid bromine is dropped into a gas jar, an equilibrium between the liquid and the gas is established. The system appears to be static, but in fact the molecules are condensing into liquid molecules at the same rate as the liquid molecules are evaporating into gas molecules.

☐ **3** *(c)*
A reaction that does not fully reach completion is known as a reversible reaction. A reversible reaction is one in which the forward and reverse reactions take place at the same time.

☐ **4** *(b)*
In a reversible reaction both forward and reverse reactions take place. When the rate of the forward reaction equals that of the reverse reaction, the composition of the mixture will appear static. This is known as a dynamic equilibrium.

☐ **5** *(b)*
When a reaction has reached equilibrium, the rate of the forward reaction is equal to the rate of the reverse reaction. This means that the concentrations of the reactants are constant. Therefore, only the first statement is true.

☐ **6** *(d)*
Once the equilibrium has been established, the concentrations of the products and reactants remain constant, but they are not necessarily equal.

☐ **7** *(c)*
The equilibrium position adjusts to oppose the decrease in temperature. Hence, the equilibrium moves to the right as the left to right reaction is exothermic.

☐ **8** *(e)*
Le Chatelier's principle states that "when conditions are changed, a system in equilibrium will adjust itself in such a way as to minimize the effect of the change". It can be seen that when the equation moves from the left to the right there is a decrease in the number of moles of gas and so a decrease in pressure. When the pressure in increased the system will try and minimize this change by moving in the direction of least pressure. In the reaction, this means moving the position of equilibrium towards the right, and increasing the amount of ammonia.

☐ **9** *(d)*
If the ammonia is removed as it is produced, the equilibrium is disturbed and the reaction will try to re-establish the equilibrium by producing more ammonia. Therefore, the position of the equilibrium moves to the right.

☐ **10** *(a)*
An increase in pressure will tip the equilibrium towards the right (decrease in the number of moles of gas) whereas an increase in temperature will favour the left hand side as the reaction will proceed in the endothermic direction. A catalyst will not alter the yield (but will alter the rate of reaction).

☐ **11** *(e)*
A catalyst only increases the rate of a reaction, it will not affect the yield. In a reversible reaction, the rate of the forward and reverse reactions are increased equally and therefore the yield of the product remains the same.

☐ **12** *(a)*
The addition of a small amount of sodium hydroxide removes a small amount of the hydrogen ions, as they react to form water. The position of equilibrium moves to the right to produce more hydrogen ions.

Exothermic and endothermic reactions

Foundation and Higher Levels

☐ **1** *(b)*
An exothermic reaction is one in which the products have less energy than the reactants. Therefore, there is a release of energy, which is usually given out in the form of heat. (See following diagram.)

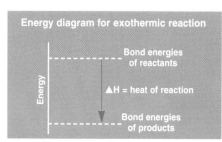

A1

☐ **2** *(b)*
An exothermic reaction is one that produces energy. Burning magnesium produces heat and hence is an exothermic reaction. The four other reactions are endothermic as they take in energy.

☐ **3** *(c)*
An exothermic reaction is one that produces energy and always results in an increase in temperature. The two reactions in which the temperature increases are i and iv, so these are the only exothermic reactions.

☐ **4** *(c)*
An exothermic reaction is one that produces energy and always results in an increase in temperature. The two reactions in which the temperature increases are ii and iii, so these are the only exothermic reactions.

☐ **5** *(e)*
When ammonium nitrate is dissolved in water, heat is taken in during the reaction and the solution gets cooler. Therefore, this is not an exothermic reaction.

☐ **6** *(d)*
The three reactions where the temperature decreases are i, iii, and v.

☐ **7** *(c)*
An endothermic reaction is one in which the products have more energy than the reactants, and therefore energy has to be taken in from the surroundings. This usually results in a decrease in temperature. (See diagram that follows.)

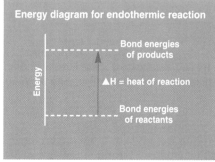

A7

☐ **8** *(a)*
The reaction vessel will feel cold to the touch.

☐ **9** *(c)*
Only reactions ii and iv have a lower final temperature. Therefore, *(c)* is the correct answer.

☐ **10** *(b)*
An endothermic reaction is one that takes in energy. The decomposition of limestone needs heat (energy) to make it happen. (See diagram below.)

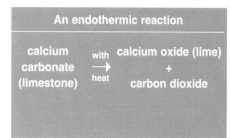

A10

☐ **11** *(a)*
That the reaction was endothermic is shown by the fact that the water around the test tube froze. In order for the water to freeze it has to have energy removed from it, and endothermic reactions need energy, which they take from their surroundings.

☐ **12** *(c)*
An endothermic reaction is one in which the products have more energy than the reactants. In order to make up this difference in energy, the reactants take energy from their surroundings, making their temperature fall. In a reaction that is only slightly endothermic, the temperature fall is only going to be very small. Hence, the answer is *(c)*.

☐ **13** *(b)*
All vaporization and melting processes are endothermic. Water has to take in heat (energy) to boil.

☐ **14** *(a)*
All of the statements in the question can occur if two solutions are mixed together.

Exothermic and endothermic reactions

Higher Level only

□ **15** *(c)*
An exothermic reaction is one in which the products have less energy than the reactants, and therefore there is a release of energy. This energy is usually given out in the form of heat. Not all exothermic reactions are spontaneous, most need a small amount of energy to start the reaction. This energy is known as the activation energy. For example, methane and oxygen react exothermically, but the reaction is only started by the flame from a match or spark.

□ **16** *(a)*
In a chemical reaction, bonds are broken and formed. The breaking of bonds is endothermic and the formation of bonds is exothermic. The stronger a bond, the more energy is needed to break it and the more is released when it is formed. In an endothermic reaction, more energy is taken in than is given out – the bonds broken take in more energy than is given out during the formation of the new bonds. Hence, the new bonds are weaker than those broken.

□ **17**
C is the correct diagram. During an exothermic reaction, energy is given out usually in the form of heat. This means that the reactants must contain more energy than the products because the excess energy is given out. As shown in the diagram that follows, the reactants are higher than the products and the difference is the amount of energy that will be given out during the reaction.

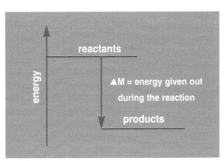

A17

□ **18** *(d)*
When energy is taken in by a reaction it means that the new bonds formed did not give out as much energy as it took to break the old bonds. Hence, they are not as strong as the old bonds. An endothermic reaction will therefore result in a compound that is less stable than its reactants. The more

endothermic the reaction, the less stable the compound. Therefore, *(d)* is the answer.

□ **19** *(c)*
In a reaction the energy taken in is used to break the bonds. If this energy is not given out when new and stronger bonds are formed, the reaction will be endothermic. The more endothermic a reaction, the more energy it had to take in and hence the bonds formed are weaker than those broken.

□ **20** *(a)*
Both of the statements are true. In fact, the first statement is an explanation of the second.

□ **21** *(a)*
The breaking of a chemical bond requires the input of energy, and is therefore an endothermic process.

□ **22** *(c)*
The correct units for bond energies are kJ mol^{-1} (kilojoules per mole).

□ **23** *(a)*
To break a chemical bond, energy is needed to overcome the force of attraction between the two molecules or atoms.

□ **24** *(d)*
One mole of propane has a mass of 44 g (the relative molar mass of carbon is 12 and hydrogen is 1). Therefore, 11 g is $1/4$ of a mole. Hence, one mole of propane would produce 4 x 555 kJ of energy = 2220 kJ.

□ **25** *(c)*
Bond formation is an exothermic process because energy is given out when a bond is formed. The energy given out is the same as the energy required to break the same bond.

□ **26** *(c)*
Bond breaking is an endothermic process because energy is needed to break a chemical bond. On the other hand, the opposite reaction involving bond making is an exothermic process and energy is given out. The bond energy is therefore the amount of energy needed to break a particular bond, and also the amount of energy given out when a particular bond is formed.

□ **27** *(b)*
Bond energies are first worked out by experiment, and when one bond energy is known, others can be worked out by calculation.

□ **28** *(e)*
Bonds broken are:
2 (H–H) = 2 x 436 = 872 kJ
(O=O) = 496 kJ
Total energy required = +1368 kJ

Bonds formed are:
4 (H–O) = 4 x 463 = –1852 kJ
Total energy given out = –1852 kJ
Heat of reaction (energy taken in + energy given out) = +1368 – 1852= –484 kJ

□ **29** (c)
Bonds broken are:
(C=O) = 743 kJ/mol (H–H) = 436 kJ
Total energy required = +1179 kJ

Bonds formed are:
(C–O) = 360 kJ/mol (O–H) = 463 kJ
(C–H) = 412 kJ
Total energy given out = –1235 kJ
Heat of reaction (energy taken in + energy given out) = +1179 – 1235 = –56 kJ

□ **30** *(d)*
Bonds broken are:
1 (C=C) = 1 x 612 = 612 kJ
3 (O=O) = 3 x 496 = 1488 kJ
4 (C–H) = 4 x 412 = 1648 kJ
Total energy required = +3748 kJ

Bonds formed are:
4 (H–O) = 4 x 463 = –1852 kJ
4 (C=O) = 4 x 743 = –2972 kJ
Total energy given out = –4824 kJ
Heat of reaction (energy taken in + energy given out) = + 3748 – 4824 = –1076 kJ

□ **31** *(e)*
Bonds broken are:
4 (C–H) = 4 x 412 = 1648 kJ
2 (O=O) = 2 x 496 = 992 kJ
Total energy required = +2640 kJ

Bonds formed are:
2 (C=O) = 2 x 743 = –1486 kJ
4 (H–O) = 4 x 463 = –1852 kJ
Total energy given out = –3338 kJ
Heat of reaction (energy taken in + energy given out) = + 2640 – 3338 = –698 kJ

□ **32** *(d)*
Bonds broken are:
(C=C) = 612 kJ (Br–Br) = 193 kJ
Total energy required = +805 kJ
Bonds formed are: (C–C) = –348 kJ
2 (C–Br) = 2 x 276= –552 kJ
Total energy given out = –900 kJ
Heat of reaction (energy taken in + energy given out) = + 805 – 900 = –95 kJ

□ **33** *(b)*
The bond energy is the energy needed to break a chemical bond. Therefore, energy must be supplied and hence all the bond energies are positive.

☐ **34** *(e)*

The greater the bond energy the more energy is needed to break the bond, and therefore the stronger the bond. The energy given out in the formation of a bond is the same as the energy needed to break the same bond. From this we can see that the carbon–oxygen bond is stronger. Therefore, it would require more energy to break it, and more energy is given out when it is formed.

☐ **35** *(a)*

One mole of any gas occupies a volume of $24000 cm^3$ Therefore, $1200 cm^3$ is $1200/24000$ moles = 0.05 moles. If one mole of methane produces 890 kJ, then 0.05 moles will produce 0.05 x 890 = 44.5 kJ of energy.

The Earth

The Earth and its atmosphere *(Double Award only)*

During the 4500 million years since the Earth was formed, the atmosphere has totally changed. It is thought that the original atmosphere was a mixture of hydrogen and helium. As the Earth cooled, the atmosphere then changed to a mixture of ammonia, carbon dioxide, methane, and steam. Millions of years later, the atmosphere became the mixture of oxygen and nitrogen that is present today. The following questions test knowledge of this area of chemistry.

 ## KEY FACTS

• **Evolution of the atmosphere:**
The Earth's early atmosphere was produced by large-scale volcanic activity as the Earth started to cool after it was formed. The early atmosphere was made up from methane, ammonia, carbon dioxide, carbon monoxide, and water vapour. As the Earth cooled, the water vapour in the atmosphere condensed to form the rivers and oceans. The formation of the oceans resulted in the reduction of carbon dioxide in the atmosphere and also allowed the first plants to evolve. The plants produced oxygen through photosynthesis. This oxygen reacted with the methane and carbon monoxide to produce more carbon dioxide and water vapour, and also reacted with the ammonia leading to the formation of nitrogen. As more plants grew the percentage of carbon dioxide decreased, and the percentage of oxygen increased. The increase in oxygen led to the formation of the ozone layer, which protected the Earth from harmful ultraviolet radiation and allowed the animal life to move out of the oceans and onto the land. The composition of the atmosphere has been constant for about 200 million years at 78% nitrogen, 21% oxygen, less than 1% noble gases, and 0.03% carbon dioxide.

• **The carbon cycle:** The carbon cycle helps to maintain the composition of the atmosphere by controlling the amount of carbon dioxide in the air.

QUESTIONS

Foundation and Higher Levels

1 For the last 200 million years the proportions of different gases in the Earth's atmosphere have remained fairly constant. What are the proportions of these gases?

☐ (a) 78% oxygen, 21% carbon dioxide, and small amounts of other gases
☐ (b) 78% oxygen, 21% nitrogen, and small amounts of carbon dioxide and other gases
☐ (c) 78% carbon dioxide, 21% oxygen, and small amounts of other gases
☐ (d) 78% carbon dioxide, 21% nitrogen, and small amounts of oxygen and other gases
☐ (e) 78% nitrogen, 21% oxygen, and small amounts of carbon dioxide and other gases

2 What is the percentage of nitrogen found in the atmosphere?

☐ (a) 1.00
☐ (b) 21.00
☐ (c) 78.00
☐ (d) 0.03
☐ (e) 45.00

3 What is the percentage of oxygen found in the atmosphere?

☐ (a) 21
☐ (b) 78
☐ (c) 45
☐ (d) 90
☐ (e) 3

4 What is the percentage of carbon dioxide found in the atmosphere?

☐ (a) 0.03
☐ (b) 78.00
☐ (c) 21.00
☐ (d) 1.00
☐ (e) 0.30

5 Which of the following gases is not found naturally in the atmosphere?

☐ (a) Oxygen
☐ (b) Hydrogen
☐ (c) Nitrogen
☐ (d) Carbon dioxide
☐ (e) Argon

6 What element, found in a large quantity in the atmosphere, is unreactive and essential for the growth of plants?

....

7 Which one of the following removes carbon dioxide from the Earth's atmosphere?

☐ (a) Photosynthesis
☐ (b) Respiration
☐ (c) Combustion
☐ (d) Electrolysis
☐ (e) None of the above

8 What is respiration?

☐ (a) The conversion of glucose and oxygen into carbon dioxide and water
☐ (b) The conversion of carbon dioxide into water and oxygen
☐ (c) The conversion of sunlight into plant food
☐ (d) The conversion of fuels into carbon dioxide and hydrogen
☐ (e) The conversion of iron oxide into iron and carbon dioxide using carbon monoxide

9 Which of the following is not responsible for maintaining the amount of carbon dioxide present in the air?

☐ (a) Decay and excretion
☐ (b) Photosynthesis
☐ (c) Combustion
☐ (d) Respiration
☐ (e) Solution in sea water

10 Which one of the following gases is removed from the atmosphere during combustion?

☐ (a) Water vapour
☐ (b) Carbon dioxide
☐ (c) Nitrogen
☐ (d) Argon
☐ (e) Oxygen

11 Which one of the following statements explains why an increase in the amount of carbon dioxide in the atmosphere increases the greenhouse effect?

- ☐ (a) The carbon dioxide traps the solar radiation
- ☐ (b) The carbon dioxide magnifies the solar radiation
- ☐ (c) The carbon dioxide increases the amount of ultraviolet radiation in the sunlight
- ☐ (d) The carbon dioxide increases the transparency of the upper atmosphere and so lets in more light
- ☐ (e) The carbon dioxide damages the ozone layer

12 Which one of the following statements about the burning of fossil fuels explains why it affects the carbon cycle?

- ☐ (a) It produces large amounts of carbon dioxide
- ☐ (b) It produces large amounts of oxygen
- ☐ (c) It produces large amounts of methane
- ☐ (d) It produces large amounts of water
- ☐ (e) It produces large amounts of calcium carbonate

13 Which one of the following is a major pollutant of the air?

- ☐ (a) Nitrogen
- ☐ (b) Oxygen
- ☐ (c) Nitrogen dioxide
- ☐ (d) Hydrogen
- ☐ (e) Helium

14 How does the burning of fossil fuels result in acid rain?

- ☐ (a) The removal of oxygen from the atmosphere increases the acidity of rain water
- ☐ (b) The burning of fossil fuels releases oxygen into the atmosphere, which increases the acidity of rain
- ☐ (c) The burning of fossil fuels results in the formation of sulphur dioxide, which then increases the acidity of rain water
- ☐ (d) The burning of fossil fuel results in the formation of ethanoic acid
- ☐ (e) Fossil fuels are acidic

15 Which one of the following is the major adverse effect of acid rain?

- ☐ (a) Damage to plants and buildings
- ☐ (b) Damage to paint work of cars
- ☐ (c) The increased weathering of rocks and minerals
- ☐ (d) Brain damage in children
- ☐ (e) None of the above

QUESTIONS

Higher Level only

16 Where did the Earth's early atmosphere come from?

- ☐ (a) Animal life
- ☐ (b) Volcanic activity
- ☐ (c) Plant life
- ☐ (d) Outer space
- ☐ (e) The decomposition of the sea

17 Which gases probably made up the early atmosphere of the Earth?

- ☐ (a) Carbon dioxide, methane, and ammonia
- ☐ (b) Oxygen and methane
- ☐ (c) Nitrogen and carbon dioxide
- ☐ (d) Water vapour and oxygen
- ☐ (e) The composition of the atmosphere has not changed

18 Which one of the following was responsible for the introduction of oxygen into the Earth's atmosphere?

- ☐ (a) Reduction
- ☐ (b) Combustion
- ☐ (c) Respiration
- ☐ (d) Oxidation
- ☐ (e) Photosynthesis

19 Where did the nitrogen that now makes up nearly 80% of the atmosphere come from?

- ☐ (a) It was released as a result of volcanic activity
- ☐ (b) It was released by photosynthesis
- ☐ (c) It was released by the action of denitrifying bacteria
- ☐ (d) It was produced by the reaction between methane and ammonia
- ☐ (e) It was produced by the reaction that occurred between carbon dioxide and ammonia

20 About 20% of the Earth's atmosphere is oxygen. Where did this oxygen come from?

- ☐ (a) It was released by the reaction of carbon dioxide and methane
- ☐ (b) It was released from the sea when the water warmed up as a result of volcanic activity
- ☐ (c) It was released from volcanoes
- ☐ (d) It was produced during the process of photosynthesis
- ☐ (e) It was released from the ozone layer

21 The atmosphere of the young Earth was known as a reducing atmosphere because it contained small amounts of methane and ammonia. Why are these gases not found in the atmosphere today?

- ☐ (a) The gases were exhausted by plant life
- ☐ (b) The gases were able to escape from the atmosphere
- ☐ (c) The gases were absorbed by the water in the sea
- ☐ (d) The gases reacted with oxygen
- ☐ (e) The gases were used by micro-organisms

22 The ozone layer protects the Earth from the harmful effects of ultraviolet radiation from the sun. How did the ozone layer form?

- ☐ (a) By the reaction of the oxygen with cosmic radiation
- ☐ (b) By the reaction between carbon dioxide and oxygen
- ☐ (c) By the reaction between ammonia and oxygen
- ☐ (d) By the reaction between methane and oxygen
- ☐ (e) By the reaction between chlorofluorocarbons (CFCs) and oxygen

Weathering *(Double Award only)*

Even the hardest rocks on Earth wear away over a period of thousands of years, in a slow process known as weathering. Weathering can be divided into three types: physical weathering, chemical weathering, and biological weathering. The following questions test knowledge on this topic.

QUESTIONS

Foundation and Higher Levels

1 What is the name given to any process that wears down a rock?

- ☐ (a) Corrosion
- ☐ (b) Erosion
- ☐ (c) Precipitation
- ☐ (d) Weathering
- ☐ (e) Hydration

2 What is erosion?

- ☐ (a) The gradual disintegration of rocks in their resting place
- ☐ (b) The breakdown of rocks by water
- ☐ (c) The breakdown of rocks by wind, water, and ice
- ☐ (d) The breakdown and removal of rocks from their original place
- ☐ (e) The effect of both physical and chemical weathering

3 Which of the following would not lead to substantial erosion?

- ☐ (a) A river in flood
- ☐ (b) A sea with high waves caused by strong winds
- ☐ (c) A mountain footpath that attracts thousands of people every year
- ☐ (d) An advancing glacier
- ☐ (e) A drought

4 Which of the following processes would you expect to be completed in the shortest amount of time?

- ☐ (a) The erosion of the bank of a river in flood

- ☐ (b) The recrystallization of limestone into marble
- ☐ (c) The formation of soil
- ☐ (d) Colliding plates to form a mountain range
- ☐ (e) Sand cemented into sandstone

5 What is another name for small pieces of rock mixed with decayed vegetable matter?

- ☐ (a) Sand
- ☐ (b) Shale
- ☐ (c) Soil
- ☐ (d) Coal
- ☐ (e) Chalk

6 Which one of the following statements explains why water entering cracks in rocks often causes the rocks to splinter?

- ☐ (a) The water carries other materials, which gradually erode the rock
- ☐ (b) When water freezes it expands, causing the rocks to splinter
- ☐ (c) Acids within the water splinter the rocks
- ☐ (d) If the water is hot it will expand, causing the rocks to splinter
- ☐ (e) Only porous rocks will splinter because they allow the water to pass through them

7 Frost shattering is the splintering of rocks, caused by the expansion of water. What else can splinter rocks?

- ☐ (a) Acids in water eroding the cracks in the rocks
- ☐ (b) Sudden changes in temperature
- ☐ (c) High winds
- ☐ (d) Other materials, such as small pebbles, being carried by water
- ☐ (e) Erosion by salt water

8 Which one of the following statements is false?

- ☐ (a) Small pieces of rock can be carried by the wind to make sand dunes
- ☐ (b) Erosion can be accelerated by water
- ☐ (c) Soil has decayed vegetable matter in it
- ☐ (d) Salt cannot damage rocks
- ☐ (e) Atmospheric pressure changes can not cause damage to rocks

9 What is the name of the process by which some rocks absorb water into their structure, causing them to expand and change chemically?

- ☐ (a) Hydrolysis
- ☐ (b) Carbonation
- ☐ (c) Osmosis
- ☐ (d) Oxidation
- ☐ (e) Hydration

10 What is the name given to any process which chemically wears down an object?

- ☐ (a) Weathering
- ☐ (b) Corrosion
- ☐ (c) Hydration
- ☐ (d) Erosion
- ☐ (e) Carbonation

ANSWERS

The Earth and its atmosphere

Foundation and Higher Levels

☐ **1** *(e)*
The Earth's atmosphere consists of 78% nitrogen, 21% oxygen, and small amounts of various gases, which include carbon dioxide.

☐ **2** *(c)*
The atmosphere is 78% nitrogen.

☐ **3** *(a)*
The atmosphere is 21% oxygen.

☐ **4** *(a)*
The atmosphere is 0.03% carbon dioxide.

☐ **5** *(b)*
Hydrogen is not found naturally in the Earth's atmosphere as it is light enough to escape the Earth's gravity. It is also very reactive and will burn to form water when it reacts with oxygen.

☐ **6**
Nitrogen, which makes up 78% of the Earth's atmosphere and is an unreactive gas, is essential for plant growth.

☐ **7** *(a)*
During the process of photosynthesis, plant life converts carbon dioxide and water into oxygen and glucose. Then the oxygen is released into the atmosphere.

☐ **8** *(a)*
Respiration is the conversion of glucose and oxygen into carbon dioxide and water. Respiration, which occurs in both plants and animals, produces energy and helps to maintain the composition of the atmosphere.

☐ **9** *(a)*
All the processes except excretion and decay are involved in the maintenance of the volume of carbon dioxide in the atmosphere. They are all involved in the carbon cycle.

☐ **10** *(e)*
During the process of combustion the oxygen in the atmosphere is used up as it reacts with the fuel to produce carbon dioxide and water.

☐ **11** *(a)*
An increase in the amount of carbon dioxide in the Earth's atmosphere will increase the greenhouse effect because carbon dioxide is responsible for trapping solar radiation that has been reflected back from the Earth's surface. This extra trapping of solar radiation will then increase the average temperature of the Earth.

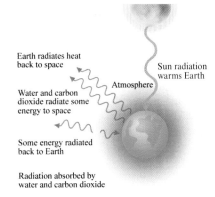

A11

☐ **12** *(a)*
The burning of fossil fuels produces large amounts of carbon dioxide. This results in a large imbalance in the carbon cycle because the excess carbon dioxide cannot be removed by the process of photosynthesis, or by dissolution in the seas. This increase in the volume of carbon dioxide in the atmosphere can lead to global warming.

☐ **13** *(c)*
Nitrogen dioxide is a major pollutant of the air. It is produced in the internal combustion engine and is released into the air through exhaust fumes. Oxygen and nitrogen form about 99% of clean air, and hydrogen and helium are gases that do not pollute the air.

☐ **14** *(c)*
The burning of fossil fuels results in the formation of sulphur dioxide due to the presence of sulphur impurities in the fuel. When the fuel is burnt this sulphur reacts with oxygen to form sulphur dioxide. The sulphur dioxide is carried up into the atmosphere where it dissolves in water vapour to form an acidic solution, which falls as acid rain.

☐ **15** *(a)*
The major adverse effect of acid rain is the damage it causes to plants and buildings. The acid can change the pH value of the soil and destroy the leaves of the trees. Both these factors could lead to the death of the trees. It can also eat into the surfaces of buildings, causing structural damage.

The Earth and its atmosphere

Higher Level only

☐ **16** *(b)*
The Earth's atmosphere came from the volcanic activity that accompanied the formation of the Earth. This original atmosphere contained mainly carbon dioxide, methane, and ammonia, with a little carbon monoxide and steam.

☐ **17** *(a)*
The early atmosphere was composed of carbon dioxide, methane, and ammonia, with small amounts of carbon monoxide and steam, but no oxygen.

☐ **18** *(e)*
Oxygen was introduced into the atmosphere by the process of photosynthesis. During the process of photosynthesis plant life converts carbon dioxide and water into oxygen and glucose. The oxygen is released into the atmosphere by the plants.

☐ **19** *(c)*
The nitrogen in the atmosphere was produced by the action of the denitrifying bacteria in the soil. A small amount of the nitrogen was produced by the reaction that took place between ammonia and oxygen.

☐ **20** *(d)*
The oxygen in the atmosphere was released by plants during photosynthesis. The diagram that follows shows how photosynthesis converts carbon dioxide and water into sugars and oxygen, which the plants then release into the atmosphere.

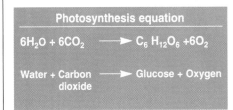

Photosynthesis equation

$$6H_2O + 6CO_2 \longrightarrow C_6H_{12}O_6 + 6O_2$$

Water + Carbon dioxide $\longrightarrow$ Glucose + Oxygen

A20

☐ **21** *(d)*
The methane and ammonia reacted with the oxygen that was present in the atmosphere (produced by plants during photosynthesis) to produce carbon dioxide, water, and oxides of nitrogen.

☐ **22** *(a)*
The ozone layer was produced by the reaction between oxygen (released by the process of photosynthesis) and cosmic radiation in the upper atmosphere. The formation of the ozone layer allowed the evolution of new living organisms.

Weathering

Foundation and Higher Levels

☐ **1** *(d)*
Weathering is the name given to any physical or chemical process that causes rocks to disintegrate. Often sand is produced as a result of this process. Weathering should not be confused with erosion, which involves the movement of weathered particles.

☐ **2** *(d)*
Erosion is the breakdown and removal of rocks from their original site. Wind, water, gravity, and ice are all methods by which the rocks can be transported. Erosion should not be confused with weathering, which is the disintegration of rocks at their original site, without their removal.

☐ **3** *(e)*
Erosion is accelerated by the rapid flowing of water, wind at high speeds, the trampling of land and vegetation, and by the advancing of ice. In contrast, a drought slows the water flow in a river, decreasing its erosive power. A drought in cold areas causes less snow to accumulate in the glaciers, decreasing the chance of the glacier advancing and causing erosion.

☐ **4** *(a)*
When a river is in flood an entire river bank can collapse in a matter of seconds. This is as a result of hydraulic action (the physical force of flowing water) and abrasion (the collision of rock particles on the river bed and banks). All the other processes can take thousands or millions of years.

☐ **5** *(c)*
Soil consists of decayed vegetation – known as humus – and small particles of rock.

☐ **6** *(b)*
Unlike most chemicals, water expands when it freezes. This means that if a crack is full of water that freezes, the crack will enlargen and the rock splinter. This process is known as frost shattering.

☐ **7** *(b)*
If rocks undergo a sudden temperature change from hot to cold, they can shatter into smaller pieces.

☐ **8** *(d)*
If salt water enters into a rock's pores and then the water evaporates leaving the salt behind, damage can be done. The salt will crystallize and, if the crystals are large enough, they can cause disintegration of the rock. This is called salt crystallization.

☐ **9** *(e)*
Some rocks will absorb water, especially during long periods of wet weather that follow periods of dry weather. The rocks' chemical structure changes. Also, the rocks expand and exert pressure on neighbouring rocks. This process is called hydration.

☐ **10** *(b)*
Corrosion is the term given to any process which chemically causes rocks to break down into smaller pieces. Sometimes the term chemical weathering is also used.

Geological Changes
Formation and deformation of rocks *(Double Award only)*

There are three main types of rocks: igneous, metamorphic, and sedimentary. These rocks are continually being formed and destroyed in a very slow process known as the rock cycle. The following questions relate to the key ideas about the formation and deformation of rocks.

 KEY FACTS

• **Rock types:** The rocks that make up the Earth can be divided up into three main types. Hard igneous rocks are formed by the cooling of molten magma, either on the surface of the Earth or within the crust. They are made up of shiny, interlocking crystals and do not contain any fossils. Examples of igneous rocks include granite, basalt, and pumice. Soft sedimentary rocks are formed when the weathered material from other types of rock is deposited and buried. The burial causes the sediment to undergo, over millions of years, the process of lithication by which the sediment is turned into rock. The rocks are made up of layers of rock fragments and may contain fossils. Examples of sedimentary rocks include limestone, sandstone, clay, and mudstone. Hard, shiny metamorphic rocks are formed by the action of high temperature or high pressure (or both) on other rock types. The rocks are crystalline and the grains are usually aligned. Examples of metamorphic rocks include marble, slate, schist, gneiss and hornfels.

• **Plate tectonics:** The theory of plate tectonics suggests that the lithosphere (the collective term for the Earth's crust and the upper part of the mantle) is divided up into a series of large plates. These plates float on the asthenosphere and move about slowly due to the convection currents in the mantle. The movement of these plates gives rise to volcanic and earthquake activity and results in the formation of major geological features.
• Where two plates move apart new crust is formed, and two ridges of mountains separated by a trench are formed, eg. the North Atlantic Ridge and the East African Rift Valley.
• When oceanic and continental plates meet, the oceanic plate is forced to sink underneath the continental plate and a deep oceanic trench is formed.

The friction that is produced as one plate moves under the other causes them to melt, and the molten rock rises to the surface to form a chain of volcanic mountains, such as the Andes.
• When two continental plates collide a chain of mountains, such as the Himalayas, is formed. Where two plates move past each other (a conservative plate boundary) no new material is formed and no rock is destroyed, eg. the San Andreas Fault.

 QUESTIONS
Foundation and Higher Levels

1 The Earth is approximately 4500 million years old. Why are no rocks of this age found on the Earth?

☐ (a) It took 1000 million years for the rocks to form
☐ (b) No half-life of any radioactive isotopes is long enough to measure the age of rocks beyond 3500 million years
☐ (c) A meteorite crashed onto the Earth 3500 million years ago, destroying all the rocks that had formed before then
☐ (d) The rocks are continually being recycled
☐ (e) None of above

2 What is the name given to the solid material that settles at the bottom of a river or sea?

☐ (a) Residue
☐ (b) Shale
☐ (c) Sand
☐ (d) Sediment
☐ (e) Clay

3 Which type of rocks are formed from the deposition of particles such as rock fragments?

☐ (a) Metamorphic
☐ (b) Sedimentary

☐ (c) Porous
☐ (d) Igneous
☐ (e) Volcanic

4 Which one of the following rocks might contain the remains of shells of organisms that lived previously?

☐ (a) Limestone
☐ (b) Basalt
☐ (c) Granite
☐ (d) Marble
☐ (e) Quartzite

5 In the diagram that follows, which sedimentary layer is the oldest?

....

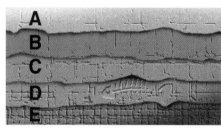
Q5

6 In the following chart, look at the time periods for the main groups of plants and animals. What time period would a sedimentary rock belong to if it contained fossils of lamellibranches, trilobites, gastropods, but not vertebrates?

☐ (a) Cretaceous
☐ (b) Triassic
☐ (c) Carboniferous
☐ (d) Devonian
☐ (e) Cambrian

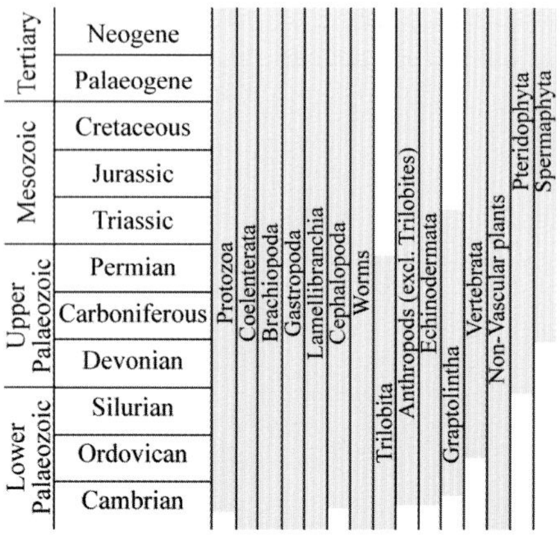

		Protozoa	Coelenterata	Brachiopoda	Gastropoda	Lamellibranchia	Cephalopoda	Worms	Trilobita	Anthropods (excl. Trilobites)	Graptolintha	Echinodermata	Vertebrata	Non-Vascular plants	Pteridophyta	Spermaphyta
Tertiary	Neogene															
	Palaeogene															
Mesozoic	Cretaceous															
	Jurassic															
	Triassic															
Upper Palaeozoic	Permian															
	Carboniferous															
	Devonian															
Lower Palaeozoic	Silurian															
	Ordovician															
	Cambrian															

Q6

120

7 In which of the following rocks are fossils most likely to be found?

- ☐ (a) Limestone
- ☐ (b) Marble
- ☐ (c) Granite
- ☐ (d) Basalt
- ☐ (e) Slate

8 What type of rock is limestone?

- ☐ (a) Metamorphic
- ☐ (b) Crystalline
- ☐ (c) Igneous
- ☐ (d) Sedimentary
- ☐ (e) Basaltic

9 Which rock is made up from the remains of sea creatures?

- ☐ (a) Oil
- ☐ (b) Coal
- ☐ (c) Limestone
- ☐ (d) Granite
- ☐ (e) Coral

10 Which rock type has all of the following characteristics?
i. Fossils
ii. Bedding or layers
iii. It would fizz when placed in acid

- ☐ (a) Slate
- ☐ (b) Shale
- ☐ (c) Granite
- ☐ (d) Limestone
- ☐ (e) Marble

11 Which type of rock is formed when magma cools?

- ☐ (a) Lava
- ☐ (b) Metamorphic
- ☐ (c) Igneous
- ☐ (d) Sedimentary
- ☐ (e) Permeable

12 Which one of the following statements is false?

- ☐ (a) Basalt is a type of igneous rock
- ☐ (b) Metamorphic rocks can be formed by intense pressure
- ☐ (c) Limestone is a type of igneous rock
- ☐ (d) Sedimentary rocks can be found in layers
- ☐ (e) Fossils often occur in sedimentary rocks

13 Which type of rock is produced by lava cooling quickly on top of the Earth's surface?

- ☐ (a) Granite
- ☐ (b) Chalk
- ☐ (c) Coal
- ☐ (d) Basalt
- ☐ (e) Limestone

14 What is molten rock called, firstly when it is beneath the Earth's surface and secondly when it is above the Earth's surface?

- ☐ (a) Basalt and granite
- ☐ (b) Lava and magma
- ☐ (c) Mantle and magma
- ☐ (d) Granite and basalt
- ☐ (e) Magma and lava

15 Which type of rock is produced by magma cooling slowly inside the Earth's crust?

- ☐ (a) Granite
- ☐ (b) Chalk
- ☐ (c) Coal
- ☐ (d) Basalt
- ☐ (e) Limestone

16 The following diagram shows three plates in the Earth. At which point – A, B, C, D, or E – would the youngest rock be found?

....

Q16

17 Which one of the following statements describes how fossil fuel coal is formed?

- ☐ (a) From the death and decay of trees, followed by high temperatures
- ☐ (b) From the death and decay of animals, followed by high temperatures
- ☐ (c) From the death and decay of animals and plants, covered up by layers of mud and sand at high temperatures
- ☐ (d) From the death and decay of trees, covered up by layers of mud and sand at high temperatures
- ☐ (e) From the fossils of animals

18 Why are fossil fuels, such as coal and oil, only formed underground and not on the surface of the Earth?

- ☐ (a) There is not enough organic matter on the surface in order to form the fuels
- ☐ (b) The organic matter is removed by erosion before it has a chance to form into the fuels
- ☐ (c) Because of the presence of oxygen on the surface
- ☐ (d) Because of the actions of man on the surface
- ☐ (e) None of the above

19 Which one of the following is formed from layers of dead trees?

- ☐ (a) Limestone
- ☐ (b) Marble
- ☐ (c) Coal
- ☐ (d) Oil
- ☐ (e) Basalt

20 Which rock type is made from rocks that have been altered by heat or pressure (or both)?

- ☐ (a) Metamorphic
- ☐ (b) Sedimentary
- ☐ (c) Porous
- ☐ (d) Volcanic
- ☐ (e) Igneous

21 If sedimentary rocks are changed by pressure or heat (or both), what type of rock is formed?

- ☐ (a) Marble
- ☐ (b) They are still sedimentary
- ☐ (c) Metamorphic
- ☐ (d) Igneous
- ☐ (e) Porous

22 If limestone is metamorphosed by pressure or heat (or both), what rock is formed?

- ☐ (a) Coal
- ☐ (b) Marble
- ☐ (c) Quartzite
- ☐ (d) Clay
- ☐ (e) Basalt

23 If sandstone is metamorphosed by pressure or heat (or both), what rock is formed?

- ☐ (a) Coal
- ☐ (b) Clay
- ☐ (c) Limestone
- ☐ (d) Sand
- ☐ (e) Quartzite

24 Which type of rock has all of the following characteristics?
i. Large interlocking crystals
ii. A lack of fossils
iii. A lack of bedding or distinct layers

121

- ☐ (a) Granite
- ☐ (b) Marble
- ☐ (c) Basalt
- ☐ (d) Sandstone
- ☐ (e) Spinel

25 The following diagram shows the rock cycle. What is found at A?

- ☐ (a) Sedimentary rock
- ☐ (b) Magma
- ☐ (c) Metamorphic rock
- ☐ (d) Igneous rock
- ☐ (e) Lava

The Rock Cycle

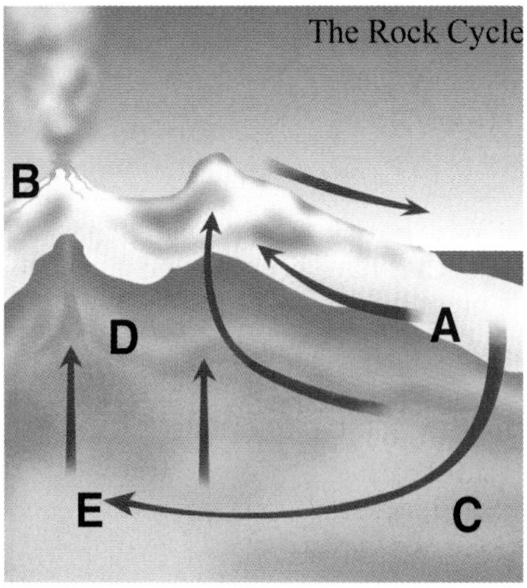

Q25, 26, 27, 28, 29

26 Which of the following is found at B in the above diagram?

- ☐ (a) Sedimentary rock
- ☐ (b) Magma
- ☐ (c) Metamorphic rock
- ☐ (d) Igneous rock
- ☐ (e) Lava

27 Which of the following is found at C in the above diagram?

- ☐ (a) Sedimentary rock
- ☐ (b) Magma
- ☐ (c) Metamorphic rock
- ☐ (d) Igneous rock
- ☐ (e) Lava

28 Which of the following is found at D in the above diagram?

- ☐ (a) Sedimentary rock
- ☐ (b) Magma
- ☐ (c) Metamorphic rock
- ☐ (d) Igneous rock
- ☐ (e) Lava

29 Which of the following is found at E in the above diagram?

- ☐ (a) Sedimentary rock
- ☐ (b) Magma
- ☐ (c) Metamorphic rock

- ☐ (d) Igneous rock
- ☐ (e) Lava

30 Which one of the following would not cause the formation of metamorphic rock?

- ☐ (a) The action of intrusive igneous rock
- ☐ (b) The action of acid rain
- ☐ (c) The action of subduction at a plate boundary
- ☐ (d) The action of burial by overlying rocks
- ☐ (e) None of the above

31 What is a crystal?

- ☐ (a) A body with no regular pattern
- ☐ (b) A body that traps light inside it
- ☐ (c) A body with a regular atomic pattern throughout it
- ☐ (d) A body made up of a few elements arranged into several regular patterns
- ☐ (e) A small, irregularly shaped piece of material

32 If the crystals found in an igneous rock are large, how was the rock formed?

- ☐ (a) By cooling quickly
- ☐ (b) Under high pressure
- ☐ (c) From a mixture of elements
- ☐ (d) By cooling slowly
- ☐ (e) On the Earth's surface

33 If the crystalline structure of an igneous rock is small, how was the rock formed?

- ☐ (a) By cooling quickly
- ☐ (b) Under the Earth's surface
- ☐ (c) Under low pressure
- ☐ (d) By cooling slowly
- ☐ (e) Surrounded by other materials

34 What is the difference between intrusive and extrusive igneous rock?

- ☐ (a) Extrusive rock is erupted onto the surface of the Earth whereas intrusive rock is formed underground
- ☐ (b) Intrusive rock is hard whereas extrusive rock is soft
- ☐ (c) Intrusive rock contains fossils whereas extrusive rock does not
- ☐ (d) Extrusive rock contains large crystals whereas intrusive rock contains small crystals
- ☐ (e) Extrusive rock is made from sediment whereas intrusive rock is not

35 From the following list of metal ores, which could you use to extract the metal iron?

i. Bauxite Al_2O_3
ii. Haematite Fe_2O_3
iii. Magnetite Fe_3O_4

- ☐ (a) i only
- ☐ (b) ii only
- ☐ (c) iii only
- ☐ (d) i and iii only
- ☐ (e) ii and iii only

36 From the following list of metal ores, which could you use to extract the metal aluminium?
i. Bauxite Al_2O_3
ii. Haematite Fe_2O_3
iii. Malachite $CuCO_3 Cu(OH)_2$

- ☐ (a) i only
- ☐ (b) ii only
- ☐ (c) iii only
- ☐ (d) i and iii only
- ☐ (e) i and ii only

37 Minerals such as galena (zinc sulphide) are normally insoluble, but can be formed into mineral veins by the movement of water in the ground.
How is this possible ?

- ☐ (a) The minerals are carried as a suspension
- ☐ (b) The water is moved by the movement of the plates
- ☐ (c) The water can dissolve the minerals because of the very high temperature and pressure underground
- ☐ (d) The water reacts with the rocks as it moves through them slowly, causing the minerals to form along the path of the water
- ☐ (e) None of the above

38 Which of the following soil composites would be the best for plant cultivation?

- ☐ (a) Clay and humus only
- ☐ (b) Sand and clay only
- ☐ (c) Sand, pebbles, and humus
- ☐ (d) Clay, sand, and humus
- ☐ (e) Sand and humus only

39 Why is it important for soil to hold water?

- ☐ (a) Water stops the soil from being washed away
- ☐ (b) Water transports nutrients in the soil to plant roots
- ☐ (c) It is not important for soil to hold water
- ☐ (d) It stops the roots of plants from drying out
- ☐ (e) Water in the soil stops the humus drying out

40 What is biological weathering?

- ☐ (a) The action of the atmosphere on plants and animals
- ☐ (b) The action of rain on the health of animals
- ☐ (c) The action of plants and animals on rocks
- ☐ (d) The action of plants and animals on the atmosphere, causing a change in global weather patterns
- ☐ (e) None of the above

 QUESTIONS

Higher Level only

41 There is a theory that South America was once joined to Africa. If this is true, which of the following statements would be correct?
i. The shapes of the continents would fit together
ii. Certain bands of very old rocks would match up on both continents
iii. All the fossils would match up on both continents

- ☐ (a) i only
- ☐ (b) i and ii only
- ☐ (c) i and iii only
- ☐ (d) ii and iii only
- ☐ (e) All of them

Structure of the Earth *(Double Award only)*

The outer solid layer of the Earth is known as the crust. Research has provided enough information for scientists to be fairly sure about the nature of the inner structure of the Earth. A theory known as plate tectonics can be used to explain the cause of such events as earthquakes and volcanic eruption. Knowledge and understanding of the Earth's structure are tested in the questions that follow.

 QUESTIONS

Foundation and Higher Levels

1 Which of the following is the name given to the gaseous layer surrounding the Earth?

- ☐ (a) The atmosphere
- ☐ (b) The crust
- ☐ (c) The centre of the Earth
- ☐ (d) The core
- ☐ (e) The mantle

2 The following diagram shows a cross-section of the Earth. What does the label point to?

- ☐ (a) The atmosphere
- ☐ (b) The crust
- ☐ (c) The centre of the Earth
- ☐ (d) The core
- ☐ (e) The mantle

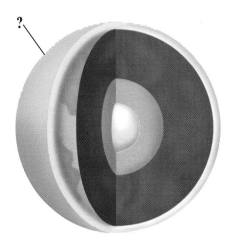

Q2

3 What is the name given to the thin layer of solid material that forms the surface of the Earth?

- ☐ (a) The atmosphere
- ☐ (b) The crust
- ☐ (c) The centre of the Earth
- ☐ (d) The core
- ☐ (e) The mantle

4 The following diagram shows a cross-section of the Earth. What does the label point to?

- ☐ (a) The atmosphere
- ☐ (b) The crust
- ☐ (c) The centre of the Earth
- ☐ (d) The core
- ☐ (e) The mantle

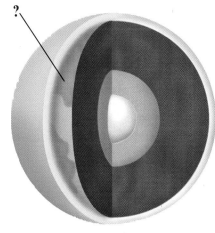

Q4

5 The following diagram shows a cross-section of the Earth. What does the label point to?

- ☐ (a) The atmosphere
- ☐ (b) The crust
- ☐ (c) The centre of the Earth
- ☐ (d) The core
- ☐ (e) The mantle

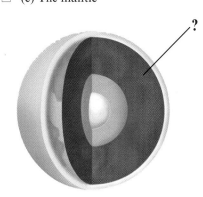

Q5

6 What is the semi-liquid section of the Earth between the core and the crust called?

- ☐ (a) The outer core
- ☐ (b) The mantle
- ☐ (c) The atmosphere
- ☐ (d) The lava
- ☐ (e) The magma

7 The following diagram shows a cross-section of the Earth. What does the label point to?

- ☐ (a) The atmosphere
- ☐ (b) The crust
- ☐ (c) The centre of the Earth
- ☐ (d) The core
- ☐ (e) The mantle

Q7

8 What is the very hot centre of the Earth known as?

- ☐ (a) The core
- ☐ (b) The mantle
- ☐ (c) The crust
- ☐ (d) The middle
- ☐ (e) The focus

9 Where does most of our knowledge about the internal structure of the Earth come from?

- ☐ (a) Guesswork
- ☐ (b) Mining
- ☐ (c) Drilling for oil
- ☐ (d) Shock waves from earthquakes
- ☐ (e) Satellite images

10 What is the term used to describe the movement of gigantic pieces of the Earth's crust?

- ☐ (a) The conveyor belt
- ☐ (b) Plate technology
- ☐ (c) Plate tectonics
- ☐ (d) Sea floor spreading
- ☐ (e) Fault movement

11 Why do the Earth's plates move?

- ☐ (a) The moon's gravitational field moves the plates around
- ☐ (b) Convection currents under the surface force the plates to move
- ☐ (c) Earthquakes and volcanoes force the plates to move
- ☐ (d) Each different season causes the plates to change position
- ☐ (e) The plates move in the opposite direction to that in which the Earth spins, due to inertia

● QUESTIONS

Higher Level only

12 How old is the Earth?

- ☐ (a) Less than 1 million years
- ☐ (b) 1 million–100 million years
- ☐ (c) 100 million–1000 million years
- ☐ (d) 1000 million–10000 million years
- ☐ (e) Over 10000 million years

13 The Shrinking Earth Theory (which suggests that the Earth is shrinking as it cools from the temperature at which it formed) was put forward to explain some of the geological features that occurred on Earth. Which one of the following features cannot not be explained by this theory, and therefore caused it to be replaced?

- ☐ (a) Volcanoes
- ☐ (b) Mountains
- ☐ (c) Earthquakes
- ☐ (d) The appearance of the same types of fossils on either side of an ocean
- ☐ (e) The formation of continents

14 When the Earth's atmosphere was first formed, it was mainly carbon dioxide. The atmosphere today has a very small proportion of carbon dioxide. What happened to most of this carbon dioxide?

- ☐ (a) It was combusted by the action of volcanoes to form oxygen
- ☐ (b) It was used up by the plants that were evolving
- ☐ (c) It slowly became locked up in the rocks and fossil fuels
- ☐ (d) It was dissolved into the seas
- ☐ (e) It was converted to nitrogen by cosmic radiation

15 Where is it believed that the Earth's magnetic field originates?

- ☐ (a) The crust
- ☐ (b) The mantle
- ☐ (c) The outer core
- ☐ (d) The inner core
- ☐ (e) The North Pole

16 At equal distances either side of the North Atlantic Ridge, the basaltic oceanic crust is the same age and gets progressively older moving further away from the ridge. What does this suggest about the relative movement of the tectonic plates in this region?

- ☐ (a) The plates are moving towards each other
- ☐ (b) The plates are moving away from each other
- ☐ (c) The plates are moving both north and south
- ☐ (d) The plates are not moving
- ☐ (e) None of the above

17 How can the geological record in the British Isles explain the theory that the plates on the Earth's surface have moved over time?

- ☐ (a) By the presence of faults
- ☐ (b) By the presence of volcanoes
- ☐ (c) By the presence of large deposits of desert sands
- ☐ (d) By the presence of gold in rocks
- ☐ (e) None of the above

18 The Earth's magnetic field reverses its polarity every thousand years, and this is recorded by the minerals of newly formed oceanic basaltic rock. The pattern of magnetism is repeated either side of an oceanic ridge. What does this suggest about the movement of the plates?

- ☐ (a) The plates are moving towards each other
- ☐ (b) The plates are moving away from each other
- ☐ (c) The plates are moving both north and south
- ☐ (d) The plates are not moving
- ☐ (e) None of above

19 What will occur due to the oceanic plates moving apart, as illustrated in the following diagram?

- ☐ (a) A deep open trench
- ☐ (b) Fold mountains are created
- ☐ (c) New crust is created
- ☐ (d) Crust is destroyed
- ☐ (e) Nothing happens

Q19

20 What will occur due to the continental plates merging, as illustrated in the following diagram?

- ☐ (a) Nothing, because both plates are the same size
- ☐ (b) Earthquakes
- ☐ (c) Volcanoes
- ☐ (d) Fold mountains
- ☐ (e) Islands

Q20

21 In the following diagram, which illustration correctly shows how the Earth's plates can move to create a rift valley?

....

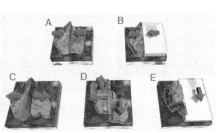

Q21

22 The following diagram shows three plates in the Earth. At which point – A, B, C, D, or E – is the destructive zone (the place where rock is being destroyed)?

....

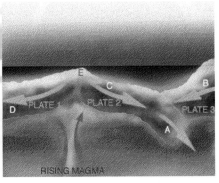

Q22

23 Which of the following geological features would be formed at a destructive plate margin between oceanic and continental plates?

- [ ] (a) A mid-oceanic ridge
- [ ] (b) A rift valley
- [ ] (c) A chain of volcanic mountains
- [ ] (d) A chain of fold mountains
- [ ] (e) An island arc

24 Which of the following geological features would be formed at a destructive plate margin between two oceanic plates?

- [ ] (a) A mid-oceanic ridge
- [ ] (b) A rift valley
- [ ] (c) A chain of volcanic mountains
- [ ] (d) A chain of fold mountains
- [ ] (e) An island arc

25 On the diagram that follows, which one of the illustrations shows a constructive boundary?

....

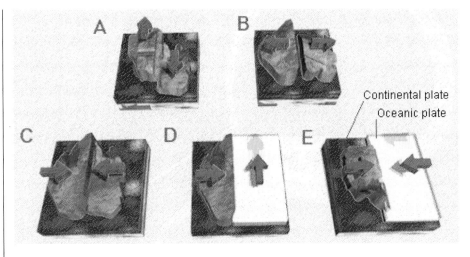

Q25

26 Evidence of folding and faulting can be seen in rocks that have been put under immense stress or strain. Which one of the following statements explains why some rocks, under this stress or strain, fold and others fault ?

- [ ] (a) The different composition of the rocks
- [ ] (b) The different nature of the rocks, i.e. whether the rocks are metamorphic, etc.
- [ ] (c) Some rocks are ductile and others are brittle
- [ ] (d) The amount of water found in the rocks
- [ ] (e) None of the above

27 Volcanic and earthquake activity occurs at the boundary between tectonic plates. What does this suggest about the cause of the activity?

- [ ] (a) It is caused by the movement of the plates
- [ ] (b) It is coincidental that this activity occurs at plate boundaries
- [ ] (c) It is caused by the shrinking of the Earth's surface
- [ ] (d) It is caused by the radioactivity at these boundaries
- [ ] (e) None of the above

28 What is the name of the scale on which earthquakes are measured?

- [ ] (a) Quake scale
- [ ] (b) Seismoscale
- [ ] (c) Richter scale
- [ ] (d) Fault-line scale
- [ ] (e) Geoplate scale

29 What is the name of the instrument that is used to measure the extent of an earthquake?

- [ ] (a) Quakemeter
- [ ] (b) Seismometer
- [ ] (c) Manometer
- [ ] (d) Richtometer
- [ ] (e) Earthquake meter

30 Which of the seismometer patterns – A, B, C, D, or E – in the following diagram indicates the longest earthquake?

....

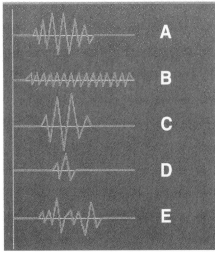

Q30

31 A fossil of a very primitive flowering plant is found in a piece of sedimentary rock. Using the geological time scale that follows, during what age and time period was the rock laid down?

- [ ] (a) 300 million years ago in the Carboniferous period
- [ ] (b) 200 million years ago in the Triassic period
- [ ] (c) 150 million years ago in the Jurassic period
- [ ] (d) 120 million years ago in the Cretaceous period
- [ ] (e) 50 million years ago in the Tertiary period

Era	Period		Millions of years ago
Cainozoic	Quaternary	First people	0–2
	Teritary	Mammals and flowering plants flourish	
		First primates	65
	Cretaceous	First flowering plants	
		Many creatures, including dinosaurs and ammonites, become extinct	135
Mesozoic	Jurassic	Dinosaurs and ammonites flourish	
		First birds	190
	Triassic	First dinosaurs and mammals	225
Palaeozoic	Permian	First conifers	
		Reptiles become widespread	280
	Carboniferous	Dense plant life covers swamplands	345
	Devonian	Animals move onto land	
		First amphibians	395
	Silurian	First plant life appears on land	440
	Ordovician	First vertebrates, including fishes, appear	500–570
	Cambrian	Increasing variety of fossils	

Q31, 32

32 A piece of rock is 140 million years old. Using the geological time scale in the previous diagram, what fossils could the rock contain?
i. Dinosaurs
ii. Conifers
iii. The first flowering plants

☐ (a) i only
☐ (b) ii only
☐ (c) iii only
☐ (d) i and iii only
☐ (e) i and ii only

ANSWERS

Formation and deformation of rocks

Foundation and Higher Levels

☐ **1** *(d)*
The rocks that make up the Earth's crust are continually being recycled by the movement of the tectonic plates that make up the crust. See diagram below. As a result, the oldest rocks have been recycled and therefore rocks of the same age as the Earth are not found. The oldest rocks that have been found are 3500 million years old. These rocks were discovered in an area of the crust that has been tectonically stable for a long time, and therefore no recycling has taken place during this time.

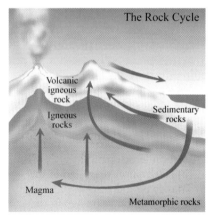

A1

☐ **2** *(d)*
The very small pieces of rock that are suspended in rivers or seas often settle at the bottom of the body of water. This newly deposited solid material is known as sediment. When the sediment is consolidated, it forms layers that make up sedimentary rocks.

☐ **3** *(b)*
Sedimentary rocks are produced by an accumulation of particles that may be transported by the wind, rain, etc. The deposits build up as layers and, as the layers get squeezed together, sedimentary rocks are formed. See illustration that follows.

A3

☐ **4** *(a)*
Sedimentary rocks such as limestone and sandstone are made up from layers of sediment that have been laid down over millions of years. This sediment may contain the shelly remains of once living organisms that inhabited the area in which the sediment was laid down.

☐ **5**
In sedimentary rocks, the deepest layers are the oldest ones because they will have formed first. Therefore layer E is the oldest sedimentary layer. The analysis is more accurate if fossils, which can be dated, are also found in the layers, because the layers are the same age as the fossils.

☐ **6** *(e)*
In the Cambrian period, trilobites and gastropods are common, lamellibranches are rare but evident, and vertebrates are absent as they had not yet evolved. In all other time periods vertebrates would be evident in the form of fossil record.

☐ **7** *(a)*
Limestone is a sedimentary rock, granite and basalt are igneous rocks, and slate and marble are metamorphic rocks. As igneous rocks are formed from molten magma it is not possible for them to contain fossils. Metamorphic rock is produced by the effect of heat and pressure on other rocks, so any fossils present would be destroyed. Sedimentary rocks may contain fossils of plants and animals that were trapped when the rock particles were deposited.

☐ **8** *(d)*
Limestone is a sedimentary rock that is composed of the shells of dead sea animals. Layers of shells are slowly compacted together to form limestone.

☐ **9** *(c)*
Limestone is made under the sea from the shells of dead animals. Movement of the Earth's plates can bring these rocks to the surface.

126

☐ **10** *(d)*
The fact that the rock contains both fossils and bedding layers suggests that it is a sedimentary rock. The sedimentary rocks in the list are shale and limestone. Only limestone would fizz in acid, as it is made up from magnesium and calcium carbonate. Marble would react in the same way in acid, but it is a metamorphic rock and therefore would not contain a fossil.

☐ **11** *(c)*
Molten rock is known as magma when it is underground and as lava when it comes to the surface. When this molten material cools, the rock formed is known as igneous rock. There are different types of igneous rock.

☐ **12** *(c)*
Igneous rocks are formed from cooling molten rock. Limestone is not an igneous rock; it is a sedimentary rock formed from the remains of marine creatures.

☐ **13** *(d)*
Basalt is formed on the surface of the Earth from molten lava that cooled very rapidly due to exposure to the air. This rapid cooling produces small crystals, which can sometimes form into hexagonal columns, such as in the Giant's Causeway.

☐ **14** *(e)*
The molten rock beneath the surface is known as magma. If this is pushed onto the surface through volcanoes, it is called lava.

☐ **15** *(a)*
Granite is formed from magma cooling beneath the Earth's crust. Because the cooling process is slow, large crystals, characteristic of granite, are formed.

☐ **16**
The rising molten magma at E cools down to form new rock. Therefore, at this point, the rock is the youngest.

☐ **17** *(d)*
Coal is formed when trees die and rot, and are then covered by layers of mud and sand. This causes high pressure which, together with high temperatures, produces coal.

☐ **18** *(c)*
The breakdown of the organic matter to form fossil fuels will only take place in the absence of oxygen. Also, both temperature and pressure are high underground – conditions that help to turn the organic matter into fossil fuels.

☐ **19** *(c)*
Coal comes from dead vegetation that has been deposited in layers. Later, this material is buried and compacted to form coal.

☐ **20** *(a)*
Rocks that are changed by intense heat or intense pressure (or both) are known as metamorphic rocks. They are so called because the original rocks have been metamorphosed.

☐ **21** *(c)*
Any rock that has been changed by heat or pressure (or both) is known as metamorphic. When limestone metamorphoses, marble is formed.

☐ **22** *(b)*
Upon heating, limestone will recrystallize and form marble, which is a type of metamorphic rock.

☐ **23** *(e)*
Upon heating, sandstone will recrystallize and form quartzite (or metaquartzite), which is a type of metamorphic rock.

☐ **24** *(a)*
Granite is an igneous rock and therefore it is composed of crystals. Because granite is an intrusive rock, it cools slowly and has large crystals. It does not contain any fossils or have any bedding or layers.

☐ **25** *(a)*
Sedimentary rock is formed here by particles that have been deposited and buried. See diagram that follows.

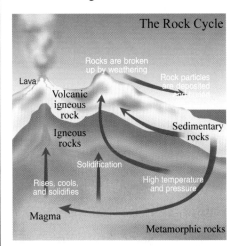

A25, 26, 27, 28, 29

☐ **26** *(e)*
When molten rock reaches the Earth's surface it is called lava. Here, the lava erupts from a volcano, as can be seen in the diagram above.

☐ **27** *(c)*
At high temperatures and high pressures sedimentary rock changes into metamorphic rock, as the previous diagram shows.

☐ **28** *(d)*
When the molten magma cools, it solidifies and forms igneous rock. See previous diagram.

☐ **29** *(b)*
When rocks move deeper underground they get hotter and hotter until eventually they melt. This molten rock found below the Earth's surface is called magma. See previous diagram.

☐ **30** *(b)*
The formation of metamorphic rock is caused by the action of heat or pressure (or both). Therefore, metamorphic rock would be formed by the action of the intrusion of igneous rock, by the subduction of rocks at a plate boundary, and by the burial by overlying rocks.

☐ **31** *(c)*
A crystal is a body that has a constant, symmetrical, and regular pattern throughout it. The crystal shape is due to the regular arrangement of the particles of which it is composed. See diagram that follows.

A31

☐ **32** *(d)*
If molten rock cools slowly, the igneous rock that is formed will have large crystals. This is normally the case when the igneous rock is formed within the Earth's crust.

☐ **33** *(a)*
If molten rock cools quickly, the igneous rock that is formed will have small crystals. This is normally the case when the rock is formed on the Earth's surface, where the air accelerates the cooling process.

127

☐ **34** *(a)*
The difference between extrusive and intrusive rocks is that intrusive rocks are erupted into the surrounding rocks, whereas extrusive rocks are erupted, in the form of lava, onto the surface of the Earth through volcanoes. Intrusive rocks have larger crystals as they have cooled over a longer period. Extrusive rocks, which cool very quickly, have very small crystals and can even be glass-like.

☐ **35** *(e)*
Bauxite contains no iron. However, both haematite and magnetite contain iron and therefore would be suitable ores from which to extract iron.

☐ **36** *(a)*
Bauxite is the only ore that contains aluminium. Haematite is an iron ore and malachite is a copper ore.

☐ **37** *(c)*
The water underground is at a very high temperature and is under very high pressure. Under these conditions the water can dissolve minerals that would not normally dissolve. As the water moves towards the surface, the pressure and temperature decrease and the minerals come out of solution, leaving a vein of the mineral.

☐ **38** *(d)*
A soil that is to be used for plant cultivation has to be able to hold water without becoming waterlogged, and it must have a good supply of nutrients. The soil composition that would provide this is a balanced mixture of sand (which allows the soil to drain), clay (which holds the water), and humus (which provides the nutrients).

☐ **39** *(b)*
It is important that soil is able to hold water because it is the water that brings nutrients to the plant roots. The soil must also be well-drained to prevent it from becoming waterlogged.

☐ **40** *(c)*
Biological weathering is the action of plants and animals on rocks. Actions such as the roots of a plant growing into a rock can cause the rock to break into smaller particles, increasing the rate of erosion in the environment.

Formation and deformation of rocks

Higher Level only

☐ **41** *(b)*
The shapes of the continents do fit together and both continents have some rocks of similar age. There are also some similarities between the fossils, but because many fossils were laid down after the continents drifted apart, they would not all match up. Suggestion *(b)* is therefore the correct answer.

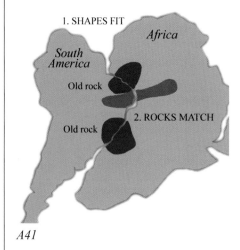

A41

Structure of the Earth

Foundation and Higher Levels

☐ **1** *(a)*
The layer of gases surrounding the Earth is called the atmosphere.

☐ **2** *(a)*
The atmosphere (a layer of gases) surrounds the Earth.

☐ **3** *(b)*
The thin outer layer of solid rock is called the crust, as shown on the following diagram.

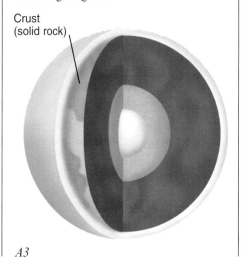

A3

☐ **4** *(b)*
The thin outer layer of solid rock is called the crust.

☐ **5** *(e)*
The thick layer of material that is semi-liquid is called the mantle, parts of which can move slowly.

☐ **6** *(b)*
The mantle is mostly solid, but some of it is semi-liquid and can move about. This causes huge convection currents that cause the plates to move. See diagram that follows.

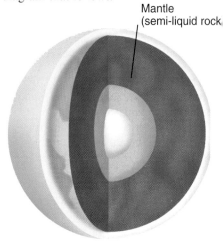

A6

☐ **7** *(d)*
The centre of the Earth is called the core, as shown on the following diagram. It consists of an inner region that is very dense solid rock, and an outer region made up of very dense hot molten rock.

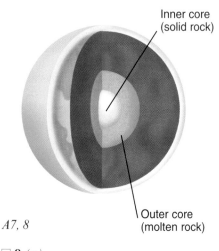

A7, 8

☐ **8** *(a)*
The core of the Earth is made up of mainly nickel and iron. The outer core is liquid, while the inner core is solid due to the immense pressure. See diagram above. It is believed that the Earth's magnetic field is due to the movement of the liquid section of the core.

□ **9** *(d)*
Our knowledge of the internal structure of the Earth comes from the interpretation of the way that shock waves produced by earthquakes travel through the Earth. There are two types of shock waves that travel deep into the Earth. These are known as P and S waves (sometimes referred to as Raleigh and Love waves). From the way these waves are refracted and the speed at which they travel, we can gain valuable information about the Earth's structure.

□ **10** *(c)*
Plate tectonics is the theory of the movement of pieces of the Earth's crust, known as plates.

□ **11** *(b)*
The semi-liquid molten rock underneath the Earth's crust has convection currents in it, which force the plates to move. The plates float on this molten rock.

Structure of the Earth

Higher Level only

□ **12** *(d)*
The Earth is approximately 4500 million years old. The age of the Earth has been determined using various astronomical and chemical calculations.

□ **13** *(d)*
The Shrinking Earth Theory can explain most of the geological features that occur on Earth, but it cannot explain how the fossils of the same land creature can appear on either side of an ocean (eg. fossil remains of the menosaurus were found in both Africa and South America). If the Earth is shrinking, then the theory would suggest that the continents are moving closer together and that they would contain very different types of fossils.

□ **14** *(c)*
The carbon dioxide in the atmosphere of the young Earth decreased to its present levels as it slowly became locked in rocks (such as limestone and chalk) and fossil fuels. The evolution of plants did decrease the volume of carbon dioxide in the atmosphere, but only by a very small amount.

□ **15** *(c)*
The Earth's magnetic field is believed to originate in the outer core. The outer core is composed of a very high density liquid (mainly molten nickel and iron), and the convection currents in this liquid are believed to result in the formation of the Earth's magnetic field.

□ **16** *(b)*
The plates on either side of the North Atlantic Ridge are moving away from each other. As the two plates move apart, a gap appears in the crust and the magma that is brought to the surface to fill the gap forms new oceanic crust as it cools. This means that the crust at equal distances from either side of the ridge is the same age and gets progressively older further away from the ridge.

□ **17** *(c)*
The fact that there are large deposits of desert sands in the geological record of the British Isles suggests that at one time the British Isles were in a position on the globe where the climate was much warmer than it is at present. In order for this to happen, the plates on the Earth's surface must have moved, and the British Isles must have been moved northwards.

□ **18** *(b)*
As the plates move apart magma rises up to fill the gap. As the magma cools the minerals in the basalt, which include iron, align themselves with the magnetic field and thus record the direction of the magnetic field. If the magnetic field is reversed, this change will be recorded in any new magma erupted as the plates move apart.

□ **19** *(c)*
The two plates moving apart will at first create a rift valley. However, new magma will come out of the gap in the crust, and new crust will be formed. Islands and submerged volcanoes can also be created this way.

□ **20** *(d)*
Two continental plates that collide will push each other upwards to create fold mountains. For example, the Himalayas were created when the Indian plate collided with the Eurasian plate. Areas where plates collide are known as collision zones.

□ **21**
Illustration C is the correct answer. When two plates move apart, they leave a rift valley between them. New magma, however, will come out to form a new crust and may create volcanoes.

□ **22**
At point A two plates are colliding and the oceanic plate (Plate 2) is being pushed down. The rock melts and is destroyed. This is known as the destructive zone.

□ **23** *(c)*
At a destructive plate boundary between oceanic and continental plates a chain of volcanic mountains is formed. As the oceanic plate is forced beneath the continental plate, the friction causes the plate to melt and form magma. This magma rises to the surface, causing the formation of volcanoes. An example of this type of plate boundary is the boundary between the Nazca plate and the South American plate, which has caused the formation of the Andes.

□ **24** *(e)*
At a destructive plate margin between two oceanic plates a number of geological features are formed, one of which is an island arc. An island arc is formed because as one plate is forced below the other, the friction generated causes the plate to melt, creating magma. This magma rises to the surface some distance behind the plate margin, forming a chain of volcanic islands. An example of this are the islands of Japan.

□ **25**
A constructive plate boundary is shown by illustration B, as when the gap appears magma comes out. This magma then cools and creates new crust, and more plates are constructed.

□ **26** *(c)*
Faults and folds in rocks are the result of the stress or strain placed on the rocks by the movement of the tectonic plates on the Earth's surface. The particular formation produced depends on whether the rock is brittle or ductile. A ductile rock will respond to stress by folding, and a brittle rock will respond by faulting. Whether the rock is ductile or brittle depends on a number of factors, the most important of which is the temperature of the rock. A hot rock is more likely to fold, as it will be more ductile than a cold rock.

□ **27** *(a)*
As the plates move against each other, the friction that is created can lead to the melting of the rocks and, eventually, to volcanoes. Any movement of the plates is accompanied by an earthquake.

☐ **28** *(c)*
The Richter scale is used to compare the strengths of different earthquakes. See table that follows.

Richter scale	
Magnitude of earthquake Log scale	**Possible effects**
1	
2	Normally detected only by instruments
3	
4	Faint tremor
5	Structural damage
6	Distinct shaking, poorly constructed buildings collapse
7	
8	Large buildings are destroyed (Mexico, 1985, San Francisco, 1989)
9	Ground visibly shakes

A28

☐ **29** *(b)*
A seismometer, as shown in the following diagram, is used to measure the extent of earthquakes. It is very sensitive and can detect even the smallest of tremors. It is designed in accordance with the principle of the simple pendulum.

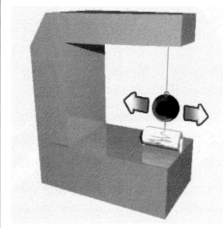

A29

☐ **30**
Although pattern B indicates the weakest earthquake (it has the least amplitude), it also indicates the earthquake that lasts for the longest period of time. As the following diagram shows, time is displayed on the horizontal axis of a seismometer.

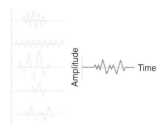

A30

☐ **31** *(d)*
The first flowering plants, which were the most primitive, were present between 65 and 135 million years ago in the Cretaceous period.

☐ **32** *(e)*
The rock was deposited in the Jurassic period (between 135 and 190 million years ago). During this period dinosaurs were flourishing, so their fossils would have been deposited. Although conifers first appeared much earlier during the Permian period, they would still be present during the Jurassic period and so their fossils could also be present in Jurassic rock. It would not be possible for flowering plant fossils to be present as they did not evolve until later, during the Cretaceous period.

Glossary

Acid
An acid is a substance that produces hydrogen ions, $H^+(aq)$, in solution. Solutions of acids have a pH of less than 7.

Acid rain
Acidic gases are produced during the combustion of some fuels. Two such gases are nitrogen dioxide and sulphur dioxide. These gases can dissolve in the water in clouds and produce acids. The rain that falls from these clouds is called acid rain. Acid rain has a pH of less than 7, and it is this acidity that causes great problems. It is thought that many trees have died from poisoning by the pollutants in acid rain, and in Sweden many lakes are so acidic that they are unable to support any biological life at all. Acid rain can also damage buildings. It is a significant cause of destruction and erosion in the modern world.

Aerobic respiration
In aerobic respiration glucose reacts with oxygen to produce carbon dioxide, water, and energy. Aerobic respiration allows glucose to be completely broken down by oxygen. There is another form of respiration called anaerobic respiration in which glucose is not broken down to produce carbon dioxide and oxygen.

Alkali
Alkalis dissolve in water producing hydroxide ions, $OH^-(aq)$. Solutions of alkalis have a pH value greater than 7. An alkali is a soluble base.

Alkaline
Alkaline solutions have a pH greater than 7.

Alkane
Alkanes are a series of hydrocarbon compounds with similar chemical properties. Hydrocarbons contain only the two elements hydrogen and carbon. Alkanes can be represented by the general formula C_nH_{2n+2}. They are said to be saturated compounds because all the bonds between the carbon atoms present are single covalent bonds.

Alkene
Alkenes are a series of hydrocarbon compounds with similar chemical properties. Hydrocarbons contain only the two elements hydrogen and carbon. Alkenes can be represented by the general formula C_nH_{2n}. They are different from alkanes in that they are unsaturated compounds. All compounds containing a carbon–carbon double covalent bond are unsaturated.

Ammonia
Ammonia (NH_3) is a gas. It is made in the Haber process from nitrogen and hydrogen. Much of the ammonia produced is used to make fertilizers such as ammonium nitrate and ammonium sulphate.

Anaerobic respiration
In anaerobic respiration energy is produced from glucose without the presence of oxygen.

Anode
The anode is the positive electrode in an electrolysis cell. Negative ions, such as chloride ions (Cl^-), are attracted to the anode. Negative ions can be discharged at the anode and electrons move from the anode to the external circuit. A typical anode reaction is the production of chlorine from a solution containing chloride ions.
$$2Cl^-(aq) \rightarrow C_{l2}(aq) + 2e^-$$

Atmosphere
The mixture of gases surrounding the Earth is known as the atmosphere. For the last 200 million years the Earth's atmosphere has been almost unchanged. It is made up of 78% nitrogen, 21% oxygen, and small amounts of other gases including noble gases, carbon dioxide, and water vapour.

Atmospheric pressure
This is the pressure caused by the gases present in the atmosphere. The pressure on the Earth's surface is about 1 bar or 100 kPa.

Atom
This is the smallest particle of an element that can take part in a chemical reaction. There are over one hundred different atoms. An element is made up of only one type of atom.

Atomic number
The atomic number of an element is the number of protons that are in one atom of that element. The atomic number is sometimes called the proton number.

Atomic structure
Atoms contain three fundamental particles and it is the arrangement of these three particles that is the atomic structure of the atom. The structure of the oxygen atom consists of a nucleus that contains eight protons and eight neutrons, as well as eight electrons that are in orbit around the nucleus.

Base
A base is a substance that neutralizes an acid.

Boiling point
This is the temperature at which all the particles in a liquid have sufficient energy to separate from each other and to become a gas.

Brownian movement
This is the random and erratic movement of, for example, smoke particles that is caused by collisions with surrounding air particles that are also moving about in a random fashion. Brownian movement (or Brownian motion, as it is also called) can be observed through a microscope.

Catalyst
A catalyst is a substance that speeds up a chemical reaction but that is not used up in the reaction. Iron is used to speed up the reaction that occurs between nitrogen and hydrogen to make ammonia in the Haber process.

Cathode
The cathode is the negative electrode in an electrolysis cell. Positive ions such as hydrogen ions, (H^+), are attracted to the cathode. Positive ions can be discharged at the cathode and electrons move towards the cathode from the external circuit. A typical cathode reaction is the production of hydrogen from a solution containing hydrogen ions.
$$2H^+(aq) + 2e^- \rightarrow H_2(g)$$

Chain reaction
This is a reaction in which one of the products reacts further and, by doing so, sustains the reaction.

Chlorine
Chlorine (Cl) is a non-metallic element. It is a very reactive green/yellow diatomic gas. It reacts with all metals to form compounds known as chlorides. Chlorine is poisonous and is used to kill germs.

Chlorine is a member of the halogens (group VII in the periodic table).

Chlorophyll
Chlorophyll is the green pigment found in leaves. Chlorophyll helps to trap energy from the sun by the process of photosynthesis. Carbon dioxide and water react together in the presence of light and chlorophyll to produce glucose and oxygen.

Combustion
Combustion occurs when a material reacts with oxygen gas, heat, and light. A flame is produced in most combustion reactions.

Compound
A compound contains two or more elements that have chemically bonded. A compound has its own unique chemical and physical properties. Water, which contains the elements hydrogen and oxygen, is a simple compound.

Compressive strength
This is the measure of force that a substance can withstand under compression. Materials with a high compressive strength, such as concrete, are used in the foundations of buildings.

Condensation
Condensation is the process by which a substance changes state from a gas into a liquid. When a substance in its gas form is cooled below its boiling point, it changes into its liquid state and is said to condense.

Conduction
Conduction is the transmission of heat or electricity through a solid material.

Cooling curve
When a substance that has been heated is allowed to cool, its temperature can be plotted against time to produce a graph. The resultant curve is called a cooling curve.

Corrosion
The reaction of metals with the air is called corrosion. Metals react with oxygen in the air to form metal oxides. Hence the shine on metals fades when corrosion takes place. Rusting is a special case of corrosion in which iron reacts with water and oxygen in the air to form rust (hydrated iron oxide).

Covalent
A covalent bond is a chemical bond that holds atoms together. It occurs when two atoms share a pair of electrons and it is this sharing that holds the atoms together. The bond between two hydrogen atoms in a hydrogen molecule (H_2) is an example of a covalent bond.

Cracking
Large hydrocarbon molecules can be broken down to produce smaller, more useful molecules in a process called cracking. Catalytic cracking uses a catalyst to accelerate the process.

Crystallization
Crystallization takes place when a solid comes out of a solution. If the process is reasonably slow, the particles present have time to position themselves in a regular arrangement, resulting in the formation of a crystal.

Decanting
Decanting is a separation technique. It is the process of separating an undissolved solid from a liquid by carefully pouring the liquid away and leaving the sediment behind. It is a quick and simple method, but it is not as effective a process of separation as filtration.

Decomposition
Decomposition is the breaking down of a substance into simpler substances.

Denitrification
This is a process by which bacteria converts nitrates in the soil into nitrogen gas.

Diffusion
This is the process by which a substance spreads out to fill all the space available to it. Diffusion also occurs in gases and liquids. It is the movement of particles from an area of high concentration to an area of low concentration.

Displacement
Displacement occurs when a more reactive metal pushes a less reactive metal out of solution. Adding zinc to copper sulphate solution produces zinc sulphate solution and copper. The copper metal is displaced by the more reactive zinc.

Dissolution
Dissolution occurs when a liquid dissolves a substance to produce a solution.

Dissolve
This is when the particles in a substance separate and spread throughout a liquid.

Distillation
This is the process of separating a liquid from a solution by boiling the solution and then cooling, condensing, and collecting the vapour produced.

Ductility
This is the property of metals that allows them to be drawn into wires without cracking or breaking. Copper is ductile and is drawn into wires that are used for the conduction of electricity.

Electrode
This is the object by which electrical current enters or leaves an electrolysis cell. Carbon is often used to make electrodes.

Electrolysis
Electrolysis is the breakdown by electricity of substances that are molten or in solution. Electrolysis affects the charge of particles by converting either ions into atoms, or atoms into ions, at the electrodes.

Electrolyte
This is a liquid or a solution that conducts electricity with decomposition occurring at the electrodes.

Electron
An electron is the negative particle present in all atoms. An electron has a charge of –1 and has a very small mass (about 1/1800 of the mass of a proton).

Electron shell
Electrons are arranged around the nucleus in positions that are called shells, orbits, or energy levels.

Element
An element is a substance that cannot be broken down into a simpler substance by chemical means. An element is a substance made up of only one type of atom. There are over 100 elements.

Endothermic
An endothermic reaction takes in heat energy from its surroundings.

This transfer of heat causes a drop in the temperature of the surroundings. Photosynthesis is an endothermic process.

Enzyme
An enzyme is an efficient biological catalyst. There are specific enzymes for specific reactions.

Equilibrium
A reversible reaction is in equilibrium when the forward and backward reactions take place at the same rate.

Erosion
Erosion is the removal of material that has been weathered. Weathering is the wearing down of rock by natural processes.

Evaporation
This is the process by which a liquid that is below its boiling point changes into a gas .

Exothermic
An exothermic reaction gives out heat energy to its surroundings. This transfer of heat causes an increase in the temperature of the surroundings. Burning reactions are exothermic.

Fermentation
This is the process by which sugar changes into alcohol and carbon dioxide when it has been treated with yeast.

Filtration
Filtration is a process that is used to separate a solid from a mixture of an insoluble solid and a liquid. The mixture is poured through a fine mesh (eg. filter paper), which does not allow the solid particles through.

Flammable
A flammable substance is one that burns readily.

Fractional distillation
This process is used to separate mixtures of liquids. The process relies on the liquids having different boiling points. Often complete separation into pure liquids is not possible. Fractional distillation allows crude oil to be separated into a number of liquid mixtures called fractions. Each fraction contains a mixture of substances that have similar boiling points.

Fractionating column
This is piece of apparatus used in the fractional distillation process. It is a tall column with a number of special exits. Substances with similar boiling points escape at the same exit.

Freezing point
This is the temperature at which a liquid substance changes to a solid.

Galvanizing
This is the process of coating iron or steel with zinc to help to prevent rusting. When a piece of galvanized iron is scratched it remains free of rust. The more reactive zinc corrodes leaving the iron unaffected.

Gas
A gas is one of the three states of matter. The particles in a gas are not in direct contact with each other. Gases spread out into all available space and therefore they do not have a definite size or shape

Greenhouse effect
Carbon dioxide in the atmosphere can act as a blanket around the Earth and, in this way, help prevent the Sun's energy from bouncing back into space. It acts like the glass in a greenhouse by trapping the heat from the Sun. This effect can cause the temperature of the Earth to increase (global warming). Global warming may cause severe problems on Earth, for example, it may cause the polar ice to melt.

Haber process
This is the name of the industrial process used to make ammonia gas. Nitrogen from the air and hydrogen from natural gas are mixed, heated, and then passed over an iron catalyst to produce ammonia gas. Much of the ammonia produced is converted into fertilizers.

Hydration
Hydration is the action of water on a substance.

Hydrocarbon
A hydrocarbon is a substance that contains only the elements hydrogen and carbon. Methane (CH_4) is the simplest hydrocarbon. Alcohol (C_2H_6O) is not a hydrocarbon as it also contains oxygen.

Igneous
Igneous rocks are those that have been formed from cooling magma. Granite and basalt are important igneous rocks.

Immiscible
This term describes liquids that do not mix with each other. Oil and water are immiscible.

Insoluble
Insoluble substances are substances that do not dissolve in water. A good example is sand.

Insulation
Insulation is a barrier that limits the transfer of heat from one place to another. Copper wires are insulated with plastic in order to prevent electricity leaving the copper.

Ion
An ion is formed when an atom (or a group of atoms) loses or gains electrons. When a sodium atom (Na) loses an electron, a sodium ion (Na^+) is formed. When a chlorine atom (Cl) gains an electron, a chloride ion (Cl^-) is formed. The ammonium ion has the formula NH_4^+.

Ionic
An ionic substance is a substance that contains ions. Common salt is an ionic substance; it is made up of sodium ions and chloride ions.

Ionization
Ionization is the process by which an atom changes into an ion.

Irritant
This term is given to substances that cause reddening and blistering when they come into contact with skin.

Isotope
Atoms of the same element can contain different numbers of neutrons. These atoms are known as the isotopes of the element.

Kinetic theory
This theory explains some of the properties of solids, liquids, and gases in terms of particle movement.

Liquid
A liquid is one of the three states of matter. Liquids can be poured and take the shape of their container. Hence, they do not have definite shape (nor do they do have definite size).

Magnetism
Magnetism is the science that examines magnetic fields and the attractive forces between metals. Iron is a magnetic substance.

Malleability
This is the property that allows substances to be bent or hammered. It is often affected by heat. Metals are malleable.

Mass number
The total number of protons and neutrons in an atom of an element is known as its mass number.

Melting point
This is the temperature at which a solid changes into a liquid. Heat is required in order to provide the particles in a solid with the energy to move vigorously and to break away from each other to form the liquid.

Meniscus
The surface (boundary) of water that is contained in a narrow tube curves upwards at the edges. The surface of mercury in a thermometer curves downwards at the edges. These curve effects, which are due to surface tension, are known as meniscuses.

Metal ore
Most metals occur in the Earth's crust as compounds. In ores, the metal compounds are very concentrated and therefore their extraction is economically viable.

Metamorphic
Metamorphic rocks are those that have been formed from sedimentary rocks by the action of heat and pressure. Marble and slate are two examples of metamorphic rocks.

Miscible
This term is used to describe liquids that form a solution when brought together. Alcohol and water are two examples of miscible substances.

Molecule
A molecule is a group of atoms linked by covalent bonds. It is the smallest particle of an element, or a covalent compound, that can exist independently.

Monomer
Monomers are small molecules that are able to join together to form large molecules called polymers. Ethene molecules are monomers that join together in a process called polymerization to make the polymer poly(ethene), which is often called polythene.

Neutralization
The reaction that occurs between an acid and an alkali is called a neutralization reaction. An acid reacts with an alkali to produce a salt and water.

Neutron
A neutron is one of the three fundamental atomic particles. Neutrons are present in the nucleus of all atoms except hydrogen atoms. Neutrons have the same mass as protons but do not have a charge.

Noble gases
Noble gases are the gases helium, neon, argon, krypton, xenon, and radon. They have a stable electron arrangement and so are extremely unreactive and form very few compounds. They make up group 0 in the periodic table.

Nucleus
The nucleus is the central core of an atom. It contains both protons and neutrons.

Orbit
Electrons move around the nucleus of atoms in regions called orbits. These regions are also known as shells or energy levels.

Oxidation
Oxidation is the loss of electrons from a particle. Reactions that involve oxygen being added to compounds are also oxidation reactions. Reduction always takes place at the same time as oxidation. One example of oxidation is the changing of chloride ions into chlorine gas. The burning of magnesium to produce magnesium oxide is another example.

Ozone layer
There is a layer of the atmosphere that contains a form of oxygen called ozone. Ozone gas (O_3) absorbs much of the harmful ultraviolet radiation that reaches the Earth from the Sun. Holes in the ozone layer allow ultraviolet radiation, which is very damaging to people, to reach the Earth.

Period
Horizontal rows of elements in the periodic table are known as periods.

Periodic table
The periodic table is an arrangement of the chemical elements. The elements are arranged in horizontal rows (periods) according to their atomic numbers. As the period is crossed from left to right the atomic number of each element increases. Elements with similar chemical properties can be found in the same column (group) of the periodic table.

Petrochemical
Petrochemicals are produced from crude oil or natural gas.

Photosynthesis
Photosynthesis is the process that takes place when water and carbon dioxide, in the presence of both chlorophyll and light energy from the sun, produce glucose and oxygen.

Physical change
A physical change is one that can easily be reversed and that produces no new substances. The melting of ice is a physical change because the only product is liquid water and this can easily be refrozen to make ice.

Pollutant
A pollutant is a material that causes harm to the environment. Acid rain is caused by the pollutant gases nitrogen dioxide and sulphur dioxide. Oil spillage from tankers is a pollutant in the sea.

Polymer
A polymer is a compound containing very large molecules and it is formed by the joining of many small molecules known as monomers. Thousands of ethene molecules (monomers), link together to form the polymer poly(ethene), which is often called polythene.

Polymerization
The process of making polymers from monomers is known as polymerization.

Precipitation
Precipitation takes place when solutions are mixed and a product of the reaction is an insoluble solid. This solid is 'thrown out' of solution and is seen to precipitate.

Products
Products are substances that are formed in chemical reactions. When petrol burns, the products are mainly carbon dioxide and water.

Proton
A proton is one of the three fundamental atomic particles. Protons are present in the nucleus

of all atoms. Protons have a charge of +1.

Radiation
Radiation is energy that spreads out from a source.

Rate of reaction
This is a measure of the speed of a chemical reaction at any given time. It indicates how many chemicals are being used up or formed per second. The units used to measure rate of reaction are mol/dm³/s. The rusting of iron is a slow reaction whereas an explosion is a very fast reaction. It is possible to measure the rate of most reactions.

Reactants
Reactants are the substances that are brought together before chemical reactions take place.

Reaction
A reaction is the name of the change that takes place when chemicals are brought together.

Reactivity series
This is a list of the common metals in order of their reactivity with air, water, and acids. It is a type of league table with the most reactive metal at the top (potassium) and the least reactive metal (gold) at the bottom. The series helps to predict the vigour of many reactions involving metals.

Redox reaction
A redox reaction is one that involves reduction and oxidation. Because all oxidation reactions involve reduction, and all reduction reactions involve oxidation, the reactions are often referred to as redox reactions.

Reducing agent
A reducing agent removes oxygen from substances and, by doing so, becomes oxidized itself. When a reducing agent, such as hydrogen, is passed over hot copper oxide it takes the oxygen from the copper oxide, reducing it to copper. Reducing agents can also be thought of as electron donors.

Reduction
This reaction involves the loss of oxygen. The gain of electrons is an example of reduction.

Respiration
Respiration is the process that

occurs in the body when energy is produced from glucose.

Rust
Rust is formed when iron corrodes in the presence of water and oxygen. It is hydrated iron oxide.

Salt
A salt is formed when an acid is neutralized by an alkali or by a base: sulphuric acid forms salts called sulphates; nitric acid forms salts called nitrates; hydrochloric acid forms salts called chlorides.

Saturated
This term is applied to alkanes, which are hydrocarbon compounds. They are said to be saturated because all the bonds between the carbon atoms present are single covalent bonds.

Sedimentary
Sedimentary rocks are those that have been formed from compacted layers of sediment. Limestone and mudstone are two important sedimentary rocks.

Sodium
Sodium is a very reactive metallic element. It has the chemical symbol Na. It has few uses but its compounds, such as sodium chloride, are common and often useful.

Sodium chloride
Sodium chloride ($NaCl$) is the chemical name for common salt. It is used as a food preservative, and during the winter it is put on the roads to melt ice. It is also an important raw material for industry, and in solution it is electrolyzed to make chlorine, hydrogen, and sodium hydroxide.

Sodium hydroxide
Sodium hydroxide ($NaOH$) is a common alkali. Large quantities are used to make soap.

Solid
A solid is one of the three states of matter. The particles in a solid are in close contact with each other and cannot move out of position (although they can vibrate when heated). This means that solids have a definite shape and size.

Solubility
Solubility is the extent to which a substance will dissolve in another substance (usually 100 g of water) at

a particular temperature. Sugar and sodium hydroxide have very high solubilities in water.

Solution
A solution is a mixture of a soluble substance and a solvent. Sugar dissolves in water to produce a sugar solution.

Solvent
A solvent is a liquid that is able to dissolve another substance, which becomes known as the solute.

Sublimation
This is the process by which a solid changes into a gas, or a gas changes into a solid, without going through the liquid state. When solid carbon dioxide is heated it becomes carbon dioxide gas, bypassing a liquid state. The carbon dioxide is said to sublime.

Sulphuric acid
Sulphuric acid (H_2SO_4) is an important industrial acid. Approximately 150 million tonnes are produced in the world each year by the contact process, which uses sulphur, air, and water as its raw materials. It has a wide range of uses including the manufacture of fertilizers, paints, pigments, synthetic fibres, detergents, soaps, plastics, and battery acid. It is also used in the preparation of steel and in the refining of crude oil.

Suspension
A suspension is a mixture of a solid and a liquid in which the particles of a solid are not small enough to form a solution and yet not heavy enough to sink to the bottom of the liquid. They remain spread throughout the liquid, and this mixture is called a suspension.

Synthetic
Synthetic is used to describe a substance that has been manufactured and does not occur naturally.

Tensile strength
This is the extent to which a material can withstand a stretching force before it pulls apart or breaks. Steel cables have a high tensile strength.

Thermal decomposition
This is the splitting up of a substance into simpler substances by the action of heat.

Thermosetting
Thermosetting is the permanent

hardening of a material (often a synthetic plastic) after one application of heat and pressure. The heat causes bonds to form between the chains of atoms in the material.

Thermosoftening
Thermosoftening plastics soften when heated and harden again when cooled.

Titration
This is a practical process used to determine the concentration of a solution. It usually involves the use of pipettes, burettes, and a solution of known concentration.

Unsaturated
An unsaturated compound contains a multiple bond between its carbon atoms. Many unsaturated compounds contain a carbon–carbon double bond. An alkene is an unsaturated hydrocarbon compound because all the bonds between its carbon atoms are double covalent bonds

Vapour
A vapour is a gaseous suspension in the air of particles. A vapour is a gas that is below its critical temperature and therefore that can be liquefied by an increase in pressure.

Viscous
This term is applied to liquids that are difficult to pour. Treacle is a viscous liquid.

Volatile
A volatile liquid is one that evaporates readily at room temperature.

Weathering
Weathering is the wearing down of rocks by natural processes such as rain and frost. Its effectiveness relies on erosion to transport the weathered materials away from their original position.

Success Guaranteed!

At Dorling Kindersley we believe that our Revision Guide books will help you achieve your full potential in your exams.

If you use this book as part of your study programme we believe that you will achieve a Grade C or higher in the relevant exam.

To back this claim, if you get a Grade D or lower* and meet the terms and conditions below, you will be eligible to claim a **FREE Dorling Kindersley book** to the same value of your choice.

Once your claim is verified we will send you a copy of **Dorling Kindersley's** catalogue with instructions for ordering your free book.

Please send claims (*following instructions below*) to:

**Customer Support Manager
(GCSE Claims)
Dorling Kindersley Children's Marketing
9 Henrietta Street
Covent Garden
London WC2E 8PS**

If you have any queries please write to the address above.

*or Scottish Standard Grade 4 or lower